Reminiscences of an ancient strategist
The Mind of Sun Tzu

Reminiscences of an ancient strategist
The Mind of Sun Tzu

FOO CHECK TECK

ILLUSTRATED BY PEGGY LEONG

Gower

Published by
Gower Publishing Limited
Gower House
Croft Road
Aldershot
Hampshire GU11 3HR
England

Gower
Old Post Road
Brookfield
Vermont 05036
USA

British Library Cataloguing in Publication Data
Foo, Check Teck
    Reminiscences of an ancient strategist : the mind of Sun Tzu
    1. Sun Zi – Criticism and interpretation   2. Strategy
    3. Strategic planning
    I. Title
    658.4'012'092

ISBN 0 566 07970 4

Typeset in Nimrod by Raven Typesetter, Chester
and printed in Great Britain at the University Press, Cambridge.

In loving memory of my mother-in-law
Quek Ah Moh

also to
my wife, Tan Chay Cher
my daughter, Foo Wen Ling
my son, Foo Shi Hao

CONTENTS

vii

LIST OF
ILLUSTRATIONS

x

FOREWORD

Emeritus Professor Peter Hugh Grinyer

Foo Check Teck introduced me to Sun Tzu's *The Art of War* in 1992 while we were working together on a book reporting a major survey of strategic planning in the ASEAN Region. In it I found a fascinating insight into successful military strategy in ancient times: bases for success; the importance of 'calculation' or planning; taking account of, and exploiting where possible, the terrain and weather conditions; the morale training and care of troops; the psychology of one's own and the enemy forces; and the use of spies and military intelligence were all there. Moreover, there were timeless but often overlooked insights into the importance of strategy and its relationship with tactics.

Strategy as Sun Tzu saw it was intertwined with the operational implications of the terrain, weather, state, and morale and relative strengths of the troops. Without good strategy to guide the nature, timing and preferred course of the battle, a general was liable to lose. But strategy without vigorous, committed and flexible implementation in the field was worthless. Strategy, tactics and implementation were interwoven seamlessly. Since the responses of the enemy could not be taken for granted, and much else in battle was variable too, the good general needed to be flexible and adapt his operations, and indeed further evolve his strategy, to take into account changing conditions.

Such lessons were delivered with vivid reference to interpreting the significance of clouds of dust as a warning of advancing cavalry and of flights of birds as a sign of foot-soldiers creeping through brush. There were word pictures of attacks on towns by burning and much else. It could have been thought that what was written was particular to the time and style of war of Sun Tzu himself and of little relevance to today's world. However, as we interpreted his principles in terms of business at the end of the twentieth century we could see considerable relevance, and for this reason made reference to his work in interpreting the significance of the statistical findings from our survey.

In this endeavour Foo Check Teck was the primary author. He read Sun Tzu in different translations and in Chinese. His interpretations of the meaning of Sun Tzu's writing had a depth and quality that my own – on much more limited reading and applying a purely Western mind – could not match. Since our book together this interest of Foo Check Teck's has continued to blossom and has led to this present work, which again shows the deep understanding he has of Sun Tzu.

In this book Foo Check Teck casts himself back in his imagination to the old age of Sun Tzu and produces what he might have written, by way of expansion and discussion, of the sources of the principles in his *Art of War*. He has sought to capture the mind of Sun Tzu to increase the reader's understanding of the work. It strikes me that this has been done very well. The imagery used is precisely of the kind used by Sun Tzu. The imagined illustrations of situations from ancient warfare have a ring of validity. The wisdom of the ancient sage and his humanity are somehow captured. The heavy use of examples from nature as sources of ideas on strategy reflects that of Sun Tzu himself, who made very effective use of the analogy with water changing course on its flow to the sea. Even the use of short sections and a willingness to repeat an important principle in a new context follows the style of the ancient master.

So effective has Foo Check Teck been that it is sometimes difficult to determine where he is actually attributing to Sun Tzu views which, while consistent with *The Art of War*, go beyond what is written there. In seeking to map the mind of Sun Tzu, Check Teck has both internalised much of the ancient wisdom and introduced much of his own understanding. But this is the nature of the timeless flow of the river of knowledge, in which what is received is creatively reinterpreted to meet the changed conditions and challenges of the age. Sun Tzu would have approved! This adds rather than detracts from this attractively written, highly readable book, and its potential for illuminating the insights of the old master strategist.

Peter H Grinyer
St Andrews
Scotland
April 1997

PREFACE

The completion of the empirical, research-based work *Organising Strategy: Sun Tzu Business Warcraft* with Professor Peter Hugh Grinyer (revised softback version *Sun Tzu on Management: The Art of War in Contemporary Business Strategy*) made me realise how truly profound a strategic thinker Sun Tzu was. *Organising Strategy* drew on the statistical evidence contained in my 1990 PhD thesis at the University of St Andrews, under Professor Peter Hugh Grinyer. I commenced work on this imaginative diary, *Reminiscences of an Ancient Strategist*, in an attempt to explore the mind of Sun Tzu. To write this diary, that captures his strategic mind, I had to transport myself 2,500 years back in time. The avid reader will realise that familiar themes in *The Art of War* are reworked, re-explored and re-examined in this diary of Sun Tzu. For me personally this book complements *Organising Strategy*. Yet the two books cannot be more contrasting. The diary is a work of imaginative exploration. Hypotheses are woven into it, suggesting how ideas in *The Art of War* might have originated. Also enduring philosophical themes are discussed. Surrealism is evoked in the illustrations. The other book is grounded in statistical analyses of survey results. Hypotheses are validated. Implications of these findings for man in the corporate world are discussed. Correlograms linking relationships dominate the illustrations. What ties them together is one man: Sun Tzu. In summary, the diary explores his original mind 2,500 years ago; *Organising Strategy* validates his work *The Art of War* 2,500 years later.

Foo Check Teck
April 1997

ACKNOWLEDGEMENTS

As with *Organising Strategy: Sun Tzu Business Warcraft*, I continue to benefit from a working environment that is highly conducive for creative research. During the course of writing *Reminiscences* (mostly evenings and early dawn) I was with the newly established System and Engineering management (SEM) Division within the School of Mechanical and Production Engineering (MPE) at the Nanyang Technological University, Singapore. Associate professor Yeo Khim Teck as the founding Head of the Division of SEM had been constantly encouraging me to extend beyond my doctoral work by thinking deeply about strategy. The MPE School under the able Deanship of Professor Lim Mong King (now Deputy President) had resulted in an organisational climate that fosters highly original and creative research. For any creativity to blossom the culture has to be right. Otherwise it is easy for one to be buried by routine. I am grateful and fortunate to draw my inspirations from such an environment.

FCT

1

1  1

THIS DIARY RECORDS the inner flow of my thoughts. Though my prescriptions on strategy are crystallised in *The Art of War,* I find it useful to record the wider, strategic thought processes. These 'pre-writings' to *The Art of War*, if I may so describe my work, are intended for posterity. You might even say that I am involved in deconstructing *The Art of War*. For in recording these images ('pre-writings') I try to present my own inner thought processes in a life devoted to mastering strategy. You may appreciate the origins of strategy prescriptions better with the help of this work that deconstructs *The Art of War*.

I have nested deconstruction around *The Art of War* to help you see the complex processes at work inside a strategist's mind. The working mind of a strategist may be conceptualised as a vessel. Despite having a residual pool of insights distilled from many years of forming strategies to draw on, crafting a successful strategy still remains for me a mysterious art.

As you will see, the mind working in search of a strategy is not simply recalling past methods, although I must admit that having a repertoire of stratagems is helpful. Nor is it performing simply an intellectual or rational thought process. Every new context calls for renewed efforts in rethinking an old stratagem: 'recontextualising' a stratagem. Anyone living the life of a strategist through these warring years will appreciate how often success or failure turns on how effectively a stratagem is remoulded to fit new, changed circumstances. Adapting a stratagem to work effectively requires a skilled strategist.

My life may be seen as a flow of confrontations with hostile environments: countless meetings, challenges, surprises, intrigues, difficulties. To survive in such contexts I am compelled to search far, wide and deep for strategies to resolve perplexing issues. In practising my art I am conscious of the possible ramifications a specific strategy of mine may have, not only on rulers, generals and troops, but also on the ordinary peasants that populate the plains. I recognise the value of human lives.

You will have gathered from *The Art of War* that I advocate as the highest form of war strategy to win without fighting. For no war is costless: human and animal lives are lost, injuries sustained, homes destroyed, families torn apart. War is savage but the irony is that one versed in the arts of war is less likely to be forced to resort to them than one unfamiliar with such arts. For it is the innate nature of the brute and savage to attack the weak and defenceless rather than the strong and armed. It is therefore for the learned, cultivated and cultured to overcome the brutish through strategy. At times there is no choice but to fight. And the countless possible variations on battle situations put demands on me, the strategist, to reconfigure strategy accordingly. At times an unexpected, complex situation may call for a unique strategy to be created. Where then do I seek for strategic solutions to the situations that confront me? What are the means through which I discover strategies to resolve issues? How do I ensure a creative flow of strategy ideas? It is to these issues that I turn next, reflecting on my past experience of generating strategic solutions to intricate problems.

Sometimes solutions are embedded in the writings etched on tortoise-shells. Some of our ancestors, some living 2,500 years ago, and others since time immemorial, have deemed it useful to convey to us the lessons they have learned. Surviving hostilities seems an age-old problem; lessons gained through surmounting them in the past may still be useful. The art of strategy has that timeless appeal of always being able to benefit from ancient works.

Time may indeed be like a river. Ancient strategists are those living upstream who cast their works afloat on the river so as to benefit those downstream. And I, being placed somewhere midstream, am now able to gain from their works. And water flows on regardless: the river of time.

And so I too have emulated the ancients by engraving my prescriptions for waging war in *The Art of War* on bamboo strips. After another 2,500 years have passed, I wonder if these prescriptions will still be appreciated by strategists. Vastly altered circumstances may render some of *The Art of War* prescriptions less directly applicable. Yet if human nature remains unchanged, then the value of the art of strategy is timeless, despite the flow of the river of time.

One merely needs to adapt *The Art of War* to the context. And survival of humankind depends on constant adaptation, whether of the art of war or of other arts. That is in the nature of things.

1 ▬▬▬ 4

At times, I derive my prescriptions from things that Mother Nature provides for us. Look at water – how it adapts to *any* vessel. The qualities of water tell me a lot about the virtues needed for human survival: adaptation to change.

I also benefit from observing nature. For animals too have to adapt to harsh environments in their search for sustenance. Again, if you have read *The Art of War* you will remember my emphasis on timing. I learnt the critical role of timing from the eagle, when he captures a mouse from high up in the air.

At other times, such prescriptions for strategy are derived as a consequence of deeper reflection. The philosophical issues of strategy are only appreciated through reflection. For example, how to win wars without waging wars.

Yet, often ideas for resolving difficult strategic issues simply float on to my stream of consciousness, seemingly from the very depths of my unconscious. On many a morning I wake up with a strategy instantaneously before my eyes. It is as if in my sleep, my mind has been searching the very depths of my soul for a strategy.

And strangely, solutions do often spring forth as if from

nowhere, just when my consciousness is about to recede into a dream-like state. This is often preceded the same evening by my searching intensely and in vain for a strategic solution to a multi-faceted problem. The strategy is remarkable in providing a synthesized solution that takes into account the multi-faceted nature of the problem. Fantasy solutions are often toyed with in dreams. These too have their uses.

It is interesting to observe how the mind works. For in the midst of conversing with people on topics totally unrelated and without any conscious effort on my part, a viable strategy to solve a complex problem may present itself.

Often, when searching for a strategy to resolve a complex problem, I find quiet necessary. Stillness enables the problem and related information to be processed in the deep recesses of the mind.

Also, at times a strategy becomes apparent when I am involved in some activity: horse riding, brewing tea, gardening.

1 ▰ 5

To capture my thoughts in writing, I search my memories. Often a remembered past event emerges without any conscious effort. Sometimes the chirping of birds triggers my memory of something so deeply buried in my subconscious that I am surprised by the vivid images that are submerged within me. Such recollections often happen unexpectedly. Like the clouds that float across my dwelling, these images come in various shades of colour, and in surprising configurations.

The memories streaming into my mind constantly serve to emphasise the crucial role that the arts of war have in determining the rise and fall of kingdoms. So I have recorded my deepest thoughts on strategy in *The Art of War*. Many have been mistaken in thinking that mastery of the craft of war will lead to even more wars being fought. Just as the art of swimming enables one to avoid being drowned and also to save lives in a storm, so too does mastering the art of strategy – at the highest possible level – help kings to avoid wars and save lives through averting unnecessary battles.

I often recall the anguished faces of kings who had to suffer due to their prolonged neglect of the study of war. Their expressions, voices and pleas seem to be permanently engraved on my mind. For in their costly mistakes are contained lessons for all who seek to prevail in the ruthless games of warfare and intrigue that kings are inevitably involved in. And words of dethroned kings keep echoing within me:

"But if I only had studied the art of strategy this would not have come to pass!"

But alas! Mastering the craft of war is impossible unless such skills are learned earnestly. It is never possible for such skills to be acquired in a short space of time. And never can they be gained in a hurry. My *Art of War* may be brief, but to penetrate deep into its meanings, understand the many hidden messages, and see its manifestations in all human activities requires many years of learning, practice and reflection. Only then can the art of war be mastered.

Like the fermentation of rice wine, strategic thinking requires time to mature. Like seeds in favourable soil and climatic conditions, that grow to become young plants, so seeds of strategic thinking, when planted in 'mind fields', should grow to become strategic plants, bearing the fruits of effective strategies. Like young seeds, strategic thinking needs to be nurtured in the right environment: too many court entertainments, too many nights with concubines and too little time for quiet meditation and reflection are not the right conditions for growth.

Fear

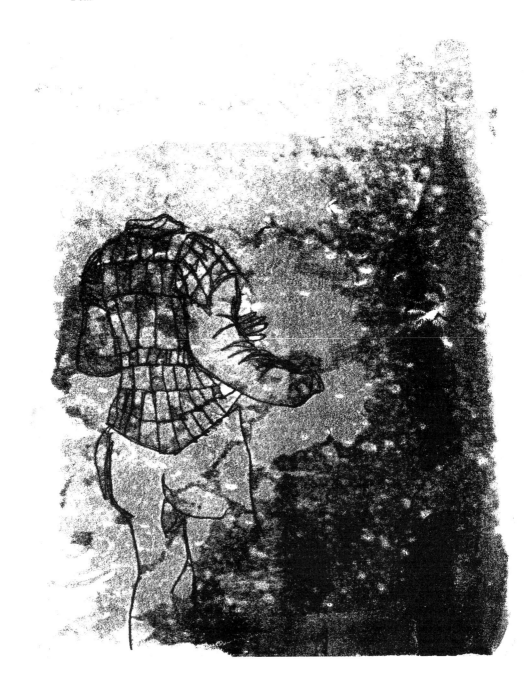

2 2

I recall the many times I have counselled kings with these words:

"Think daily, deeply, and in a disciplined way about strategy, for on that alone is your throne of power preserved and strengthened."

Alas, these words are uttered in kingly ears that hear but will not listen. Then there are kings who listen but do nothing else. Some act in kingly ways but fail to think. And yet there are those kings who think but do not reflect. Some kingly reflections may be experienced but do not come from deep pools in the mind. Few kings then reflect constantly, profoundly and devotedly on the art of war. And only the king who is strategically skilled knows the true value of advice as proffered by strategists.

2 3

Much can be learnt from the king who turns to the art of strategy in despair. This scenario is often replayed in my mind: kings echoing words of despair, regret and remorse:

"Hearing battle cries outside the walls, and seeing some generals with their troops deserting the city, I suddenly realise the price I have to pay for neglecting the warring arts. And despite my offer of bountiful rewards of gold and silver, no strategists are willing to come forward with sound advice."

Kings especially must excel in the art of war. I know kings have many distractions: ceremonies, concubines, hunts, fine arts, music. Yet all these arts pale in significance compared to the arts of war. For our history tells us how the survival of many people rests on a king's mastery of warcraft. And, indeed, even if kings survive such a crisis, they are constantly haunted by the cries of their country folk, whose blood colours the rice fields red:

"Oh, I live in fear of the night! For in my sleep my people haunt

me: their headless bodies or bodiless heads come into my dreams, beseeching me to take revenge ... but how can I now, in such a dire state, ever dream of raising another army?"

And these kings ask me how they can continue living with such guilt and remorse. No priests seem able to shield these once great kings from such dreams.

Of all the arts, none is more difficult to master than the art of war. And the art of winning wars through strategy may at times be complex, subtle and profound. Even the most intelligent may take many years to completely master it. So for all kings and kings-to-be, I must urge you to study the art of war relentlessly. For it is on the mastery of the art of war that the future of an entire state depends.

Who but the king should be author of strategy? The stakes are high. Just as a brilliant strategy can deliver a country, a strategy poorly conceived may lead to the ultimate collapse of a kingdom. So all prospective kings should heed my advice to study the arts of war and especially to develop skills in thinking strategically.

2 ▄▙▄ 4

The art of strategic thinking must be cultivated over time. For deep reflections on strategic issues are needed. On occasions the strategist needs to draw lessons from antiquity. Essentially the art of war is about how to triumph over people who are your enemies. People now and in the past differ little in their chemistry: thus the principles of *The Art of War* can be as valid now as they were 2,500 years ago and may remain relevant for 2,500 years hence. For this reason I am setting *The Art of War* afloat on the pristine stream of time.

According to *I Ching* (*The Book of Changes*), there is but one constant in life: change. And in the ebb and flow of life, one must acquire the skills of flexible strategic thinking. Skills in flexibly applying the precepts of *The Art of War* distinguish the true expert from the novice. Such abilities are found only in those who are true followers of *The Art of War*.

In life there can be many ironies. The highest purpose behind mastering the art of strategy is not always to win through war-mongering. Instead, the highest skill consists in the mastering of strategy so that kings may prevail without having to wage *any* war. In terms of attainment of strategic skills, the taking of a city intact is far superior to capture through endless battles. So it is a sage king who is able to use his strategic skills to avert wars and yet achieve his goals.

Fearlessness

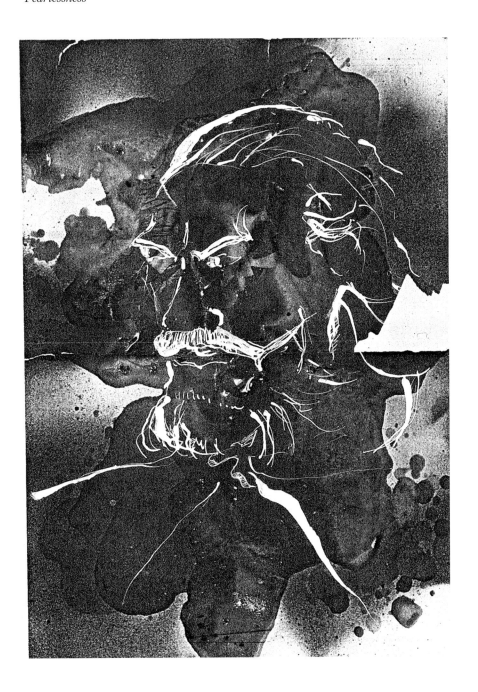

Besides kings, generals too must never neglect the art of war. Again I recall many a general who lost his head because he neglected the study of various arts of war. You may say that generals who are waging war directly and hands-on must, even more than kings, have that blend of personal values, qualities and attributes to succeed. For many a brutal and daring general fails for want of wisdom as much as through sheer neglect in the performance of his duties. The latter may be rectified through diligence, but the former requires that the general continuously profit from his warring experiences. I recall the soft yet distinct voice of the mighty general who prevailed over many battles whispering in my ears:

"But there can be no fixed rules, for there are endless permutations, variations and surprises on the battlefield. As in the game of chess, one has to continuously profit from the varied experiences gained. Each confrontation with an enemy has in it lessons even for the most seasoned of warriors."

A wise general should continuously sharpen his strategic thinking through his many war encounters. For *The Art of War* cannot be but a summation of the key principles.

Another quality shared by many a successful, wise general that I have met, read about, or heard of is reputation for personal courage in the midst of danger. As a soldier related to me of his general:

"Fires inside the camp rose to tree-level, dancing wildly to the tune of the howling winds, slashing our faces. The howling of the winds seemed to harmonise with the crackling sounds of the woods. Few of us soldiers could turn our faces in the direction of the camp. And although we were outside the camp, the heat of the scorching fires seemed so intense as to burn our skins. Yet our general, despite the immense dangers in such a situation, dashed right inside the camp, into the heart of the wild flames. Such bravery in the face of such odds stirred in us a deep admiration. Within moments, the general emerged clutching the sacred Imperial Sword. Since then he has been revered and loved by us and we name him the Brave One."

With such a demonstration of kingly devotion, the general moves the hearts of the ordinary soldiers, uplifts their fighting spirit. By his acts he exemplifies, besides bravery, loyalty and devotion to the king. By his conduct he moves the soldiers to aspire to achieve the impossible in the soldierly arts.

Yet on another occasion, this soldier recalled about this same general:

"As the army was retreating from a hopeless battle scene, a fellow soldier lay wounded on the battlefield. Galloping on horseback towards the body were enemy troops with shining spears. The sight of the wriggling body seemed enough to stir in the general a sense of soldierly obligation to rescue this body, about to be trodden underfoot. Silently and without any hesitation, he turned around and singlehandedly charged at the bewildered enemy troops. The mere sight of a single man charging so determinedly at them was all it took for the enemy troops to beat a retreat. And we were so moved by his action that we were all willed by his courage also to charge at the enemy, thus turning unexpectedly the tide of victory."

And though possessed of incomparable personal bravery, these generals are not lacking in humanity. Indeed, each battle seems to add to their sense of humility. Oddly, though war encounters are anything but civilised, such a general seems to become more noble through each encounter. Also the general seems to grow ever wiser after each battle. The savageries of battle only add greater depth to both his humility and his wisdom.

Their discipline springs not from mere blind adherence to military rules but from the will to achieve a higher good. Take the rule that all soldiers need to clamp a stick between the teeth during night manoeuvres. Without such precautions, some soldiers might talk and so unwittingly give away their position to the enemy.

But besides the disciplined general there are other factors which often determine military success or failure.

The next factor is how well the army is organised.

3 2

From a good general, a king often inherits an army that is tightly yet flexibly organised. In such an army ranks are duly worked out, duties properly assigned, work fairly allocated. Needless to say such an army is well supplied. For in excellent organising lies the secret of a responsive, properly equipped army. For organisation in itself is a crucial factor that may determine success on the battlefield. Ranking in equal importance with organisational skill is the general's capability in utilising what nature gives him to his best advantage. Two aspects of nature are of strategic value: weather and terrain.

13

3 3

Just as there are times when a person's blood seems to boil due to the anger rising within him, so there can be summer days when the heat scorches the soil beneath our feet. And in winter there are days when winds are icy cold and days when sunlight gives a comfortable warmth to the air. So the wise general chooses the time most appropriate for implementing his strategies. He will think of infinite ways to subject his enemies to the worst of weather conditions and at the same time secure the best possible climatic conditions for his own troops. Thus the general as a strategist lures the enemy to march out in the middle of a storm amidst the howling winds while his own troops rest in sheltered comfort behind the city walls. However once the storm has subsided and the morale of the enemy troops has been drenched in wetness and chilled by the wind, he will speedily lead his well-sheltered, rested army to slay the enemy, as a soldier told me:

"The enemy troops dragging their soaked, hungry bodies along the jungle path was an ugly sight. Despite the forest winds, the banners failed to fly. After each blast of wind came the shivering looks on the tired, desperate faces. The sneezing of the horses added harmony to human noises. And when we emerged from the trees with our flags fluttering in the air, the enemy troops were simply overawed, seeing us in high morale, dry, and charging towards them wielding swords. In no time, we crushed the enemy troops."

Thus a master strategist is one who, when conceiving a plan, uses weather as a weapon too. Sometimes, the general combines the effects of weather and terrain when engaging the enemy, for example, the general who confronts the enemy at a battle site just after a howling storm, with the enemy's back towards the deep gorges of rushing waters. And whilst the enemy troops are hungry, soaked, and tired after marching through stormy weathers, the general's troops are well-fed, rested, and eager for a fight, having left the camp after the storm. And I recollect a soldier saying this:

"Seeing the enemy troops in such dire straits emboldened us. With roaring waters to their back and us bold and majestic standing before them, many of them felt cornered. Many gladly downed their arms when offered the chance to surrender. And indeed, many of them opted to join our ranks and fight along-side us. We all share one thing in common: deep admiration for the genius of our general."

Terrain across the earth is as varied as the weather: marshes, deserts, forests, gorges, cliffs, grasslands, plains, hills, mountains, caves, underground hollows, slopes, flat lands, sandy beaches, rivers, valleys. The weather conditions: summer, spring, autumn, winter, sunrise, sunset, moonless nights, full moon, howling winds, gentle breezes, hurricanes, storms, mid-day, evening, dark clouds, twilight, stars. The general who has mastered the art of war takes all these into account when waging war.

4 ▦ 1

Today autumn begins: a day appropriate for reflecting my experiences. What more do I want than to pen my thoughts in the midst of the sounds of fluttering birds and sweetly scented mountain air? And despite the quiet beauty that nature holds, below me men continue to strive to triumph over other men!

From my years of battlefield encounters, in which I have witnessed the success and failure of countless bloody battle engagements, I am able to distil seven major factors that weigh heavily in determining final victory or defeat. Yet men often fail to learn from the past; mistakes are often repeated again and again. If only future strategists can grasp these truths, cries of war already predestined to fail will not be heard and countless innocent lives spared.

For the benefit of future strategists I shall explore these reflections in writing. And for present strategists, if they can grasp the essence of these thoughts, then they should be able to apply them at all times, even in vastly altered circumstances. For so long as there is conflict among men then a thousand years may flow past and yet the essential truths remain substantively the same.

4 ▦ 2

First, the ruler. Who among the rulers vying for central control of the plains is known to be the strongest on matters related to morals? That king who is most discerning, most filial, most loyal, most faithful or, to sum up, the most honourable one; that king shall ultimately triumph over all men. Thus the one who prevails in long armed struggles among kings will be the one known by people to be the strongest on morals. For it is in the nature of things that Good shall in the long run prevail even though Evil seems to be thriving during troubled times. The king whose words are widely held to be worth their weight in gold is more able to secure compromises than one whose words nobody ever trusts. So when a number of kings are locked in conflict over supremacy, then all I need do to identify the likely winner is to enquire:

"Whose words among these kings would you take to be the most reliable, honourable and trustworthy?"

People are attracted to good, honourable kings like bees round a honey pot. And one sure test of honour is whether promises are kept. People yearn for wise kings. A wise king who loves his people, and engages in wars only when all else fails is rare indeed. A promise from such a king, once given, is never dishonoured. Among the kings contending for supremacy, the one most respected for his morals is likely to gravitate towards the central role. This has been so since time immemorial.

Such a king is also likely to attract into his service the best of generals: humane, loyal, wise, devoted, dutiful, courageous, hard-working. For like all human beings, good generals seek to serve the most noble and honourable of the lords. Thus a king whose reputation for observing morals exceeds that of all others is most likely to attract into his service the best of generals – even the enemy's. Above all, the general who has mastered the art of strategy is the most valuable.

4 3

Second, the general. The simple question I ask is:

"Whose generals among those of the contending kings are most skilled in applying the art of strategy in the heat of battle?"

Knowing that, I will be able to predict which king is most likely to prevail eventually. For the outcomes of wars are not predicted just by reckoning the numbers of soldiers, chariots, swords, spears and other weaponry. Mastering the art of strategy also takes intelligence, time and effort. It is only possible through continuous practice, deep meditation and long deliberation.

So how do I assess the strategy skills of a general?

From the analysis of his actions as well as non-actions in a specific war situation I should be able to discern the extent to which he has mastered the skills in *The Art of War*. Although what is stated there may be brief, there are many possible levels of application. First is the simplistic. Next, is the literal. Third, is to read multiple meanings into the words of the text. Fourth, is to use it metaphorically. Fifth, is to search for its deeper significance beyond the words to the consciousness of a strategist.

Thus I admire a general who, though well-versed in *The Art of War*, yet departs from it when circumstances dictate, such as when the enemy anticipates his manoeuvres from his application of the art of war. For at the very core of strategic thinking is the view that any strategy that may be read like a book is easily countered by the enemy and as such is useless. So a general must strive to be flexible in applying the art of war. No strategy should ever be repeated elsewhere. Just as there are myriad configurations of clouds in the skies, there must be infinite ways to configure strategies. And like the dancing movements of the clouds, strategy sequences should unfold in ways difficult to anticipate.

The general who is able to blend strategy with whatever advantages nature has in store is truly remarkable. This brings us to the third factor.

4 ▭ 4

Third, the side able to secure most from what nature has to offer is likely to win, for instance, the side able to secure the best ground in a given terrain. If your troops are the only side which must charge uphill or march across tricky marshlands then that will surely count against you.

Fourth, the side which is better controlled and which is more likely to implement orders. Soldiers, no matter how valiant in the battlefield, are useful only if they obey orders. An army is only effective if its troops are able to act in unison, complying with orders on battle formations.

How then do you instil discipline among troops? By showing that military orders are meant to be complied with.

I recall having to chop off the heads of a king's favourite concubines – despite his strong protests – for failure to comply with my direct orders. These two concubines were each leaders of a squadron of female troops. The king wanted to test my skills in the art of war. I had no alternative but to order their executions. For to spare their two lives at that time might have endangered the lives of many in the future. Troops may perceive that it is still permissible in some circumstances to disobey orders. In war situations it is often impossible to reveal every intended move, and troops must simply act as and when instructed.

Besides being obedient, such troops must themselves hunger to fight. This brings me to the other factors concerning troops: the fifth factor, troops' hunger for battle; the sixth factor, training of troops; and the seventh factor, motivating the troops.

4 🕮 5

Fifth, the side that hungers for battle is the stronger. Thus the side with a stronger moral purpose behind them for waging the war is more likely to be hungrier for battle. But such hunger alone is inadequate. Training is needed to translate these battle-hungry troops into formidable fighters. This is the essence of my *sixth* factor: the training of men. The better trained side is the more likely winner. Strict, disciplined training in the various techniques of war, such as the different weaponry, also toughens the troops, enabling them to bear the inevitable hardships that wars bring. And finally, besides training, motivating troops is equally important. That is my *seventh* factor: the side better motivated through rewards or punishments is the more likely to win.

Change

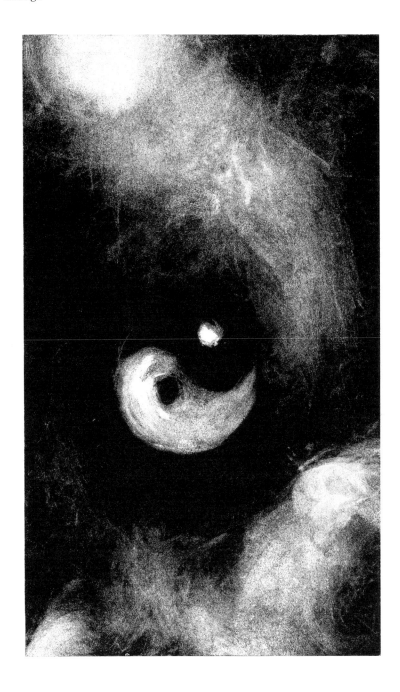

5 ⚏ 1

Another day and I shall see the coming of snow. How quickly time passes. Look at the forest animals, how they adapt to the coming seasonal change! The animals are preparing for the wintry months ahead: below, burrows are being dug, and above, birds are migrating. And the trees too are shedding their leaves in anticipation of change.

How interesting that the forest snakes, river frogs and toads in the pond all hibernate throughout the severely cold winter and emerge from their deep sleep only with the stirrings of spring. Even the bats, who are inactive in the day, choose to hibernate during the coming wintry season. So for these animals, winter is a period of rejuvenation. For an army too there should be a time for rejuvenation before another major military undertaking is embarked upon.

Such cycles in nature – spring, summer, autumn and winter – may have a deeper purpose. And that may be to alert us to adapt to change.

5 ⚏ 2

All manifestations of adaptations in nature contain useful lessons for the observant strategist, who must always study them. For my part, I must capture these inner reflections on adapting to change before my thoughts float on to other matters or recede deeper into my mind. One of the most difficult skills for any strategist to master is to be able to adapt strategy to changing situations. The best strategists are those capable of formulating adaptive strategies. Such a task is however mentally demanding, for there are any number of possibilities in a changing world. But a general incapable of acting flexibly in a changing and shifting war situation is unlikely to sustain victory for long. Such a general may be physically strong and majestic-looking but, like tall, mighty trees that are often seen to be uprooted during stormy weather, he may be brought down by swift, unexpected turns of events. Yet a tiny blade of grass on a mountain side, because it is able to bend with the changing winds, will survive stormy weather. What an irony! Indeed the stronger, the more deeply rooted and therefore more inflexible the tree, the greater the risk of it being uprooted in howling winds. And no matter how strongly and in which direction the winds may howl, the lowly grass will outlast the mighty tree.

Chance events often alter the balance of net advantage accruing to any one side in a war. So those responsible for implementing the strategy must be quick of mind in taking actions necessary to counterbalance any negative developments. Thus reinforcements scheduled to arrive today may be delayed by stormy weather. The generals who can survive such crises are those able to figure out what possible actions – alternative defence strategies – to take when unexpected events occur.

5 3

In my forest walks I recall meeting an animal that inspired my thoughts on an instantaneously responsive defence. I saw a strange animal whose skin seemed to be very well-armoured. I later asked around and found the animal was known as the pangolin, which eats ants. What is most remarkable about this small animal is that when threatened with a stick, it quickly rolls itself into a ball of scaly armour. Is it not possible too for troops to be trained to adapt quickly to signs of immediate threat – say, sprays of arrows – by rolling themselves tightly together and using hand-held, metal shields for protection?

On another occasion I saw a strange animal whose body may be curled up, with sharp spikes sticking out, when it is endangered. So, unable to avoid danger by making a speedy escape, these little animals have taken to arming their bodies throughout with prickly spikes. I later learnt that these animals are hedgehogs. Can generals train their troops to respond likewise when faced with dangers? That is, when enemy troops attack unexpectedly, his soldiers could quickly form themselves into a tight group, with spears sticking outwards?

When seeing a tortoise along the river bank I am reminded of how it will recoil into its shell at any sign of danger. Do you not see a parallel between this behaviour and how our villagers will quickly rush to be inside the mud walls when there is a warning of danger? Indeed, in some villages, the mud walls seem to be constructed according to the idea of quick withdrawal. Perhaps the ancients were inspired by the tortoises in constructing villages with protective walls. Generals should always ponder on how troops should respond intuitively to any early signs of danger.

5   4

Even more dramatic are insects in the forest that are able to change their skin colours to harmonise with the bark of trees they land on, so generals as strategists versed in the art of strategy can redefine their strategies in the light of changing environments. Insects unable to do so will then be easy prey for birds on the hunt. This is due to the contrast between the colour of their bodies and that of the trees. Green insects on green leaves are more difficult to spot. Generals should therefore learn from nature and adapt their strategies to changing circumstances, as does the brown lizard on brown tree-bark. Such adaptive behaviour of insects and animals enables them to elude certain death when faced with their enemies, the birds. For this reason certain insects are experts in these elusive arts: bodies shaped like twigs or leaves escape the sharp-eyed birds. The best is however the chameleon lizard: on the sands, it is yellow; on the rocks, grey; green on leaves; brown on tree-bark. And if needed, patterns of spots and stripes can appear on its skin! Similarly, generals should master elusory skills by being able continuously to adapt strategies to changing contexts.

5   5

Another aspect of adaptive change is reflected in metamorphosis, found among some insects in the forest: the caterpillar transforms itself into a chrysalis and though immobilised for twelve days, emerges as a butterfly. The essence of the process is to be able to change into something radically different. For whilst the caterpillar only crawls, the butterfly can fly. An analogy may be that of an adaptive general able to recruit, train and equip farmers who work by day and secretly transform them through training. Out of the intensive training emerge mighty warriors, ready to launch nightly raids on unsuspecting enemies. Like the bats that rest in the day and hunt at night, these soldiers work on their fields during daylight and come out to prey on enemies during the night. With further training, these soldiers become expert night hunters, like the much-feared owls who hunt rats. Or they become like the vampire bats whose skills lie in being able to suck the blood of their victims without them even knowing!

Another principle of adaptation is evident even from watching simple, everyday happenings, for example when drinking wine. Notice how wine adapts itself to whatever shape of vessel it is poured into. The variety in the sizes and shapes of containers does not matter. Wine simply adapts. Another example is the flow of water from the mountains through the changing terrain into the sea. And how easily water adapts itself to contours of the land! Like animals that hibernate in the cold, so waters become inactive during the winter: they lie motionless on the river as ice blocks. So the strategist must draw from nature lessons of adaptation to change. Change is the only constant in life. The current situation is what it is due to a balance of forces. New developments may unsettle the equilibrium and thereby create imbalance. So the wise general counteracts to correct such imbalances.

Today, the sun seems to shine a little longer than in previous days. And the winds do not seem as cold as before. With the coming of spring the forest turns green. I welcome the greening of the forest for that is when I renew my learning from nature about the hidden secrets of strategy.

With observant eyes anyone can learn much from studying Mother Nature. I recall how amazed I was on seeing plants trapping flies and even bees. Yet how deceptively harmless these plants look! Indeed, they seem very attractive on the surface and I believe also appear so to the unsuspecting insects. In such simple observations are found profound lessons for generals who aspire to be master strategists.

An essential ingredient for a general's success as a strategist is the mastery of skills in deception: how to entrap the enemy. For that to work, detailed understanding of the weaknesses and strengths of the enemy is required. One idea is to work on his weakness so as to defeat him. Another is to use his strengths to work against him. In the art of fighting, the idea is to redirect the force of the fighter towards himself. The mastery of these talents, I believe, is one of the hallmarks of a wise strategist.

For any trap to work, it must deceive the enemy completely. The idea is to encourage the enemy to be complacent and unguarded, or to take immediate, unthinking, rash and care-less actions. For a trap to work, lures must be used to draw the enemy forward. Although these are the principles, in practice there are infinite variations on the setting of traps. Just as plants differ in how they trap their prize enemies, so must a general vary his approaches depending on the circumstances.

Some plants snap their leaves together quickly to catch an enemy bee. An insect is unlikely to be aware that plants can kill with such rapid snapping movements. If only these insects were able to watch for themselves the swift killing actions of these plants! Herein lies the deception: although able to snap quickly, these plants give *an appearance of being unable to do so*. Such deceptive devices are less likely to

25

succeed if plants openly display their capabilities before the eyes of the insects. For then the insects are likely to sense danger and be on the alert for quick escape. So the strategic deception is, *when* able, appear to be *unable* and catch the enemy unprepared.

Other plants trap by drowning. I remember the sweet smell of a pitcher plant. Such a smell must have lured the insects to venture inside the 'pitcher' in a greedy search for the tasty nectar. That is exactly the same principle applied by our ancestors when laying traps to capture wild animals. To lure a wolf into the open doors of an iron cage, put a fat chicken inside; for a tiger, use a goat as bait. So, depending on his enemy, the general must devise different lures.

6 3

To lure an enemy carelessly to enter and attack a city, make it appear to be unguarded. For at the heart of deception is the use of *appearances*. An enemy that rarely besieges cities may still be lured to attack an army camping out in the country if it *appears to be disorderly*: for one human weakness of warring generals is the desire to gain a reputation for quick, decisive and easy victories. So feigned inferiority may be the key to lure the march of enemy troops.

Sometimes one may need to *anger* the enemy general into taking rash actions. Even young beautiful women can be used as lures to win wars. How? To distract the attention of enemy generals on matters related to war. And when beautiful women are given as gifts, this may cause the generals to lower their military preparedness on account of their preoccupation. So in this way beautiful women fulfil the same role as sweet-smelling nectar in plants.

The construction of these pitcher plant traps are worthy of close study: inside, the vase-shaped leaves are hairy and slippery with liquid. Insects do not seem able to crawl out once inside these leaves. Indeed, the hairs inside point downwards to the nectar at the base of the leaf. This makes it difficult for insects with wet legs to crawl out of the pitcher. The slipperiness caused by wetness ensures that the sheer weight of the insects drives them downwards too.

So the general must pay close attention to how traps are

constructed. If enemy troops are to be trapped into dug-out holes with spikes protruding from the sides, ensure these are dug deeply and sharp spikes are planted. For if the holes are poorly constructed, enemy troops may be able to crawl out of the traps and retaliate. Attention to detail is as crucial to success as is the broad picture. A trap that fails to kill will make it doubly hard to apply in the future.

6   4

Besides plants, insects are equally adept at laying traps. The strategist can benefit from studying how the spider in the garden lays traps that are effectively deceptive. It spins its web made of such fine silk that it is almost invisible to the eye. Insects in flight are caught unawares. So in the same manner our ancestors mastered the art of using nets to catch fish. For nets placed in the murky waters of the river are equally invisible to the fish.

And see how strategic are those spots in the house where the spiders choose to spin their webs: often dark corners, sheltered from strong wind. And the fishermen I have spoken to tell me that where they lay the nets is of equal importance in determining how successful the catch!

From the point of view of the spider's enemies – the various insects – all seems quiet and inactive. Yet in reality, the spider is fully active, lying hidden and waiting for action. So the wise general *feigns inaction* while preparing for rapid action to slaughter the enemy. So to lure enemies to go along a path deep into the thick undergrowth of a forest, troops waiting on the sides for the kill must be so disciplined as to remain motionless. Not a human sound must be heard until the signal for slaughter is given. And at that moment the troops must be so stirred up as to charge ferociously and intimidate their enemies.

6   5

And observe too *how* the spider approaches its prey. As the spider waits for the trapped victim to be tired out with struggling, it spins even more silk round it. I notice how patient the

Deception

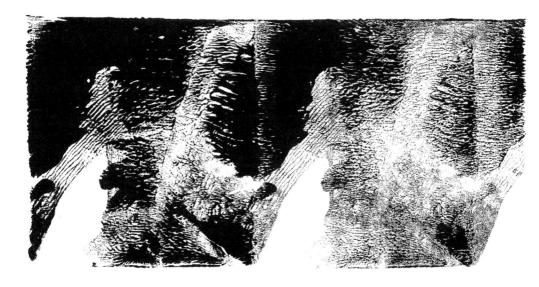

spider can be. In this manner the spider is capable of killing an enemy insect many times its size by simply waiting for the trapped enemy to wear itself out. So size alone is not necessarily decisive of the final outcome. The wise general, when countering a much larger enemy, should devise a strategy to *strain the enemy and weary him.* And like the spider that fights the insect only when it is completely exhausted from fruitless struggle, so must the general only fight large enemy troops when they are utterly dispirited and tired. For only then does the spider attempt to move the insect to the centre of its web so as to devour it.

So the thoughtful general must study and reflect on the art of deception to win against the enemy. Strategic lessons are transferable by analogy from the plant or insect world through keen observation and deep reflection. Make use of changing circumstances and enemy information when devising deceptions for trapping enemy troops. Generals must also never rely on old tricks but should constantly strive to engineer new deceptions.

Prediction

7 ▦ 1

Today, I am opening this book again, stirred not by nature but by men. Another general has just left. The question he asked unsettled me deeply: Can outcomes of wars be predicted?

His question stirred me to ponder over and over again: Are the destinies of strategists written in the stars or discoverable through the crackling of tortoise-shells?

Some believe that war outcomes are etched on eyes, eyebrows, noses, ears, palms and indeed the faces of generals. Some look to omens to predict outcomes.

Are wars necessary as part of a wider scheme of things in nature? Do they lie within the manipulative powers of nature?

Or are they more the result of men themselves seeking to resolve conflicts inherent in the very essence of human society?

7 ▦ 2

I am certain that whatever sway nature may have over the destinies of men, outcomes of wars are predictable on the basis of a handful of critical factors. Or to put it more strongly, based on precise assessment of these factors, I am able to say which will be the winning side. For the side that wins must have had a critical advantage. The master strategist does not wage a war unless his side is certain to prevail from the very outset. Like the insects in nature, with highly complex traps to capture enemies, so must the strategist sharpen his perceptive skills for evaluating battle outcomes. His powers reliably to form conclusions from the particular to the general are basic to his role as strategist. Needless to say, thinking skills – involving data or information collection, analysis, interpretation, and generating stratagems – must be honed daily in the mind of the strategist, so that deep, unfathomable strategies may evolve in times of need. The mind of the strategist is deeply reflective and only from such a well of thought can winning strategies be finely crafted. For the mind is the essential tool for the master strategist, a mind that is able to estimate the chances of victory.

Contextual elements such as these have to be taken into account:

1 The people–king relationship – how harmonious are the people with the king?
2 Natural forces that pervade the earth – in whose favour are these: winds, gales, thunderstorms, rain, coldness, heat, mist, wetness, dryness, earthquakes?
3 Geography – who has the advantage in terms of distances traversed, bridges, narrow paths, rocky terrain, swamps, deserts?
4 Qualities of leadership in war – who is most humane and daring, and has the most agility of mind, character, trust-worthiness, respect of his soldiers?
5 Organisation in the army – which side is better in terms of discipline, people, material, equipment, tools?

So before formulating war tactics, one must estimate the relative strengths of the people king relationships of those in conflict. For war may become a long drawn-out affair, and the willingness of the people to support the king will determine success.

Natural forces have also to be considered: a country devastated by earthquakes is obviously in a weakened state. So is the side that has been through a period of drought. And troops that have to journey through swamps and wind-swept plains before engaging the enemy are likely to be more weary and less eager for battle than those well-rested.

And surely, the army led by a quick-thinking general, one able to adapt battle formations to changing circumstances, is better poised to win than one known to be inflexible. For nothing remains constant for ever, especially in war.

Moreover, the general level of organisation in the army is critical. A wild mob of people with knives, sticks and choppers is less formidable than organised, uniformed troops: these fight under high-flying banners, equipped with specialised weapons, assigned to clear tasks and roles.

If on balance of these factors, your side predominates, then war should be contemplated. Otherwise, the strategist should be very careful about engaging the enemy. If your side is the weaker through such reckoning, then it is better quietly to build up strength.

For besides these, the following related, more specific factors are equally relevant in determining which side wins:

1 The side whose king has higher moral standing;
2 The side with a more skilled general;
3 The army as a whole more capable of exploiting natural forces and geography;
4 The army that is more tightly regulated, wherein instructions are rigorously implemented;
5 The army whose soldiers are eager and hungry for battle, but angered when asked to withdraw;
6 The army that offers continuous, intensive training for officers and men;
7 The side with a motivation system in place that rewards effort and punishes wrongful actions.

I shall elaborate by comparing hypothetical cases. First I would ask about the moral standing of the two kings. The tendency of people is to rally round kings known for their virtuous characters and moral conduct. Cruel, strict, tough kings may, through inspiring fear, seem successful in the short term but their victories are difficult to sustain. Second, I would enquire which general is personally better versed or trained in the arts of war. No matter how grand a strategy is, generals are still the ones at the battle front directing the war. A poorly skilled general may fail to implement a grandly conceived strategy. A resourceful general may be able to turn the tables on the battlefield even if the strategy is weak. Closely linked to the quality of the general is the overall capability of the army and its officers. Are they able, when fighting on ground away from the supervision of kings and generals, to adapt strategy to take advantage of whatever nature has in store?

And yet another associated factor: how tightly knit and regulated are these troops? Or are they no more than an *ad hoc* gathering of people aroused on the spur of the moment to fight?

No doubt the will to fight is essential for victory: nothing is worse than well-armed, trained and disciplined troops who are sapped of the will to do battle because they do not

Spears

share in the cause. Conversely nothing can stop a people's army whose wills are forged together in determination to lay down their lives for a cause.

But such a people's army needs intensive training in the military arts. It can only become a potent force when there is in place a proper, graded system of recognition, reward and punishment so that people will be motivated to do their utmost.

For a strategist to excel he must develop the ability to weigh up these factors in predicting the winner. And a strategist capable of accurately judging these factors is a priceless treasure to the state. For he will be able to counsel kings and generals against rash battles that only deplete resources: human lives, precious grain, scarce horses, swords, spears, armour, uniforms. But to counsel inaction when victory is certain is also erroneous. For the idea of strategy is to fight when victory is certain, to fight a war that is already won.

2

1 1

IT IS A full moon in the Summer of the Year of the Rat. And the brightness of the moon reminds me how moonlight has instructed me in strategy. I recall how the moon shows up remains on the battlefield! But what contrasts – the glorious morning with its scented air in battle-readiness and the gloom and stench of evening weariness; the thrills of seeing armed troops with banners fluttering and the terrible sight of wretched bodies strewn among dead horses.

Among the dead are the headless, the armless, legless, eyeless, earless, fingerless, the footless. And blood that still oozes out of cold, lifeless bodies now nourishes the grass. Tattered banners, broken wheels, dented armour, shattered chariots: once symbols of kingly might now lie as worthless as little stones on the grass.

How costly war is! If only someone could reckon the cost of war! And yet kings can wage war just on the spur of the moment! The tally of war costs is written on the wide expanse of that battlefield. If only the kings would come with me just to add these up: a thousand four-horse chariots, a thousand four-horse, leather-covered wagons, and many more thousands of troops.

So if only kings could be more conscious of the cost of war, and count more carefully before they declare war. And to think that kings can be keen to wage war just to wreak revenge for a verbal insult! For what is lost on battlefields is lost for ever: bodies, horses, carriages, banners, armour. Dead bodies cannot till the land. And without grain, cities will have no food! So is it not wiser just to let anger subside than to wage useless wars and stir up emotions even further? For an

Costs

angry person may yet become happy, but the soul does not return to a dead body.

1 ▰ 2

As I reckon the costs of war, I begin to realise how substantial the amount really is. For what is immediately apparent as the cost of war is what lies as waste in the aftermath of battles. Less immediately apparent wastes are just as costly. Every chariot requires lacquer and glue in the making. Every soldier wears clothes made of cotton. Every weapon is made out of metal and wood. Every wagon requires leather. And so on and so on. Just imagine how much better people's lives would be if these raw materials of cotton, wood and metal were put to uses other than war!

Besides the visible costs of war, whose accounts are written on the battlefield, so much more money needs to be expended on the invisibles costs; transportation, grain, food, stipends for advisors, gifts and money for volunteers. For troops and horses on the battlefield have to be fed, and grain and food must be transported across the country to battle sites. And fees must be paid to advisors on various aspects of waging wars. Expert advise is needed on the best routes of attack. Advisors can also give insights into the enemy's battle strategies or training methods. Account has also to be taken of expensive gifts made to volunteers able to render help in the war effort. Through the help of such volunteers advance routes may be mapped.

Even less visible, if not invisible, and thus more difficult to estimate, are the costs of bribes paid for secret information from spies. Yet provision must be made for this. Spies vary in their greed for money. Some are willing to provide information on account of their own hatred of the enemy. Others are more scheming and demanding of rewards. But even these are a pittance compared to the overall cost of waging wars. And indeed such spending, if effective, may even save unnecessary costs in the war effort – especially if victory is possible by using spies rather than waging war!

And also unaccounted for are the efforts put in by ordinary people to provide for the additional needs of war. A high cost often left unaccounted for is the value of goods forgone: valuable things that may have been produced by men but are taken away to the battlefield. And what of the metal from farm tools melted down to provide spears? Spears cannot produce valuable food which farm tools could. How does one account for such losses? Farmers are deprived of what is their due through lack of farming implements.

The losses for some families are enormous: not only may farm animals, metal implements, and whatever is useful for the war effort be confiscated, but lands may be left unattended for years for lack of farm hands. And in the families of the dead and gone, it may simply be too much even to estimate: young, strong males who, were it not for the war, would have provided for their parents through their old age. Thus the cost of war is so incalculable that kings must use war only as the very last resort; on no account should any war be waged lightly.

So the wise king will consider carefully the social costs of war before contemplating any aggressive moves. And for any wars so planned budgets must be set and cost per activity estimated in terms of taels of gold required. The king's treasury should not be depleted unnecessarily through poor control in the spending of gold.

For the same outcome, as many feasible alternatives should be considered as possible, and each evaluated in terms of the weight of gold needed to achieve it. Thus if enemy kings may be persuaded by a beautiful woman to avert war, such a woman should be sought for and offered. She should feel proud to be chosen. For through her singular efforts, massive suffering, thousands of lives, taels of gold and much more are saved. And her name will be remembered for eternity by those who benefit from her sacrifice. And if an enemy king desires one of our priceless jade ornaments, foolish is the king who wages a war just to keep it. For whilst new jade pieces may still be carved from blocks of stone, lives and kingdoms once lost are gone for ever! There is little value in having a priceless piece of jade when all else is lost on the battlefield.

In the world's turmoil, wars are often inevitable. Wise are the kings who recognise these truths and work from them. So to avoid wars, one must always be ready for them. To be always ready and yet not deplete the king's treasury is the golden rule in budgeting for wars. Let me explain. To keep huge, standing armies will only drain the state's resources.

But having a population of farmer-soldiers with a core group of highly skilled generals, officers and select troops is a strategy of war-preparedness that does not deplete resources. For farmer-soldiers to fight well, regular training in use of weapons is needed. But such war exercises also enhance their physical health. And there is a need for quick mobilisation of these farmer-soldiers in time of emergency. Thus cities must have the means to activate troops quickly. Regular troops guarding the border must be alert to any sign of enemy manoeuvres. If such an alert mobilisation system is in place enemy kings will be unable to gain quick victory through surprise attacks.

No state, however rich, can wage wars without regard to the resources consumed as a consequence. Costs of war should be estimated with care and understood by generals charged with the responsibility for waging them. I estimate for a major war that direct, visible costs can easily add up to more than a thousand taels of gold daily. So if an alternative exists, do not wage a war. Exhaust whatever stratagems are available. Use whatever schemes there are. If pushed to the limit, then muster your forces to scare the enemy through a show of strength. When conflict is inevitable, fight a short but decisive battle. Never wage a prolonged, epic war. For there is little to gain on either side in any long drawn-out clash of arms.

A prolonged autumn. I notice that when things in nature become prolonged, problems start to emerge. Like the swelling of rivers due to prolonged rains. The waves of water from the glutted rivers sweep away livestock; children are lost, washed away to unknown places. And I recall in the Year of the Ox the prolonged failure of rains to come. The drought that followed was just as harmful to the people. For with dry wells no seedlings may be planted, just as with swollen rivers they are wiped away. The consequences of prolonged rains or their failure are that whole families have to seek food in faraway lands. Such poverty is due to prolonged natural phenomena. In relation to wars, one can learn from such natural calamities how important is the role of time in determining outcomes. Operations in wars, because they are so costly, and so consuming of resources, should never on any account be prolonged. Time is a critical variable in war and must always be considered.

In the distant past, blunders are recorded to have been made in being too swift when waging war, but there is not a single instance of any well-conceived operation known to have been prolonged. Generals in their eagerness for wars sometimes forgot that the primary objective of war is victory and not prolonged engagement in locked battles. Some people, because of their emotions from having suffered the loss of loved ones in battle, may see war as revenge; the general must realise that lives lost in war are irretrievably gone. No prolonging of wars can bring back lives. Wars only fuel more hatred, more resentment.

Always remember too that any prolonged bullfight only hurts both fighting bulls, to the benefit of waiting tigers. For two states locked in prolonged conflict are likely to be easy prey to neighbouring states. And finally, even if a bull survives the long struggle, such a victory is but short-lived. For a hungry tiger is unlikely to let an opportunity of certain victory pass: it will pounce on a battle-scarred bull. The prize of victory is just too tempting for restraint to have any effect: two bulls for the price of one! And the sly tiger does not want to wait. Why? With each passing day the bull is recovering a little from its wounds. No strategist of any repute will fail to advise the tiger to seize the opportunity that lies before it. I doubt whether in such dire circumstances anything can be done to rescue the ailing, badly injured bull. If only the fighting bull had known the ill-effects of prolonging war and the immense danger of a neighbouring tiger lying in wait!

Like the fighting bull that gets a little more injured, hurt or wounded by the exchange of blows through time spent locked in battle, each day, week, month or year of war that passes means more people are injured, more dismayed, more disabled, more materials consumed, more troops exhausted, more weapons dulled, more chariots lost, more animals dead, more depletion of the king's treasury, more officers dead, more people frustrated, more horses worn out, more people battle-weary – more problems. Each extra day of war means less enthusiasm for battle, less shining armour, less sharp the edges of the sword, less grain in store, less ardour among soldiers, less discipline.

2 3

The passing of time in war must be seen through the eyes of the people. Prolonged sacrifices to war efforts without certainty of outcome only serve to diminish their faith in the king. And such changes in the perception of war take place with the passing of time. Inconclusive wars are to be dreaded by generals and kings alike. For people's trust and faith in those who lead the war efforts must diminish when the meaninglessness of war dawns on them: they see their sacrifices lead to nothing but a continuing need for even more sacrifices. And therein lies the danger that kings lose the support of their people for the war efforts. Nothing is worse than having to quell internal rebellion when engaged in external wars.

What of the individual soldier? Trained to obey orders, soldiers have little choice but to fight as commanded by their generals. But even then there is a difference between a war fought on one's own conviction and a war that is merely an act of one's profession. So in a war the advantage lies with the side that fights on strong moral grounds. However, with the passage of time, the early euphoria of war is likely to quieten

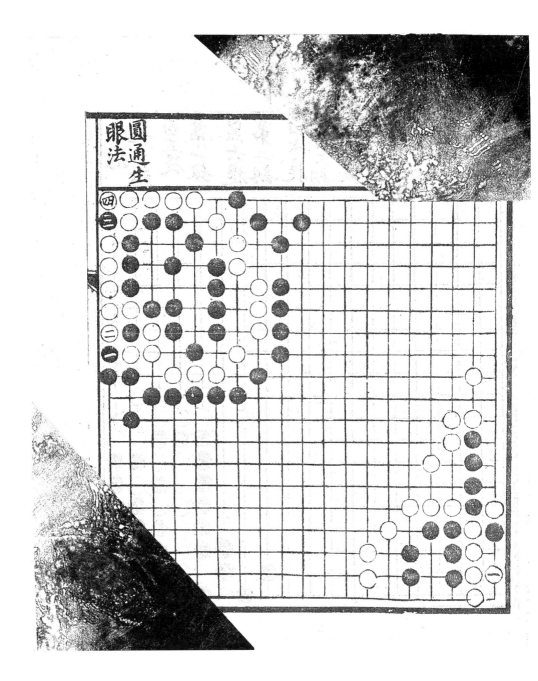

down. Remains of euphoric feelings, if any, are likely to evaporate on seeing pile upon pile of dead, disfigured bodies. As time passes without clear resolution on either side, the thirst for revenge is likely to be quenched by the realisation of the senselessness of waging endless bloody wars. Disillusion with war may even emerge if wars drag on inconclusively and with that problems of discipline among troops, of insubordination and of desertion will become ever more common. To all these may be attributed one root cause: prolongation of wars. So kings and generals must constantly be alert to the influence of the passage of time on the will to continue to fight.

2 ▰ 4

All things in nature have an inherent cycle: seasons of spring, summer, autumn, winter; birth, growth, maturity, decline, death; the moon's cycle of total darkness, arc-shaped light, half, three-quarter, full moon, three-quarter, half, arc-shaped and back again to nothingness. So war too has a cycle of possible psychological stages: the wait, preparation, march, clash, suffering, regret, remorse.

In more detail the cycle is as follows. First, an initial phase of heightened consciousness when preparing for war: soldiers eagerly sharpening their weapons, getting ready for the mission on the battlefield. Then there is the elation and euphoria of marching down the city roads with people waving, showering flowers, cheering, shouting themselves hoarse. Next comes the long, lonely march down seemingly endless winding paths among the cheerless trees and merciless sun. Then there is the camping under moonless skies deep inside dark forests, accompanied by the music of the insects. Later, drums, gongs, fluttering banners, hand signals, glittering spears add to the tension before the clashing of swords. Charging forward, the troops search for bodies into which to thrust their blades and draw out red, warm blood, at the same time offering their bodies to be slain. After the dynamics of war comes the stillness of fields littered with dead and wasted remains: animals, human corpses, wagons, weapons, banners, gongs, drums. And suddenly, the inner voice, often buried by war propaganda, begins to ask: what is the meaning of all this?

Paradox

Late into the night, cold and wintry, with winds howling through the windows, I crawl out of my bed. The winds are so strong that I cannot light the candles. Yet there is a burning desire in me to set my thoughts on paper. For the events and characters are so vividly etched on to the pages of my mind. And strangely, in these circumstances I seem more able to recollect the moving scenes of war. I must really get down to writing and take advantage of the brightness of the moon: light streams into the corners of my room, unperturbed by the winds. For despite the disadvantages of cold winds circulating in the room, my mind seems as bright as the moon, lighting up ever more sharply images of war buried deep in hidden closets. How strange. Yet at times when I am well prepared, with brush in hand, my mind remains barren. On occasions like these, with cold winds about me, I seize the brush to capture these thoughts on paper, using whatever moonlight there is.

In life there are many circumstances, including war, when advantages coexist with disadvantages. I might even say that advantages are inherent in disadvantages; it is a question of whether one is able to see them as such. A person in disadvantageous situations should grasp at the 'opportunities' to realise the advantages. And going back to what has just been said: it may be precisely because I am about to immerse myself in sleep that my mind recollects floods of memories so vividly. The flow of thoughts is so irresistible as to move me to the writing table. Contrast this with the situation when I am well equipped to write – seated under the candlelight with brush in hand – and yet the thoughts hardly flow! And I see in life the equivalent of this experience: the principle of disadvantages in advantageous circumstances. Perhaps that is nature's way of developing and testing the inner resolve, strength, will and determination of men. Thus nature tests me in my resolve to put my thoughts on paper by letting them flow in the most unexpected of circumstances.

If I may set out the principle more generally, it is simply: what often 'is' actually 'is not' and what perhaps 'is not' actually 'is'. So what may appear to be an advantageous time to write is not necessarily so. And when it appears to be disadvantageous to write, it is often the time to capture the rich flow of ideas. The person who succeeds is one able to apply this principle to cope with worldly change. For he sees, in the disadvantage, seeds of the advantage and conversely, seeds of the disadvantage buried deep in the advantage. Thus an empire reaching its height of glory often plants within itself the very seeds of its decline.

For the paradox is that in strength there is weakness, and in weakness there is strength. Through the passage of time strong becomes weak and weak strong. So no empire is everlasting. For on reaching its pinnacle of power weaknesses begin to evolve and manifest themselves within it.

I shall illustrate this principle, drawing on my experiences of war.

3 ▰ 2

What applies to my writing situation is also applicable to wider contexts of life: it is equally true for war. Regular, professional troops, well fed, housed, equipped and paid, may be an advantage. But therein lie possible disadvantages. These troops may lack the will to weather a long and determined struggle. So used are some of them to the quiet life of simple guard duties inside city walls that the prospect of bloody wars waged far out in the wilds may be chilling to them. How different are the farmers, wrongly dispossessed of their lands by the enemy! Even though they may lack basic military skills these farmers, once trained, are often the bravest fighters in spearheading the charge of the army. The outrage of having being dispossessed of their lands drives them forward relentlessly, without fear. Such farmers turned troops are capable of enduring unimaginable hardships. And many a capable army officer has that background of a farmer whose home has been destroyed by enemies.

Thus the wise general, in times of calm and quiet, anticipates danger through recognising this principle long before others. He makes sure that his troops are exposed, if necessary by rotation of duties, and hardened by nature: camping in the wild, traversing deserts, marching long distances over difficult terrain. Also, military skills are constantly tested and graded, involving the use of swords, spears, arrows, halberds, knives and fire. For nothing is worse than to have regular troops seasoned to city life. The general recognises too that his army may be considerably strengthened by absorbing and using enemy troops who have given themselves up. Instead of slaughtering enemy troops – what is the use of dead bodies? – he tries to convert them to his own advantage. This is to turn what is initially dangerous to oneself into something useful. Thus the general treats captured enemy troops humanely. And through acts of kindness he tries to win their loyalty and belief in his cause. He tells them about the moral cause he is fighting for and tries to win them over. For once their loyalties are pledged to him personally the general may then be able to deploy these troops against his new enemy forces.

3 3

Often one finds that strength may itself induce weaknesses. Thus I remember the story of a former king who lost his kingdom due to his neglect of military affairs on account of its size *vis-à-vis* its neighbours. If your kingdom has an army ten times the size of the largest of your neighbours, the tendency is for you to grow complacent. And as a result of its numerical superiority the generals also become equally arrogant, counting on sheer numbers to overawe the enemy. Worse still, the generals neglect the study of the various arts related to warfare. And because of their numerical inferiority, the generals in the neighbouring states study and investigate deeply the various aspects of the art of war. What is worse, the officers and commanders in the numerically superior state become equally arrogant over time and neglect the study of the arts of war. Precious money, intended for purchases of weaponry, is diverted to fund elaborate parties. Whilst the numerically inferior states, conscious of their weaknesses, devote efforts to study of war and especially how to confront a numerically superior foe. And money is poured into building an arsenal of ever more potent weapons, weapons that can help these smaller states overcome their limited numbers. And fearful of being suddenly overrun by the numerically superior state, the smaller states invest in resources to build an extended network of spies. And thus as a result of this devotion to effort, the smaller states are able to send false information and wrong signals to the numerically superior king, such as how weak, unprepared and fearful the kings of the smaller states are. This information in turn encourages ever-growing indulgence by the stronger king in pleasures of the body, again to the neglect of military arts. People living in the stronger state too become more and more disillusioned with their king who, in his indulgence, has neglected stately affairs. As part of an overarching strategy to contain the military prowess of the stronger king, the smaller states send their most beautiful women, best wines, foods and treasures to him. With each passing year the strong, despite their numbers, become weaker and the weak strong as a consequence of their efforts, preparation and unity. But it takes time for strength to become weakness and weakness to become strength. And the signs of collapse begin to become visible when the people of the stronger state rise up to rebel against their king for his gross neglect of the affairs of the state through his overindulgence in bodily pleasures. Every uprising among the people is cruelly crushed by the bloated but poorly trained and ill-disciplined army. The soldiers take the occasion to plunder their own people and enrich themselves. So when the neighbouring states unite to conquer their once superior neighbour the people quickly rise to declare their allegiance to the conquering states. Allegiance is further fuelled by how kind the conquering armies are towards the people of the conquered state. Invading armies even return articles wrongly snatched by their own armies in quelling the uprisings! The news of such civilised behaviour of the invading troops spreads like wildfire across the countryside and village after village begins to welcome the invading army instead of rising up against it. And generals of the once strong state are unable to be sure of the loyalty of their troops, for many have also begun to defect to the other side following the changing fortunes. Some switch sides right under the noses of the generals by refusing to engage enemy troops and instead surrender as groups of soldiers led by their officers. Since the ministers of the superior state have been bribed to the core, none cares to bring the truth to the king, taken up as he is with his own bodily desires and pleasures. Indeed, it is only when the flames of war are burning in his palace that it dawns on the king, still in bed taking his pleasure, how costly are his passionate fires. Unable to confront reality the king asks his bedfellow to plunge the royal sword, studded with jewels, into his bosom. Alas, strength has turned into weakness and, with invading armies now awaiting orders to march inside the palace gates, weakness has become strength. Nothing, as is said in the *Book of Changes*, remains constant, and in the ebb and flow of life what was once strong is now weak and what was weak strong.

I am glad to have captured these thoughts in writing amidst the now icily cold winds circulating in the room. The night skies have become so clouded that only the most determined of the moon's rays reach into the room. Yet my mind remains so illumined that almost every piece of memory can easily be seen with the mind's eye. And my body seems to be kept comfortably warm by the mere brightness of my inner thoughts and the vigour of my brushstrokes. For I have overcome weakness and become strong by being able to record these thoughts despite difficult external circumstances. And with these thoughts now so freshly brushed on paper I too need to retire before night becomes morning. And knowing that I have succeeded in leaving what thoughts are on my mind for posterity I would be glad to catch the night's sleep. Sweet is my sleep now I know a key point in strategy has been brushed on to paper for eternity.

I have just returned from a long walk across the forest tracks. I have been observing how animals survive by living in the wild, taking enough for their needs from what there is in nature. Down below in the ponds and rivers the fish must take what they need from what is there. Up in the blue skies I see flocks of birds flying in beautiful formations. At this time each year I see them fly; they leave and return again months later. At such height, I cannot see each bird individually but it is clear that none seem to be carrying with them stocks of food. Some birds seen flying high above still dive for food within the thick of the forests. Keepers of sheep and horses in the far north are also known to traverse vast distances in the search for food among new pastures. And the eagle that I have now learnt to recognise, staying high up in the mountain peak, also hovers above treetops hunting for rats or rabbits as prey.

What should men do about food when they journey long distances?

Men who journcy far across mountainous regions should learn to take for food what is found in the forests. If men have to rely on their usual daily food packed on their backs the weight will be unbearable. Some longer journeys are simply impossible if men rely only on packed food brought from home.

Generals especially must train their men to survive in the jungle by finding food from among the thick vegetation. In forests many wild plants may be eaten. There are also wild fruits. Although some roots are poisonous there are those which are nutritious. Besides the fruits, roots and vegetables, men could hunt for meat. Hunting skills must be developed in order for men to survive through a long arduous journey across these forests. Soldiers should be tutored in the arts of laying traps to capture animals for food. Birds may be shot with arrows to provide a delicious evening meal. The skill in making fire from dried wood must again be mastered. For without fire, no cooking is possible. Basic cooking implements have to be carried by the men, such as knives, pots, skewers and plates.

Another factor for survival is the availability of water. The journey must be planned so that there are places to refill water containers. Water too is needed to keep the soldiers clean. If the main route is across mountainous regions, places where water is to be found must be enquired into. Where the planned route cuts across rivers soldiers may then master the art of spearing fish for food. The rivers are also ideal places for soldiers to take a refreshing bath. Bathing can invigorate the spirit after a long and tired march.

These are vital considerations especially when waging a distant war. For soldiers suffering from acute hunger pangs cannot be expected to be enthusiastic about fighting wars. At the same time their strength should not be depleted on account of having to shoulder heavy war provisions. So generals in their formulation of strategy must consider this factor carefully: how best to ensure there is food for the soldiers throughout a journey.

On a larger scale, the question often arises as to how often the ordinary people should be made to contribute to the war effort: sons for soldiers, grain for food, cloth and other supplies? No war can be sustained for long without the people's support. For the king's troops are but fish swimming in a sea of people. And whilst wars can be waged indeterminately, the resources of people are limited. People become weary with long drawn-out conflicts on distant battlefields, especially if these require regular requisitions of human and material supplies. And when people get tired of wars, victories at the battlefront may even seem empty. What use is there in winning wars when people no longer rejoice in the victory?

So the wise king must ensure that if wars are unavoidable, the people should not be taxed more than once to get what is needed: once and once only. Estimate correctly the requirements and be sure that all that is needed is obtained in a single requisition. This must be done before the start of war. Seek decisive and quick victories from wars. There is no profit on either side from lingering on the battlefield. What is especially wearisome for people is when such battlegrounds lie far away at the border. If possible, the army should forage foods from the enemy rather than rely on people to shoulder the burden of dragging grain across difficult, undulating, barren and isolated terrain. Other ways must be sought to satisfy the soldiers' hunger pangs. If the ordinary people are made to undertake such tasks, the strain on families is tremendous: who then shall provide for the aged, the young and the sick? How long can families support wars when the strain is intolerable?

So never make it the practice to supply food to distant battlefronts. No good strategist will rely on that. Instead the army, like the high-flying eagle I saw in this morning's walk, sharply eyeing its prey in the thick of the forest, should keep a close eye on enemy movements. As the animals are killed for food by the eagle, so should the army hunt the enemy for supplies and provisions.

Many a king has lost his throne through neglect of the impacts war, especially when long drawn-out and inconclusive, can have on people. Remember that with each passing season in war, people's support and enthusiasm are likely to become more and more strained. Even victories seem empty when the associated burdens and costs are too high.

The strategy should be for soldiers to take with them equipment including cooking utensils, but to depend for food on surprise attacks on enemies. Troops should be exhorted and motivated by generals to prey on enemies for food. Spies must be planted inside enemy quarters to provide vital information. And an enemy deprived of food and provisions is a weaker enemy, especially when supply routes are endangered. The cutting of supply routes will surely demoralise even the enemy's elite troops. Such successes in securing enemy supplies should be celebrated, for they relieve the people of the untold suffering of transporting food and provisions across unknown terrains.

This is an ancient lesson of war. I recall the story from antiquity of the collapse of a once popular king who chose to fight on two fronts and taxed people to supply food and provisions on both. To wage wars successfully, kings and generals must be alert to the extent of deprivation forced on the people. Given a definite population size there is a limit too on the resources that may be available for war.

This king from antiquity chose to wage wars rather than settle disputes through diplomatic means on both the northern and southern fronts. At the beginning the people were supportive of the king in his northern expedition to rid the country of nomadic raids on the farms. Seeing a just cause, many a person eagerly volunteered to transport grain across the wide northern expanse of uninhabited lands.

The king was so buoyed up by the enthusiasm of his

people for his war efforts that he became intoxicated by it. So when the southern state failed to bring the stately tributes expected each year, the king without hesitation declared war unilaterally. His pride was hurt badly and he wanted to punish the southern state for it. No consideration was given as to how battle at yet another front was going to burden the people.

Unlike the wars fought in the north, which had a justifiable cause, those in the south found little popular support. Having made his decree, the king was loath to withdraw his mandate. Instead, people were arbitrarily taxed and compelled to make even more contributions. The population became so vexed by war on two opposite fronts so distant from each other and from the capital that many fled as immigrants to the neighbouring states.

For when war has become an unnecessary burden in the eyes of the people, doubts are raised. The people ask themselves what meaning there is in a life of burden. Why risk one's life criss-crossing the terrain pulling carts of grain sacks? With a diminishing population, those remaining must be taxed even more for the continuing war effort.

In such dire circumstances, the kingdom could not last. In the end the people rose in bitterness to topple the very king whom they once so loved and admired. For they simply could no longer endure the unrelenting sacrifices demanded of them. There must be a limit on the hardships that people can be made to endure. The rich and the not so rich have become destitute as a result. Many have abandoned their homes, seeking relief from such burdens. Those who remain in the lands are so poor that some resort to cooking meals of grass, insects and treebark just to sustain their bodies.

What began as a battle with a cause ended in bitter misery for all. So kings and generals should never wage a war without the utmost consideration of how it will affect the people's lives. Never assume that the feelings of people are unchangeable.

5 📖 1

As I sit here gazing through the window I remember again passing the old withered tree at the bend in the road. Unexpectedly, images of hobbling skeletons float before my mind's eye. Some years back I journeyed through a border city. The scenes of emaciated people and their living skulls, with sunken eyes, tottering past me remained strongly carved in my memory. Though these are just memories they make me feel so nauseous that I would vomit whatever I had just eaten. These living dead glared at me with such hungry eyes. I could even hear the groaning in their stomachs. They became hunger personified: some were driven to madness through severe hunger.

So driven, indeed, that my flesh would seem like a delicacy to them. For they had long known the taste of raw human flesh through biting the flesh off corpses that lay dead after savage battles. In agony they waited for the aftermath of the next battle to feed themselves! Such depths of depravity that can be wreaked by wars should always be remembered by strategists. How high the price of war for humanity to be sunk to such depravity! I must record such thoughts as lessons for mankind.

5 📖 2

I was seated in a horse-drawn carriage meandering through intricate city lanes. This once prosperous city has been so reduced to shambles that its glorious past seems like a dream, a myth, a heaven. From what I learn the city once flourished in splendour through centuries of cross-border trade. That is until the day the city became the site where pitched battles were fought. Now instead of stalls laden with food and goods on the sides of the streets, you find heaps of human bones. As I was passing there were opposing armies encamped nearby. That day war was declared, and the dream city became a living hell – just like that, they said.

Nothing was ever the same again when those armies came, the man serving me said. The impossibly rich who chose to stay sank irretrievably into unheard depths of poverty. Many who owned stalls turned into scavengers. Money quickly loses its glitter when the army arrives, and everything shot up in price. Lawlessness prevailed, for nobody could stop the army on either side from plundering. Those who left for the mountains were the wisest. For only they were able to preserve their humanity.

Such haunting scenes remain in the very depths of my memory. Every time I see something decaying, withering, wilting, my mind quick replays these scenes. And I am overcome with sadness about what men can do unto themselves.

5 — 3

What a contrast! The cheerful faces that I see in villages deep inside the forests or high up in the mountains, and the skeletons haunting these border fringes. Hardly any flesh is left on their bodies. In the dark these moving shapes will surely turn the city to a ghostly haunt! And in the city I am shocked at how prices of simple necessities: salt, rice, clothes, have escalated beyond imagination. No wonder their lives are even worse than those of animals in the forest. Some scarcely cover themselves with leaves.

Is any war worth such deprivation of humanity?

Even the foodstall where I stopped for a meal has little else besides grass soup, fried insects and cooked tree-bark. These, according to the man, are now prized items in a war. For whatever is useful has been forcibly taken away by soldiers from both warring states. And the story is that even the soldiers themselves, with the war dragging on, also become desperate for a good meal.

What an irony it is that soldiers themselves often rely on battles to overcome their pangs of hunger. For after a fiercely fought battle, these soldiers will behave like scavengers, scouring the battlefields for dead horses to cook for food. At least they are eating cooked horsemeat, unlike those skeletal forms that gnaw the raw, dead human bodies, and slurp red, warm blood.

How can one be sure of the sanity of humankind when wars like these could on and on? Of what value are they? Thus strategists can learn from the mistakes of waging indecisive wars. No joy, no gain, no reputation, no meaning can be wrought from senselessly continuing wars – depravity is the only outcome.

Depravity

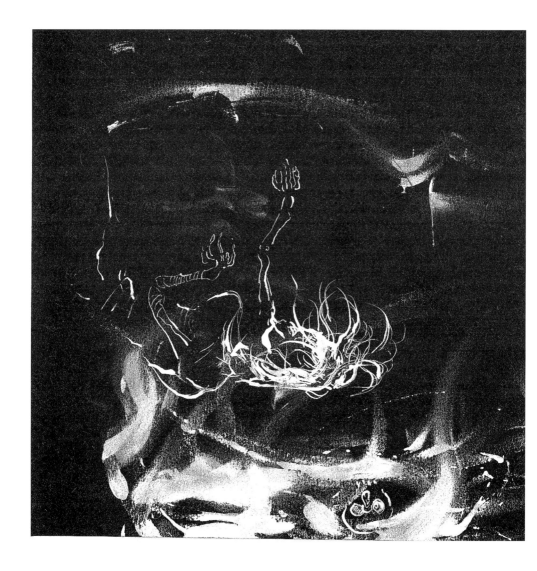

5 ⚎ 4

Although I have recorded memories of depravity inside border cities ravaged by continuing wars, there is suffering too in the capital city when wars are waged at the border. Prices in capital cities too shoot up on account of war. Whatever there is for the people must first go to the war effort. For the chariots, horses, armaments (crossbows, arrows, lances, shields, helmets, armour, spears), animals and wagons lost or destroyed in battle must be replaced. So what is produced from the farms goes into supporting the continued war effort. There is no certainty that money alone can secure enough grain for the family. All metals are wrought to make war implements, so the rich cannot have new carriages. Even the king's treasury becomes quickly depleted if war goes on and on. Even if people are summoned to contribute to the war effort, spies in neighbouring states must still be bought with gold and treasures.

How do you expect food to be plentiful when the able are conscripted for the battlefield? Food prices soar while rice fields lie unattended for want of labour. War produces only people who are medalled, disappointed, vengeful, hurt, crippled or dead. Little true happiness can ever come from wars, especially those fought over a long time. For prolonged war only produces more misery. So the strategist must always plan for a swift and decisive war. Never fight a destructive war, a war in which all that is civilised is destroyed. War is all-consuming.

However, wars may at times be inevitable.

5 ⚎ 5

At such times I counsel many a general on how critical it is to secure supplies to feed the soldiers. So I advise you, as generals, to contrive stratagems to feed your troops off the enemy. Enemy troops may be demoralised when they learn that their supplies have been raided. Inside the enemy camp discontent is likely to be stirred up when soldiers have to go hungry for lack of grain. Such captured grain saves the soldiers the agony of transporting supplies over difficult terrains. The enemy troops, so suddenly deprived of their food, are likely to begin to question the capabilities of their commanders. Food shortages may be made even more severe through repeated, surprise and successful raids on supplies.

Some enemy soldiers may become so distraught as to consider deserting their own army, having lost faith in their own general. Imagine troops returning from a long, hard battle to be told there is no meal for them! Tired, hungry, injured, weary – and no food. Surely such raids on the enemy's granaries, if sustained over time, must dampen the motivation of soldiers to continue to do battle.

The morale of enemy troops is sapped. And while the enemy troops go about hungry, your own troops feast in delight. Also, while the enemy troops may be driven by hunger to plunder their own people or nearby villages for food, your troops remain rested. Your troops, to win the hearts and minds of border villagers, may do the exact opposite, using the enemy's captured supplies: redistribute them to the farmers!

Before long, word will go round inside the enemy's country how beloved your troops are. If such a state of affairs continues, the outcome of war will be easy to predict. If the enemy troops continue to slaughter their own people for food it will not be long before rebellion grows from within. Few kings can wage an external war and at the same time quell uprisings from within their country. Thus I say that in war situations a bushel of your enemy's provision is worth as much as twenty of your own. For captured fodder has other effects than just depriving the enemy of their meals!

Equally, a hundredweight of fodder stolen from the enemy is worth twenty of your own. For horses cannot be expected to go on charging on empty stomachs. No warrior can look gallant on the battlefield with weak, hungry horses. How could troops' morale remain high when they ride into battle knowing that their horses are weak from want of fodder? So attacking enemy supplies of fodder is as important as attacking the enemy directly. Even better than killing an enemy soldier is to win him over through such stratagems as weakening his trust in his own commander.

Strategically, a dead body is of no use to the general, but one that is alive, loyal and committed to the moral cause of war is a true asset.

So be a wise general and keep the enemy ignorant of the

location of your own granaries. And these must be tightly guarded at all times. Never divulge which supply routes you are using. At all times these routes must be protected from possible enemy raids. Send false information to the enemy about your granaries and supply routes. Keep even your own troops ignorant of their whereabouts.

A few days have passed. And looking back at what I have just recorded I should, for balance, add how wars may reinvigorate. Given human nature as it is, many more wars can be anticipated in the years to come. So if wars are truly inevitable then strategists must assiduously study the art of strategy. The astute practice of the art of war could help humanity avoid some of the worst horrors associated with war: utter desolation, depravity, dehumanisation, and so on. Although I have said in *The Art of War* that the highest skills of a strategist lie in his accomplishing goals without ever going to war, wars may simply be inevitable in some circumstances. If that is so, then a strategy to wage a war is needed to strengthen one's position. 'Is that ever possible?' you may ask. My reply is, 'Yes, absolutely'.

The secret lies first in a mastery of human nature and second, in the efficient use of resources, especially the enemy's. For people and resources seized from your enemies should always be used for the purposes of winning the war. Let me touch first on human nature. No matter what ingenious weapons are devised, they are still wielded by human hands. And it is whose hands that wield the weapons that matters. For the meek and cowardly, no weapon is ever good enough. To the courageous seeking revenge, even a farmer's plough is weapon enough.

Men in ordinary circumstances fear death. Those who have never seen battle may boast of bravery. But once in the heat of a fight only the truly brave can calmly sail through with their momentum unaffected. For those who are truly fearless, there are no doors by which death can enter. Some, on seeing how easily head and arms are lopped off, are shocked into inaction. On the battlefield headless bodies are often seen, still on horseback, spurting out blood. The spiritual eyes seem to be seeing for the rider in these last gallops. There is nothing like the battlefield for revealing the true colours of men, displayed like the rainbow after rain. Some seem for a moment to defy death, their bodies stuck with arrows, but still wielding the sword ever so powerfully. Others are shocked into inaction.

6 ≡🦜≡ 2

After the heat of the battle comes the chill of the night. Images of war bring for those who survive many a nightmare. Cries can be heard, especially among the surviving recruits: they scream out in their dreams. The camp after pitched, inconclusive battles is so unlike its former self. The bloodied, dead, wounded, crippled and desolate now fester where the colourful, lively, energetic, majestic and boisterous once were.

The old, professional soldier who has fought in many pitched battles is less enthused by war. He has seen both faces of war once too often. Peer into his eyes and you can tell whether he is from the old stock. He is never elated before victory, nor downcast on defeat. His eyes have that distant look. An old soldier I knew long ago told me how year after year of ongoing wars had deadened his emotions. No longer did he care whether he were dead or alive tomorrow. On many occasions he should have died, but did not. So many of his best friends had gone over to the other side of the river that he no longer feared death. For he believed that once across he would be received by those who preceded him. Many a time he had sat by the fire asking why he still remained when so many had gone. For such an old soldier no exhortations by any general can move him. It is as if he is the living dead. He has become an emotionless, fearless fighting machine. So efficiently does he fight that no arrow, sword or spear can find on his body a place of entry. Such a fighting machine is at the same time the worst and the best soldier. For having heard so much and served under so many a general, no words of any general can move him. But few could match his calm in the thick of battle.

6 ≡🦜≡ 3

Yet in my recollection even a hen can be transformed into a fearless creature. I remember seeing how fierce a hen can be when her chickens are threatened: she can frightened off a big cat. All the fears she ordinarily holds simply evaporate. She is just overwhelmed by motherly love for her young. That triggers off determined, clawing movements aimed at the

Soldiers

cat's eyes. The cat on this occasion was so shocked that it just dashed off. In triumph, the hen went cackling after the cat. So the hunted becomes the hunter! Even the hen herself may be surprised by the change wrought in her.

So it must be with human beings. Anger the people, let rage overcome them and you will find in them soldiers brave enough to storm headlong into the enemy's cavalry. For to fight fearlessly in combat, one's inner state of mind must also be stirred up. That is why the moral cause in war is so critical for success.

Since time immemorial good has always triumphed over evil. Why? One reason may be the inexhaustible source of energy that is released when the human conscience is deeply disturbed. For deep in the hearts of men lies goodness. So evil acts, being contrary to the very psyche of humanity, simply cannot sustain themselves.

Soldiers come from the people. So a people enraged by cruel acts of an enemy is the fuel that drives an army to victory. In a given war, the side motivated by a strong moral cause is more likely to prevail.

6 ⚔ 4

When you are victorious in capturing enemy territories be civil towards the people. Mete out punishments if you must, but fairly. Never slaughter those who surrender on their own accord. Enemies are made and may also be unmade by the skilled general. For many more will down their arms if they learn that their lives may be spared. No ordinary man wants to die. Treat those who cross you with humanity. On hearing of these kindly acts towards prisoners of war, even more may come over to your side. Inspire them with acts of justice and fairness. For enemy soldiers, being human, can also be moved. If you doubt their loyalty use them as slaves. Salvage the talented and the skilled from slave labour, for these are scarce. But do remember that since ancient times, many former enemy soldiers have been known to sacrifice their lives for the general they once fought bitterly against. For soldiers yearn for strong, just and kind leadership. As ancient history has it, there are many enlightened generals who care for soldiers as a father cares for his sons. They in turn fight with great ferocity in the name of their generals. Many a doomed battle has been won through troops fighting to repay their gratitude to the general who spared their lives.

There are those who are moved by booty. The wise general will reward the first in every ten who seizes the enemy's chariots. Look at the forest monkeys. What does it take to lure them down from the trees towards men? Nuts. For the monkeys these are prized items. So lure those who hunger for wealth with promises of treasures if they spearhead the charge at city gates. The fearless are needed to lead the fearful. Besides treasures, however, people hunger for something far more intangible.

Some people hunger for status. Devise a hierarchy of honours and titles. The king should confer these titles as befits the contributions. These honours often stir some to admirable acts of sacrifice and bravery. For beyond food and shelter, people hunger to be recognised. They hunger not just to obey but also to achieve. And when titles are there to be earned through brave deeds and sacrifices in wars, some will gladly even lay down their lives to seek immortal glory. So the wise king grants titles even posthumously so that the living may too be motivated. Such titles move not only this generation but also the many that follow. And to sustain the honour of the family through the generations, many future offspring will strive to make sacrifices. For people yearn for their family ancestry to be honoured in the course of the river of time.

6 5

In war many things are heedlessly destroyed by vengeance. After victory many a general has released his emotions through wild destruction. I remember the scene of a capital city set on fire. It burned for days. But of what use is a burnt-down city to the living? Like dead corpses that need to be disposed of, so ruins must be cleared. As corpses cannot till the land for food, so burnt implements are equally useless. When all the bitterness has subsided, people will begin to realise the wisdom of retaining intact things of use in the confusion following the triumph over enemy troops.

Some of the treasures stored in the city's burnt-down

palaces are lost for eternity. Such treasures, crafted by reverent hands, are very rare and beautiful; they might enthrall many generations but are now lost in one. Things in themselves are neither wrong nor right. Burn the enemy flags if you must to appease anger. But the poles upon which the flags once flew must be salvaged from the fires. They can be used to fly *your* flags. Indeed, why reduce an enemy's flags to ashes when they can serve as rags? Many physical resources like these should be preserved for later use. Physical objects are in themselves neutral. So the wise general, when capturing a city, will take pains to rein in the revengeful emotions of his troops. In so doing he will minimise the damage wreaked on those conquered in wrath. Special troops will be assigned to protect city palaces and to prevent pilferage, acts of arson and blind destruction. For in moments like this wisdom must prevail over emotion.

I recall now how a self-created king once built up his tiny army from bandit size to a grand army simply by making the best possible use of whatever the enemy forces had abandoned. Nothing was ever left to waste. So even the uniforms of the enemy are kept and later used to clothe his troops, fighting on a different front. Even dead troops lying on the battleground were stripped bare of anything that could possibly be reused. No enemy troops were ever slaughtered on account of having lost the fight. Orphans of war became his adopted children.

As a result of his practices, now, in his old age, many divisions of troops are led by his adopted sons, fighting as generals in successful battles. For in his view, usable things are derived from human ingenuity. No wanton killing is ever allowed. The king values human lives above all and is thus loved for his humanity, even by the conquered peoples. Such kings are divine.

7 🕮 1

A night of full moon: no wind; silence except for the sounds of the forest. But with my brush in hand I find my mind empty, wandering away into nothingness. I stare out into the darkness of the night, across into the forest. In the depths of the forest darkness, I know are countless invisible lives. Yet all I can see is stillness and quietness, in spite of the diversity of lives which the forest nurtures.

I know that in the forest the tiger cub I caught in the hunt, now fully grown, will be on the prowl for food. Also the white owl, that many villagers see as an omen of evil, will be out searching for its prey. But once the dinner is eaten both the tiger and owl will retire and rest through the night. Even the tiger and owl do not kill all day long without purpose. That may be why the forest appears so quiet despite being the home of so many diverse living things. Forests seem better able to sustain themselves than some mighty cities. Why? The secret may lie in the fact that the forest takes care to nurture the lives within it. So fight wars if this cannot be helped but do not love wars for its own sake. There is never true, lasting joy from prolonged fighting.

Oh strategists, remember well that words on strategy are not only found in *The Art of War* but are spoken through acts of nature! For what I now write comes from my own inner reflections, from observations I have made of nature. Often I am able to see how the past melts into the present, and to peer into the future scheme of things.

7 🕮 2

The seasons have their cycles. Imagine what would happen to life around us if winter were unexpectedly prolonged for ever? Many creatures would suffer and freeze to death for lack of food. I wonder if animals could hibernate for ever through the deepest cold? Even if foods are stored for the wintry season, there must come a time when they become depleted. And nature, knowing this, limits the wintry season to its proper span. No winter can be excessively prolonged without threatening many a living thing.

See how natural is the transition in the cycle of the

seasons! It is as if nature deems it necessary to help the living adapt to change. Immediately after winter comes spring and then summer arrives. Nor does winter come abruptly thereafter. Summer is succeeded by autumn. So the cycle goes on of spring, summer, autumn, winter. Living bodies experiencing and coping with moderate warmth, heat, moderate cold and cold, each in its turn.

The same is true when the summer heat is prolonged unexpectedly. With the earth is scorched, no crops may profitably be planted. Hunger pangs are felt by the living when food becomes scarce. And when the wells dry up under the mid-day heat, the living also suffer from acute thirst. Those alive may begin to perish from either hunger or thirst. Such heat often cause fires to erupt inside the forest. When such fires burn, they render homeless countless creatures dwelling in the very depths of the forest. Unlike prolonged winters, when forces of life may lie dormant awaiting the coming of spring, fires take away all possibility of revival.

Or what if pouring, streaming rain never stops? Many seeds, seedlings, soil, domestic animals and entire farms may be washed away when the mighty rivers overflow. Once in my life when these rains didn't stop for many moons, I remember seeing, from the mountain-top, villages lying in seas of water. Like the birds on the trees, families were perched on the rooftops shivering in the cold. What a sight! What was once green, fertile land lay submerged in water. I looked as far as I could to the horizon and yet there was nothing but water dotted with rooftops. The living perished with disease, hunger and cold.

Strategists must be careful when wars are being prolonged. Little good can ever come of such wars.

7 ☰ 3

There is yet another characteristic of war: the sudden release of stored human energy. Looking at nature, you see that when cosmic energy is released, it happens in short, intense bursts. Once released, nature restores everything back to normality. So after intense activity comes the quietness.

Look at the skies. Fierce as storms may be, with their sudden, impressive and frightening bursts of energy, most

Dead kings

last only for a moment. The winds may howl ever so loudly and seem enough to blow the roofs off. Thunder seems able to rock the earth and tear down city walls. In the darkness of the night, lightning seems able to light up the entire city. Yet shortly after these outbursts in the midst of the pouring rain, peace and quiet return. It is as though nature intended that once destructive tension is unleashed there should be a period for quiet restoration.

Earthquakes do not last for ever. The earth opens up and moves. Buildings may tumble and collapse but all is over in a moment. As with the storm, once it is over, nature becomes quiet. Nature seems to be telling us it is time for reconstruction after destruction. For no rebuilding is ever possible if the earth rocks very often and for very long.

So wars which involve sudden release of human energies on the battlefield should never be waged indefinitely. Even nature does not seem to have the resources to sustain long outbursts of energy; how can earthly men do so?

7 📖 4

In my tired state of mind, the past seems to merge with the present. And I can see it reeling in front of my very eyes. I am not even clear if I am dreaming. For though exhausted, I lie sleepless on my bed. Such a state enables me to see clearly the root causes of things – causes transcending time. For this reason I am moved to record these recurring images, thoughts, feelings and inclinations. For I must leave something behind for the generations and generations of people coming after me.

In this ponderous state of being, I see images in my mind of disastrous wars. In my dream-like vision, faces of many once victorious warrior kings emerge bodiless. Kings and non-kings alike, only their decapitated heads hang on poles outside the capital cities of their once beloved kingdoms. Blood still drips from these bodiless heads of kings. I strain my ears but cannot hear their voices. All I hear is 'Uh!...Uh!' I see pain as they struggle in vain to speak. Some I know had their tongues dug out to prevent them speaking, even when dead. Oh what cruel fates have befallen these kings! Such a plight of these once mighty kings! I study their eyes and they seem to have a story to tell. All their eyes are tinged with the deepest regret. If only their experiences could be recorded as lessons for future kings. But there was one king who indeed spoke.

One bodiless king appeared to me, floating amidst all the splendour of his palace. He cried out:

"Sun Tzu, if only I had studied your Art of War *with diligence and mastered its principles! For I have realised only too late that the true warrior often goes unrecognised because he wins wars without bloodshed! I chose to fight so many wars and what did I get in the end but an endless stream of agonies! I want to share with you my own experiences and show you as vividly as possible the stages of my transition from a glorious, victorious king to a bodiless one!"*

Suddenly, the image then transformed itself, revealing the multi-faceted stages of decline in the history of this king. But he spoke with such a haunting voice. I seemed able to distil from his utterances the essence of lessons in the art of strategy. For the images seemed to follow a predictable sequence to that which I had anticipated when giving pre-scribing in *The Art of War*. First, glorious victories, giving rise to riches and splendours of his palace. These treasures were seized from the kingdom and peoples who lost the wars. And I see thereafter images of more wars on different fronts, each of increasing duration.

For the king seemed so confident of victory that he continued to wage wars. Next images appear of starving peasants, worn-out troops, disillusioned faces of generals. Suddenly uprisings erupt: people fighting with dispirited troops. Many troops in turn fighting other troops of the same colour! In the distance, troops of a different colour scaling the city walls, meeting resistance by some but often assisted by others. These images capture the downfall of the empire due to fighting too many wars on too many fronts and hence embittering the very people who once supported the king. Alas, the scene of the king being beheaded and his head hung from a pole at the city gates!

Now if only my *Art of War* can guide these kings in their strategic actions! Because he neglected its major principles such as the policy of never prolonging the agony of war, this king has lost his life and seems to be suffering in eternity.

What a price to pay!

3

1 ⚏ 1

THIS MORNING IS quiet as usual, yet there is stirring inside me an urge to walk up the mountain path. And that is how what is written here was inspired. Words flow as I take in the views unfolding before me. How strange yet again that ideas, memories and images seem to be locked beneath the rocks in my mind when I am all set to write, but gain a new freedom with the movement of my body. It is as if bodily movements thaw the mind. And as it thaws words begin to dance before my eyes. These word movements conjure up inside my head abstract scenes, vague images and views as I walk along these paths.

Wandering up to the peak, my body is caressed by the cool air which envelops me. I pause by the edge and my mind is flooded with memories of collections of paintings I have seen in the palaces of kings. How these works of art capture the essence of reality! One painting I recall evokes feelings almost identical to my feelings on seeing the same scene unfolding before me now. It is to do with how the cloud is configured. So similar to what is now in a slow, almost imperceptible dance before me – but not quite the same! I remember feeling absorbed into the vista of mountains, streams and clouds. I feel myself transposed into the picture to become one with the little dot of a man sitting in the pavilion. So immersed am I in the painting that I often become that dot, that man. I wonder who is happier: he, in the painting, or I, out here in the world?

Clouds float below me and joy pervades my body. Now I understand what moves so many to capture these timeless scenes. Standing here I can imagine the passage of a thousand

Variations

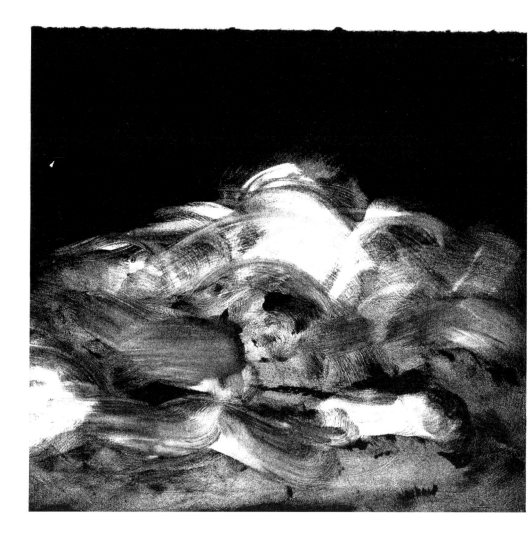

years and then another man crossing these paths to share the same inner wonderment by simply looking at these cloud formations. Countless variations of cloud pictures and yet not one is exactly the same as another. These clouds seem to be imbued with life, seeming to breathe as they move ever so gently by. They seem to be free from worldly cares. Their dancing movements are so unconstrained. No wonder that poets sing of their desire to float along with these clouds.

As I bathe myself in these cloud scenes I begin to recollect a fundamental principle in *The Art of War* – one which should dwell for ever in the hearts of strategists, like these clouds that clothe the mountain.

1 ⚏ 2

The following may sound paradoxical since what I am talking about is the art of 'war'. The precept simply put is that those who win wars without fighting are to be considered as having truly mastered the finer skills in the art of war: they win wars but through *non*-warring, peaceful means. That is, anyone who claims to have reached the apex of strategic skills must succeed by prevailing through strategy rather than through fighting. Strategy, like the clouds, is capable of countless variations depending on circumstances. A general who is always fighting, exhausting troops, depleting resources, is like a painter who is always painting clouds but failing to capture their essence. Such a general has yet to penetrate to the very essence of my *Art of War*. Many paintings of cloud formations may be found but only a few in royal possession truly capture their essence. In such rare paintings, the clouds come alive, retain their vitality and power of endless transmutation. These clouds seem to depend for their existence on the paintings of themselves: nothing is added or taken away. If only time is unfrozen, these clouds in the paintings will transmute themselves. Likewise a wise strategist is one able to win a war without a war: nothing seems to happen and yet he prevails.

To capture a city intact is far more difficult, requiring the consummate skills of a talented strategist, than to seize it through force. The worst case is when piles upon piles of soldiers lie dead outside the city walls, having acted on orders of a rash general to scale them.

A city won intact is like a painting obtained in one piece. Whilst a city may be fought for and won, inevitably there will be losses of troops on either side and destruction of many valuable things such as houses, possessions, treasures, palaces, artifacts and antiques. Even though a city may be restored, the labour and costs of reconstruction are better devoted to other causes, such as building a new city.

A reconstructed city is like a torn painting pasted together. And as anyone who cherishes paintings of morning clouds will realise, nothing can quite compare with the original, intact work in its beauty. Even if the repair may have been excellently done, the fact remains that such efforts are better put into creating another painting. So it is with pottery. No matter how good the craftsman, a rice pot once cracked is never quite the same as before.

So a wise king seeks to prevail over a city through strategy rather than through waging war. An intact city retains its beauty as well as its productive skills. Yet throughout our ancient history, there are kings who take pride in slaughtering city inhabitants and flattening streets through war. Such vengeance may appease the anger of the moment but at what a huge price for what is forgone! Strategists should ponder on this and ask: Is wanton destruction ever justified? Not only should a general take a city intact; the astute strategist should be able to gain an entire army without fighting. I would say that every attempt should be made to act likewise when countering a battalion, company, platoon or even a group of soldiers. For the basic principle is the same, be it an army, division, battalion, company, platoon or a squad.

Success lies in having latent power. To wield such power, nourishing it and never depleting it is the secret of maintaining supremacy. Thus to order troops to charge up city walls in an all-out effort to prevail in the war is certain to deplete military strength unnecessarily. A general tempted to do this should learn the virtue of patience rather than seek fleeting glories through a blood-bath of his troops. Even if a victory is won, it is a hollow one. For the price paid is far too high. The piles of dead, rotting cavalry soldiers – some among the best in the army – lying outside city walls can no longer be used. Far better to surround the city, cut supply routes and wait for the decline in the morale of enemy troops. Weaken the morale of enemy troops behind city walls by ensuring they catch the aroma of sumptuous dinners on the wind. Have eerie music played in the dead of a moonless night accompanied by wails to stimulate a hellish atmosphere: drive fear into enemy soldiers that guard the city walls and gates. Spread rumours of ghosts lurking in the dark, waiting to catch departing souls. In the morning stage glorious military displays of cavalry troops in their sober uniforms brandishing newly polished swords, spears and arrows. Have banners fly high in the strong wind and demonstrate with excellent coordination the formation of troops before the eyes of enemy troops on guard. Let the ground tremble with the sound of drums. The intention is to weaken the enemy's resolve to fight. For seeing these displays may impress on enemy troops what a mighty army they are facing. Disseminate as widely as possible the message to enemy soldiers that their lives will be spared if they down their arms and surrender: drive a wedge between the enemy's troops and their leaders. If the leaders truly lack the moral support of their troops and their people, then in these critical moments assassination attempts will be made. The strategy is to force the leaders quietly to flee the city and induce their troops and people to pledge their loyalties anew. If this is successful, not only is the army enlarged by such defections, but an entire city's resources are now available to support the war effort.

Such a strategy requires successful implementation of the consummate skills of a master strategist. And even though not a single soldier is engaged in physical combat, yet such skills distinguish the master of the art of war from a mere practitioner. For the ordinary people, unaware of its multi-layered intricacies, such an outcome does not even seem worthy of a true warrior. But among strategists such achievements are hallmarks of one who has mastered the art of war and deserves veneration by all. For the true strategist the most difficult and intriguing skill to acquire in the art of war is how to achieve one's goals without resorting to war!

So engrossed am I with the dance of the clouds that a sudden gust of wind almost sweeps me off the mountain's edge! I resume my path upwards, content that these clouds have helped me unfold the most profound principle in the art of war: to win but not always through fighting. So if *yang* is the direct, fighting side of war then the indirect, *non*-fighting side is the *yin* aspect. In waging a war both aspects must be employed. The art of war uses this *yin–yang* polarity to convert an enemy's advantages into disadvantages. Taking the earlier example, the enemy has an edge in terms of being perched high up, behind city walls, with an excellent view of the battlefront. Thus a direct assault means that many lives must be sacrificed to breach those walls. On the other hand, these advantages render the enemy troops vulnerable to indirect approaches that work on the morale of the soldiers: for example, enemy troops high above the city walls should be able to witness for themselves how formidable our troops are. Time is also on our side: the enemy must have great difficulty in securing supplies for a city population. So from the vantage point of the city walls, the resolve of enemy troops to fight can be slowly weakened through the aroma of cooked food. For in their minds doubts are being aroused about how they could possibly fight such an impressive army on empty stomachs. So at the critical moment, an open message may then be sent declaring that the lives of enemy troops and the city population will be spared if their king and generals abandon the city. The idea is through such indirect measures to cause the city gates to open of their own accord and for the defences to collapse by virtue of their own weight!

An unexpected downpour of rain brings freshness to the morning air. Through the filters of falling rain I gaze at the forest trees. All life seems so still amidst the rains. In the skies I see no birds that fly – not even the eagle from the mountain-top. These rains have a heavenly quality about them. They are so timely, coming to clear the haziness brought about by a distant forest fire. And sometimes the only thing a man can do is to wait. For who else can put out the roaring fires in the forest except such a heavy downpour? And as I turn to the brush lying on the table, in a flash I recall that it was precisely at a time like this that a general devoted to the study of *The Art of War* came rushing in. Unlike others, who merely read the work for coining stratagems, he fully appreciated its deeper underlying philosophy and belief: the ideal solution to inevitable human conflicts lies not in wars themselves but outside them. He grasped that the fundamental purpose of *The Art of War* as a book is to avoid unnecessary bloodshed. Despite his depth of understanding, he seemed visibly shocked, disturbed by the turn of events. I too was surprised to see him so emotionally distraught – so unlike his usual collected self.

With bloodshot eyes, blotted with an ugly red, he entered in a soaked, heavy uniform, panting and gasping for breath. In a moment his story was told. All his humanitarian efforts had failed to move the enemy. His command to spare an entire village (home town of the enemy general) on the outskirts of the border city from slaughter had been interpreted by the enemy as fear. His restraint from using his best troops to seize certain victory had fuelled growing arrogance among the enemy troops. His troops, under his command not to retaliate, were being sneered at openly. More than once, his troops had been ordered to back off from an imminent engagement on the battlefield. And worse: messengers sent by him to convey his protests about the misbehaviour of enemy troops had their ears chopped off and tongues torn out. The families of the messengers handicapped in this way screamed for revenge: 'An eye for an eye' and 'A tongue for a tongue'. His officers had risen in protest against inaction, asserting that the role of the army is fight, not flight. So in desperation, feeling wretched, he came seeking me out. His heart desires an

The meeting

all-out assault on the enemy's walled, frontier cities to punish them for their heinous crimes. Indeed if it were not for the strategic alliances struck between the enemy state and its neighbours, it would be timely to strike at the heart of the enemy troops. A battle cry would be like falling rain clearing the haze brought about by forest fires. His troops and people were resolutely behind him in their desire to sacrifice for the war effort, given the atrocities meted out by enemy troops to nearby villages. His enemy troops were swollen with pride, over-confident of their superiority; they could be lured out of fortified cities into the forest planted with booby traps, and massacred by the thousand.

2 2

Seeing me so calm despite having heard the story helped to quieten his spirits. His officers, fully dressed for battle and waiting in the rain, had begun to show signs of impatience. Even from the distance and through the falling rain I could faintly sense the spirit of latent rebellion among the officers. Revenge was hot in their blood and no rain seemed able to cool it. Yet the general's eyes showed his reluctance to pursue this path; he knew what the final outcome would be: a total disaster if the march were ordered. For the enemy's cities were not only well fortified but they had strong military alliances with neighbouring states. Though he did not speak of it, I knew the purpose of his visit at such a critical moment. He was beseeching me with a wordless, delicate show of expression on his face to advise his officers against such a march. A task he knew was beyond him. He would simply be swept aside given the flood of emotions, with the officers themselves taking the initiative. So I invited the officers in and served them tea. Sipping the warm tea seemed to help ease their tension.

Words may be few, but if well chosen can move mountains. Therein lies the beauty of words. I speak slowly, unemotionally, factually. To lay siege to fortresses with the rain pelting down on your faces like stones? Scaling up wet walls using slippery platforms? Why provide human sport for the enemy troops? The enemy troops will have the fun of a lifetime with their games of archery! And this time not only will they gather ears and tongues as prizes but entire bodies as well. Never let the heart command the head. Happiness lost may still be retrieved but a dead army remains dead for ever!

The secret of victory lies not in attacking enemies well entrenched in high fortresses but to counter the enemy directly through a well-conceived, integrated strategy. Negate their strengths – lure them out into the open from inside their walled cities. Let them win skirmishes and retreat so that it becomes their habit to venture out of their cities to pursue a fight. Use their arrogance against them. If they often ransack villages, study their behavioural patterns. Encourage them in such behaviour, so that it becomes their habit. Thus, when villages in neighbouring states are ransacked, these actions are linked to the enemy troops. Encourage them to be heedless, reckless and careless; better still, to neglect training and the practice of military arts. Let them be so bold as to operate in small groups which may be led into traps. Work towards undermining their strengths so as to eventually defeat them. Better to tolerate the shame of having messengers handicapped than to have an entire army eliminated through a courageous but ill-fated scaling of city walls. For if that happens entire villages of people will become handicapped by the ruthless enemy troops. What is preventing these actions now is the presence of the highly disciplined but restrained army. Work on the arrogance of the enemy troops to beguile them to slacken their military preparedness for wars. Channel emotions wrought by the inhumane actions of enemy troops to advantage: quietly build up fighting capability. Train the people to fight in different scenarios: scaling walls, open-field battles, charging down hills, along river banks, deep into the valleys.

2 3

Another round of tea drinking among the officers. The rains poured ever more heavily and the faces of some began to betray signs of inner relief. The general's eyes revealed that from his perspective the worst was over. The thickness of the falling rain seemed to shield the forest trees. I implored them to think why the enemy dared to be so audacious. Then, leading them to the open courtyard in the middle of the house, I pointed to creepers that grew entwined round the four pillars. The creeper, by rallying round these pillars, has been able to scale the heights. In the same manner the enemy have been able to act as they did mainly because they were allied to the more powerful neighbouring state to the north. So unless a wedge was driven to sever such an alliance, the enemy troops were unlikely to be reined in. For they were confident that in the event of their cities being invaded, their north-western neighbour was likely to counter-attack swiftly with its calvary. In that event officers and troops must not only suffer the punishing rain of arrows whilst scaling those walls; they were likely to be chopped into pieces by knives from their rear. In which circumstance, a debacle was assured.

More faces seemed relieved. As the soldiers stood by the courtyard the sounds of falling rain on the roofs must have been even more reminiscent of battle. The silvery reflections of heavy rain pelting down on the courtyard floor must have conjured up inside their minds war scenes in which they charge right into a rain of arrows targeted at them. It is not difficult to imagine these bloody scenes: thick heavy rain washing out spilt human blood, oozing out of open, gaping wounds. Even for those unhurt in the rain of arrows, their uniforms are likely to be painted red as soldiers collapse and die in their climb up the city walls. Sudden spurts of blood may rain on their faces as more soldiers at the top are slaughtered. Why seek certain death? That is not the art of war!

Another cup of tea followed. I emphasized all-out efforts to build strong alliances with neighbouring states. Equally, work must be directed towards disrupting the currently strong alliance between the north-western state and the enemy. The general seemed less tense than before. It was already clear by now that an audience with the king had to be arranged to discuss these state matters.

And since the officers were so attentive and absorbed in the transactions of our meeting, I continued with the role of the army. I urged them in the meantime to consider ways of surprising the enemy by luring them out of their fortresses and making shock attacks in the depths of the forests.

So the discourse on the art of war continued, unabated in intensity. It was way past midnight when the officers took leave of me, thanking me profusely for having indirectly saved the army from certain death! Even more important, they felt, was the opportunity to grasp the deeper meanings of *The Art of War*. And the rain continued.

Towards the end of autumn. A rainy spell. The rains have continued unabated. These rains, pouring so fiercely, remind me time and again of arrows, especially when the autumn air turns icy cold. That is when rain becomes hailstones, turning into pellets of ice that are shot down from the sky. The sounds of the falling bits of ice on the roof goes rapidly: *tut, tut, tut, tut, tut, tut* ... I am transposed back in time to the moving war scenes that are now so vivid in my mind. Right there before my eyes on this blank piece of paper I could see the icy-cold walls of the city reflecting the rays of the early morning sun. It was many years ago...

It was one of those occasions in the course of my military career when I had to watch, to my dismay, the costly scaling of the city walls. Inside those walls, our soldiers captured by the enemy were being slaughtered one by one and served as fodder for wild animals in captivity inside the city. Each time a prisoner was chopped into pieces his head would be flung across into our camp. Due to the extremely cold winds, the blood froze at the base of the head. It was a pitiful sight, the head without the body. Some of the soldiers became so enraged at the savage acts that they even charged madly and head-on into the walls of the cities, only to be brought down by a rain of arrows.

The general was himself impatient for action to be taken. Only immediate action could appease the troops. All were crying out for revenge to be taken. He would not hear of delay. But deep in his heart he knew how difficult it would be to scale those walls. It seemed as if Heaven was out to test their endurance and patience. How could they launch attacks against a walled city in these bitter cold wintry winds? The wind-swept walls were themselves slippery with ice. Enemy troops had poured water over the walls which immediately froze in the cold winds. The general saw the problem as mainly how to scale those vast and mighty walls. Perhaps his soldiers could use the trees in the forest to construct ladders to scale them. And if the attack were launched in the darkness of the night a successful attempt might still be possible.

3 ⚋ 2

The first wave of attacks was launched in the dead of a moonless night. The general had hastily ordered that ladders be made and troops were to use these to climb up the city wall after advancing in pitch darkness. But it was not only moonless; it was also very still and surprisingly windless. The enemy troops were indeed taken by surprise. But then the walls were too slippery and the ladders so badly constructed that many men suffered terrible injuries simply from falling off them: some of the steps could not support the weight of the soldiers. By then the alert had been sounded and enemy reinforcements were at hand to deal with the very few that managed to stumble up those shaky ladders.

88

The reinforced enemy troops encountered little difficulty in pushing the ladders off the slippery surface of the walls. Sadly, too, some of the ladders themselves were too short for the high walls. Those who were crippled by their falls ended up as easy prey for arrows that rained unabated from above.

Yet the thirst for revenge drove these soldiers to struggle on. Such bravery had not been witnessed for a long time. Even the enemy were taken aback by the determined charge of these soldiers. But still the obstacles ahead were just too much for them. So when it became clear that these attempts were leading them nowhere the general sounded the drums for immediate withdrawal. In the dead of the night, many wounded lay there unseen. The weather changed suddenly: the bitterly cold winds blew and snow fell. Little by little and in the thick of darkness the snow buried those still alive. And what could they do but accept their fate? If they struggled this would only attract attention from above, with a rain of arrows. By early dawn, when the dead and casualties were counted, it became obvious how costly these attempts were. No less than a third of the troops sent on the mission were either dead, injured, buried in snow or simply lost in action. The general was stunned by the price he had to pay to learn this bitter lesson. What had the general gained by acting so rashly? Only more dead and nothing in return.

3 ⚜ 3

After this sad episode, the troops, though humiliated, were less inclined to charge blindly. For now they knew the cost of being rash and the need to preserve their numbers if they were ultimately to prevail. And now the general appraised the task less optimistically. He sent for more reinforcements from the capital, requesting skilled craftsmen and especially master carpenters. For after the tragic deaths of so many soldiers from poorly constructed ladders he was determined to ensure that no more lives be wasted. Every morning he studied the city walls from a distance. He noted the three gates: central, eastern and western. It was during one of these trips that he chanced upon a hedgehog which led him in a flash to conceive of a burrowing stratagem. How strange that strategists were often inspired by strategies from the most unexpected sources! In the middle of the night the plan was discussed among the general, myself and other key personnel in his command centre. The idea was to dig a deep tunnel right from the camp to below the central city gate. The tunnel was to be large enough for at least three men to push or squeeze through at one time. The tunnel would be dug so that soldiers could quietly get inside the city and open the gates. Since the gates appeared to be heavily constructed it would be difficult to ram them down. The city walls too were so thickly built that it would be impossible to cause even a dent in them. Although the stratagem seemed possible, there were yet many unresolved difficulties: how could one ensure that the tunnel headed in the right direction? Could experienced diggers be found able to lead the tunnel in the right direction? Could it be done with speed and accuracy? Someone present recalled names from among the soldiers who were excellent grave diggers! Then at the point of the central city gate the tunnel was to be diverted into two opposite directions, towards the eastern and western gates. Someone else said that two or three soldiers could direct the digging towards any particular spot. But then how to ensure secrecy while the tunnel was being dug? The soil had to be disposed of without arousing any suspicion. This was the thick of winter when the days were short and much of the soil disposal could be done during the long nights. A ruse was suggested. How about issuing orders that all dead soldiers were to be buried in a

89

mass grave instead of being burnt? Enemy troops were less likely to suspect a burrowing stratagem if such orders were implemented: excavated soil could be visible from the high walls. Having weighed up the situation the consensus of those present was that the stratagem should be implemented.

The general ordered that every precaution be taken to maintain total secrecy for the whole operation. Those involved in the digging were carefully screened. The policy for burying the dead was made known among the troops. Indeed the enemy troops, on seeing these actions from the high walls, thought that an early retreat was being planned! For jeers were shouted by the enemy troops. And celebrations could be heard from outside the city walls. A letter was sent from the enemy that taunted with this message:

"No retaliation if troops were to take your many dead by the wall for burial: that would remove the filth and stink."

But the arrival of the reinforcements must have quickly dispelled such thinking. For after that the celebrations seemed to quicten down. The spot where the tunnel began was precisely the most tightly guarded of all camps – the general's personal headquarters. It was amazing how these men worked. For those selected had vengeance in their eyes. Each had deep grievances which could only be redressed through humiliating the enemy by destruction of their city. The routine: working through the night and sleeping in the day. Before long the work was done. Just a couple more hours of work and the tunnel would push upwards through the earth to its opening: inside the city gates. And the season of winter was approaching its end.

The general and staff including myself met to discuss another offensive. This time the ladders were properly constructed. Not only were there ladders, but eight huge wheeled platforms. These were built to be above the height of the city walls. The platforms were to be pulled by bulls and to carry archers at the top. Soldiers trailed behind these ingenious structures so as to charge up the well-constructed steps. Enemy troops were flabbergasted when they saw these structures. Most importantly for us these structures seemed to suggest to the enemy what our new strategy of attack was to be. The general directed that these structures be placed facing the enemy. For the enemy these structures seemed targeted at the various towers dotted along the wall, rather than at the city gates. Enemy troops responded almost as quickly: more guards, archers, soldiers seemed to mingle around the towers. Also it was obvious that those on guard above the city gates were somewhat diminished. Again the general waited for a moonless night to launch the assault.

The stratagem worked. The general worked out a detailed deployment of forces. In the first phase, the forces appeared to be focusing their attacks on the towers, with the colossal structures the centre of attention. Ladders were also being carried. These structures were advanced in a slow, deliberate fashion. The idea was to lead the enemy on to believe this to be the major thrust of the attack. From the vantage point of these high platforms, the archers saw that many of the enemy troops were being diverted from the walled enclosures on top of the city gates to the towers. The general also briefed the commanders to deflect their columns towards the city gates and abandon the long ladders once the gates were forced open from within. The whole operation was well coordinated. Enemy troops were engaged in countering the attacks from the wheeled platforms, totally ignoring the security round the city gates. The enemy officers had been entirely taken in by the stratagem. And when the tunnel pushed through inside the gates there were very few enemy troops around to resist. The gates were quickly flung open to admit the troops. And it was through such careful, painstaking efforts that the city defences fell. I recalled as I entered the city again that the weather changed suddenly, and became so cold that the rain turned to ice as it fell, and the sounds of *tut, tut, tut* could be heard … Then I captured these recollections in writing.

Elusiveness

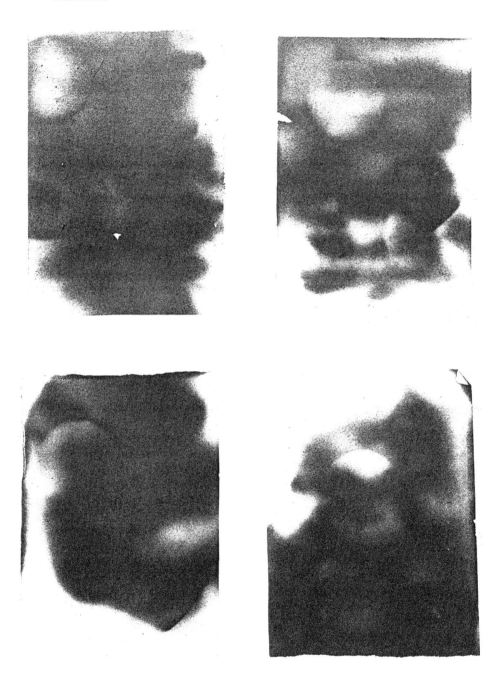

4 ▰ 1

Many moons passed before I again found the inner calm to sit here, and collect myself. I reflect and brush on to rice paper my thoughts as they settle in my mind. This time it is the moonlight that draws me to my writing table – and so alluringly.

Nothing in my view is quite so exquisite as the moon on a cloudless night. For there she is, just outside the window, looming bright behind our aging apple tree. From my bed I can see her rays filtering resolutely through the room. The dust is transformed into glittering jewels in the flow of light.

Standing by the window-sill I become absorbed in the sheer pleasure of her presence. She is at her peak brightness: so wholesome, so total, so complete, so reassuring, so inspiring! What a waste to slumber through the night when she is right at the doorstep asking for dialogue.

Her beauty seems enhanced many times over when viewed from across, the mild, windy grass plains. Her magnificence is truly manifested when she graces the snowy mountain range. For when she is fully herself the entire mountainous range seems to project her heavenly ambience.

Could the moon be reached were I at the very top of the highest mountain peak? And since when did this moon reign over the night sky? I ponder. Over this same night sky, sometimes starry, at other times clouded, I had watched the moon traverse many times – how many more? I often ask.

She seems to continue ceaselessly on her cycles of rebirth, re-enacting the stages of birth, growth, maturity, decline, death, rebirth.

In her course of many lives, she too must have observed the many wars that have raged below. Like any human being she seems to possess a range of emotions. I have found her sad, seeming to weep above the grass plains in the aftermath of many savage battles, when countless mutilated bodies lay strewn to satisfy a king's search for illusory victory. She must have often asked, as I do, whether such killings are necessary in the art of war. So when I see her happy and radiant I often wonder if she might have witnessed how wars have been averted.

How I wish to have her vantage point from which to research and test my prescriptions as found in *The Art of*

War. She must have in her memory an extensive collection of many interesting episodes of war.

Our ancients from the very beginning of time have been full of praise for her. Beauty. Majesty. Magnificence. Forbearance. Permanence. Elusiveness. Changeability.

I am sure through this vast expanse of time and space she must have borne secret witness to how endless strife has led to countless wars. In the depths of her memory must be etched many lessons for the strategists in the practice of the art of war. For she must have been privy to many behind-the-scene intrigues when man struggled against man in order to seize ultimate power.

Her presence can be felt in every corner of the city, camps, plains, mountains, river, forests . . . If only I could hear her speak! But then we do on occasion communicate through the use of a language of signs and symbols.

4 ▆▆ 2

I often gaze into her face in search of a richer, more symbolic side to my work on the art of war. Once when I dwelt in the heart of strategy whilst deeply involved in writing *The Art of War*, she alerted me to reflect more deeply on the role of the king. The symbol of king (three horizontal strokes and a vertical down the centre) seems to be what she tried to convey through the contoured dark patches that clouded her otherwise shining face.

My mind flashed back to events which I had long forgotten relating to royal blunders made in waging war. These reflections led me to prescribe that generals should exercise their judgement based on changing war circumstances. They need not obey royal orders if the circumstances dictate otherwise. And as if she too agreed with what I had written, the moon appeared before me in queenly glory the next evening. Smiles could be discerned on her face.

Whenever I am conscious of her presence, I sense she has some message for me. But the message must be deciphered, intuited. So when I study her facial features in the evening – especially when she is at her peak of brilliance – I can even read a word or two from those dark cursive strokes.

At other times it is simply her juxtaposition with

worldly objects – appearing behind trees stripped of leaves – that communicates. And how she chooses to shine through those branches! Some of these configurations seen on a windy, cold wintry night are calligraphic masterpieces. Even better than the static pieces hung on the wall, these, in their ballet to the music of the winds, illustrate the possibilities of transformation of the characters so portrayed.

The clouds that clothe her often portray by their configuration a flow of ideas: you must however be patient to wait for them to unfold. It is at moments like these that my inner thoughts on strategy surface in my consciousness.

4 ▰ 3

Unlike the sun which may in fury scorch the earth, causing hardship for the people, the moon is milder, kinder, gentler and soothing in her glow. Her radiance brings quiet splendour wherever she chooses to go. On many occasions in my research and reflection for *The Art of War* I found delight in her company.

Her omnipresence across so many battlefields in varied places helped me to crystallize some of my thinking on the key principles of warcraft, such as that the best strategists are those who prevail without fighting. Certainly, they do not believe in armies charging uphill, nor in ravaging cities by scaling defensive walls. Their strategies begin with mastering the art of taking cities whole and intact. Rather than assaulting well-entrenched fortresses, the strategist attacks the enemy's strategy.

Ever alert to the cycle of changes inherent in nature, such as the ebb and flow of the tides, the strategist seeks out opportunities in the dynamic of change to undermine the strengths of the enemy: weakening the enemy's alliances through a creative flow of stratagems that cause inter-state relationships to go sour; luring the enemy out of their lairs before engaging them; never prolonging battle campaigns that dampen the fighting spirit and so on.

Strategists win wars through secret stratagems rather than human lives. For warriors bent on savagery the art of war begins only with the wielding of the sword. But for strategists a sword fight is but a phase – a possible one – in the infinite ways of waging war.

A glance, a word, a whisper, a gift, a dinner, a marriage, a display and many other signs are all within the range of possible fragments of strategy in action. Even the moon during her sojourn in the night sky has a role in strategy. For many secret acts of assassination of key officials or spies are carried out in pitch darkness during the dead of the night. And many celebrations followed by attempted assassinations as part of the strategic act are convened during her glorious moments of fullness under the night sky.

Her cycle of absence, crescent presence, growth, maturity and decline are studied with care by seasoned strategists. Her phases may be represented as such: growing moOn, mature mOOn and declining mOon. Strategists must study her cycle when formulating military strategy, for her cyclic presence determines the ebb and flow of tides in the rivers and seas. Some military actions are more likely to succeed when implemented during her maturity whilst others are associated with her weaker presence in the night sky.

Nobody can possibly be more familiar with the intrigues of strategy than she. For with her omnipresence many a whispered secret is within earshot and many a mysterious act is done within sight. Intriguers feel more at ease to coin stratagems in the dead of night rather than under the scorching sun. Thus the moon is more likely than the others to be able to piece together the strands in strategic thinking as it unfolds.

And she too has a vantage point from which to witness the enactment of a stratagem. So in this way across the immense passage of time she must have accumulated a wealth of knowledge on strategy. Perhaps this explains why I find inspiration in strategy formulation when strolling under the moonlight.

At times she is evocative of illusive eroticism. With her exquisite beauty she is simply too enchanting even for heavenly kings. No wonder that many strategists in their plans include feminine charms as an aspect of their grand strategy. For in luring away an enemy king's attention from war and state affairs nothing is more effective than a lady of incomparable beauty.

So in winning wars the willing sacrifices of such a lady are often as valuable as a general himself. Such a lady, given as a gift to the enemy's king, may often be more effective in preventing the onslaught of troops than a good general. For whilst the general faces an enemy brandishing swords, she acts to counter the very origin of strategy – the king – whose orders gave rise to the drawing of swords. She therefore attacks the roots of the tree of strategy whilst the general attacks its branches.

I am retiring now, having expressed my thoughts in writing. While I sleep I am certain the moon will journey through the darkness of the night as always. In some far-away place she will see the unfolding of yet another strategy.

5 🕮 1

A quiet windless morning. The air is so still that when a leaf falls I can imagine myself vibrate inside with a *thud* as it lands on the earthy soil. Unlike the rush on windy days, the descent of the leaf is so gentle. In this dream-like state I seem to hear with the inner ear a monotone *thud ... (a long pause) thud ... (even longer pause) thud ...* Subconsciously I begin to count just as monotonously with my breath: *one ... five ... ten ... twenty ... a hundred.* Suddenly the *number of soldiers* looms large in my consciousness. *Numbers* and the tallies of one's own army versus the enemy. I ask myself if I emphasised this sufficiently when writing *The Art of War*.

In this meditative state I seem to be transposed back in time: to the moment of my first verbal utterances on this *number* principle, long before its prescription in *The Art of War*. I was talking to a night gathering of key army officers in the tent of the general and these words resonated inside me: 'If it is assumed all else is equal – weaponry, arms, equipment, intelligence, skill, courage, morale – then absolute *numbers* matter in determining the outcome of war ... These are objective conditions which must be carefully evaluated by the general. But of course, to win we must move beyond assumptions and secure exact information.'

I begin to probe more deeply into my consciousness for the origin of this *number* principle in shaping military strategy.

5 🕮 2

Whence did this principle of overwhelming the enemy through sheer *numerical* superiority first emerge to be of significance to me? What did I see that reinforced its importance to me?

Perhaps the principle originated in the visual recollections in my memory of a variety of scenes from the insect kingdom – the army of red ants that overwhelmed and feasted on a wriggling worm, the swarm of bees that stung a monkey dead, the waves of locusts that devoured whole trees in their paths – these scenes seem to underlie for me the significance of collective action.

By themselves these insects are of little consequence: the tiny red ant, the buzzing bee or the lone locust. Yet they are formidable when acting collectively. Look at the animal kingdom and you can find the same principle of collective strength.

I could feel the earth tremble when the wild, war-horses of the north galloped in a wave-like fashion across the plains. The bulls too when they were made to charge in a body. Whether insects or animals, they are capable of wreaking havoc when acting together as an army. Also once, when the birds in the forest flew together skywards, how they even blotted out the rays of the setting sun.

So when peasants act in concert as an organised force of soldiers their potent destructive power must never be under-estimated. For lying quietly in the villages are latent forces. If these peasants are transformed a general should be able to deploy massive hordes of soldiers against the isolated few.

5 ▬▬ 3

I picture in my mind military success as embedded in the fine art of channelling these waves of potential energy in their flow towards given objectives. By virtue of their inherent cumulative strength and power these movements often induce an awesome sense of fear and respect in the observer.

So much so that I believe if one is far superior in numbers then the mere display of prowess may be all that is required to cow another into submission. Thus if one has numbers so overwhelmingly large versus the enemy, say 100,000 against 10,000, then actual physical fighting may be avoided. For enemy soldiers when staring in the face of defi-nite defeat often capitulate. Driving fear into the hearts of enemy soldiers through such tactics is part of the consum-mate skills of a master strategist.

I have argued for the importance of gathering accurate information as part of the strategy process. Of the range of information possible, the precise numbers and deployment of enemy forces are essential. Such numerical information should be enriched with qualitative insights concerning the enemy troops.

Some of the issues worth probing are: How many

soldiers are encamped? How many in the reserve army? How fast could the reserves be mustered? What weapons are they equipped with? What are their skills in handling specific weaponry? Besides these, other factors should also be enquired into: their discipline, loyalty, morale, fighting spirit, tactics, deployment in the field. How susceptible are they to superstition? Could we manipulate the human fear of the unknown, the mysterious? Are they well trained in specific battle formations? What about their provisions?

Such information is vital before an enemy is engaged. And depending on how these numbers relate to the information gathered, I then evolve war strategies for fighting the enemy. War is fluid and I often try to impress on generals that they too must be equally flexible. And even though I have worked out in *The Art of War* a range of generic strategic alternatives: surrounding, attacking, dividing, engaging and eluding – their application in practice should be adapted to the changing circumstances of war.

5   4

I turn now to these strategy prescriptions based on the consideration of the *number* of troops alone.

And here I list the alternatives for the future strategist – whether he aspires to be a general or a strategy adviser in the courts – who may open this page of my diary:

Surrounding. If all else is equal, and, as I have prescribed in *The Art of War*, if you are far superior to your enemy in number, say by ten to one, you should have your enemy surrounded.

For they may simply capitulate on seeing what an awesome force they are now encountering. Give the sense of awe and fear in the enemy troops an opportunity to do its work for you. The best outcome possible is for you to assimilate the enemy troops who surrender into your own army. In this manner the size of your army grows through the absorption of enemy troops.

Attacking. Strictly on number, and going down the scale of relative strength, you may still attack the enemy if you are superior by at least the order of five to one. For the odds of success are in the favour of the larger army – assuming an equal match in other respects.

Dividing. But if you are lower on the scale, say two to one, then you must divide the enemy troops before launching any attack. By attacking a division of enemy troops you retain the advantage of numerical superiority.

Engaging. I am against any engagement with the enemy unless you are at least equally matched in size, other factors being equal in a given situation.

Eluding. Clearly if you are numerically inferior you must master strategies for eluding the clutches of the enemy.

Again I must emphasise that these are broad principles of strategy.

5 ▆▆ 5

Skills of elusion become critical when a much smaller force has to survive against one many times its size. Like snakes that elude capture through developing slippery skins, so must the smaller side have stratagems worked out in detail to avoid capture by a much larger force.

Despite small size, there is still the possibility of ultimate victory. In such circumstances, the skills of a strategist are truly put to severe test. The strategist must initiate stratagems to counter the enemy's numerical superiority.

One stratagem is to wreak maximum damage on the enemy base camp by use of fire – strike at a time when the enemy is least prepared. Occasions such as the return of troops from an exhausting expedition should be exploited: attack them in the late evening or early morning when they are deep in slumber. Another good time is the late night feast celebrating the birthday of the general: even warriors when drunk or bloated with food make poor fighters. Do not however be tempted into engaging the enemy if they are numerically very superior, but quickly slip away into the deep forest as the fire devours the camp. Another possibility is to infiltrate deep into the enemy's camp and secretly poison the enemy's supply of water. If necessary use heavy bribes to get inside information on how best to wreak havoc among the superior enemy troops. The secret is, once the destructive act is initiated, to melt stealthily into oblivion. This is the art of self-preservation for a possible future showdown when the numbers are more evenly matched.

Sunlight has now penetrated my room. And with it the winds seem to be stirred into motion. The rustling of fallen leaves is beginning to be audible ... *shiz, shiz, shiz shiz shiz...*

Utterances

6 ▰ 1

Today the sun seems to be especially early in rising. I feel the vigour in these early rays with the pleasure that radiates from them. Like the sun this morning a wise and brave king can invigorate an army by his mere presence at the battle-front. The morale of soldiers is often heightened on seeing the king there in person with them. And even more so if the king is visibly sharing the hardships along with the common soldiers.

As every day the sun brightens the sky, so can a king lighten the hearts of people through his concern for their daily lives. But then the sun can also bring untold sufferings when there is unabated scorching of the earth during a dry spell. A king can likewise bring suffering, especially when he persists in acting against sound military advice in directing operations of war.

I recollect my early conversations with an aged, retired general now dead and gone. He spoke of the irretrievable loss of excellent soldiers suffered by his army due to the interference by the king in military matters. And his eyes suddenly widened as he spoke. In the eyes of this silver-haired old man you could sense how intensely he felt about what he was going to say. It was as if something deep inside him was suddenly being awakened. His hoarse voice was melancholic and yet full of strong conviction as he slowly intoned his advice:

"Never ever let a king meddle in military affairs; that is a sure path to ruin of any army, no matter how glorious or mighty."

His utterances were made with such a quiet force that the words remained carved in my mind. And so when I sit to reflect deeply on the role of the king – as when writing *The Art of War* – his voice seems distinctly audible inside my ears. And at such times, I often see with my mind's eye the very tiny glistening beads of tears at the corners of his eyes. These grew to the size of pearls as he struggled to speak. The tears rolled slowly down his contoured face as emotions welled up inside him. Biting his few remaining isolated, blackened teeth on his lip, scarred by a knife wound – as if to hold back the anger rising in him – he continued with his story:

"The king had grown vainglorious after I fought hard and won for him battle after battle ... he thought of himself as the invincible ... and our army, especially that core group of troops that took me a lifetime to muster and train – the most loyal of officers, sharpest archers, most courageous soldiers in our kingdom – were sunk and lost to the deep and mysterious sands. And all because of the horrendous mistake of the royal command to cross these deserted sands..."

Now his voice echoes on within me.

6 2

I recall vividly the images of chaos distilled from my memory of these conversations: soldiers drowned by sand-storms, the futile struggles to rise above the shifting sandy seas, heads disappearing into sandy depths, never to be seen again. Spears, swords, arrows, weapons of all kinds, armour, warhorses, chariots were of little use against an unseen enemy that seemed to be everywhere present – an indefinable monstrosity wielding the mighty powers of nature: the howling winds, the dancing sands. Such is the might of these sand-storms that the bodies of uniformed soldiers were cowered into submission. They waged on, trying to cross the sandy land quickly so as to satisfy the lofty wishes of the king.

The crying winds and swirling sands are but a prelude to something far more frightening: the gobbling up of bodies by something that seems to lie beneath these golden sands. But strangely, such deaths leave no trace. No blood is ever spilled. No remains. No burial is ever needed. All that is left to be buried are memories of the writhing faces of soldiers struggling in vain to avoid suction into the earth. These memories are even more difficult to bury than remains of the dead.

How agonising it must be to learn of the bloodless, traceless, painless, mindless slaughter of one's very best troops. But then even if the general had been at the scene, what could he have done except to watch and wait and hope? And all soldiers must each be wondering:

"Shall I be next?"

What is so saddening in waging a losing battle against these sand-storms is their indifference. The best of warriors could often survive gruesome and bloody battles with enemy troops by their sheer mastery of the weaponry. But the best swordsman or archer is almost as defenceless as the next soldier in this war with the sands. Once a warrior is locked deep in combat with the gobbling sands there seems to be only one possible outcome: certain death. For the more strongly one struggles, using every martial skill, the faster one sinks into the depths. These sands are as mysterious as the stars!

The general described the last moments of his deputy who had long fought alongside him. He was ordered by the king to command the army in place of the general. These words were related to him by those who witnessed his last moments:

"*Suddenly he fell off his horse which must have been quick to sense the movements in the sands. Despite all the majesty of his new outfit as Commander of the King's Army, he was dropped into the sand like any other soldier. Even though half his body sank quickly into the sand he remained surprisingly calm. His last actions were to extract the royal edict from his body and toss it towards the soldiers. Despite the stormy winds and sands, his last words could clearly be heard. They were words of duty, assigning to another fellow-in-arms the role of Commander of the King's Army!*"

What a tragedy to lose such a devoted soldier to the sands! And not only this one. Many of the vanguard, the leading soldiers, sank deep into the sands. For many of those who lunged forward with outstretched hands to rescue the sinking were themselves dragged into the sandy whirlpools. In such circumstances the more chivalrous the soldier the more likely is he to be drawn deep in. Many of the survivors were from the rearguard. The army was the best and bravest the kingdom had ever mustered and the soldiers that belonged to it feared no enemy, not even the monstrosity that lies beneath the sands, which drowned so many of them in the call of duty.

6 ⚜ 3

No wonder the ancients had warned against crossing these sandy lands. The sandy fury unleashed had never before been experienced by these brave troops. And despite the odds the army of 100,000 men simply soldiered on. Is the soldier's role just to obey and die? For death is certain for those who defy the imperial command by retreating. The general seemed despondent when he said these words:

"... and of those that survived the ordeal, only I remained till old age to tell the story. Many an evening I feel tormented, thinking how those men buried in the sands must have felt betrayed by my absence. These are the very men in the vanguard who fought side by side with me, enduring many hardships so as to secure victories for the king who is now despised and hated by many ... Only by retelling the story to as many young men as possible can I assuage the guilt residing in me."

His eyes had that distant look as these words were spoken. And by the time the story had unfolded it seemed as if he had transposed himself into another time, another world. The story-telling so tired him that it showed on his wrinkled face. His face looked unburdened when the story was told.

6 ⚜ 4

These shocking scenes are due to blind compliance to a silly edict issued by the king: to make the deceptively short but suicidal journey across sandy lands. The king interfered in military affairs even though he was unfamiliar with the conditions of the terrain. He relieved the general of his duties because he protested vehemently against the royal edict. The general had planned a much longer but well-trodden route to the enemy's capital city.

The king was then riding on the crest of several resounding victories in war. He decreed an early attack against the walled capital city of his arch rival. The reason behind the hurry seems frivolous in retrospect: his intention was that such a victory would serve to crown his tenth anniversary – a massive celebration was being planned – as ruler and conqueror over the wide expanse of yellow soil. Whether it was the tenth or the eleventh year of rule that was chosen for city-wide celebration ought really to have been of little consequence. But to lose the elite, the very troops behind every successful battle victory? And all in haste to glorify oneself?

That certainly is far too extravagant. For dead troops can never be revived. Dig in the sands as deeply as you may and search as widely as you can but the dead are gone for ever. For it is unheard of, since time immemorial, for those who disappear into these quicksands ever to come back. Only in memories do they live now.

6 5

So his story inspired me to state as a cardinal principle in *The Art of War*: the king must never meddle in the operations of war. These fall rightly into the province of the seasoned generals.

Interestingly, the aged general himself then lamented the reason for his refusal to comply with the king's edict: he had been instructed in this principle from yet another ancient story with the similar underlying theme, told to him in his own youth! And at least in his case the story had indirectly saved him from the clutches of the sands. But I wonder if kings will ever learn from the past. Perhaps future kings may benefit from following *The Art of War* and avoid mistakes, thereby saving many lives!

I have long planned to embark on this journey that will take me to the city and across the border to a neighbouring state. The beginning of summer – and this one in particular – seems so ideally suited for such an undertaking. Even the raindrops that have fallen over the past few days seem different: tinier globules of water than before, and hardly visible through the windows.

Such light rains – even 'rain*drop*' is too coarse a description – are so fine that there is joy pure and simple just to stand in the midst of them. The rain does not soak you and yet it settles dusty roads. These tiny dots moisten and freshen the air so that it is a delight simply to breathe.

I often wonder if people in high offices are able to refresh themselves through these gifts of nature. Most are too deeply embroiled in political intrigues – gaining for themselves ever more power and influence – to be in that frame of mind to appreciate such gifts. Once power is gained there follows the debilitating struggle to keep it for ever – a most difficult task. It is the nature of things that whatever reaches the apex will decline.

So often I have witnessed how quickly persons in positions of power become aged. Perhaps only those of us now retired up in these isolated mountain-tops are true connoisseurs of the transient delights of nature: the early morning mist, dew on leaves, winds moistened with fine rains.

Indeed since I retired from active engagement in worldly affairs I have been loath to leave my residence. Quiet is essential for thoughts on strategy to collect and settle in one's mind. Reflecting on these thoughts and capturing them in writing is what I had always wanted to do for self-renewal in my old age.

Still I feel that there is benefit in remaining in the know about worldly affairs as I reflect and write these thoughts on strategy. There is the subtle joy of seeing old faces and renewing contacts. I must say that with the passing days, fewer and fewer old acquaintances remain. What was left from the wars of my generation of friends have now been taken away by diseases and old age.

The wars that still rage on in some parts of the lands below have left some of the most beautiful scenery I knew during my youth badly scarred. An idyllic lake now stinks with carcasses – war animals, men, women and children. A stretch of greenery turned charcoal black as a result of a general implementing a scorched-earth strategy.

During these journeys I often replay in my mind my role as a strategist and a general doing battle out in the field. The journey is long and tiresome. As the mule drags the cart on and on my recollection of the past becomes more vivid. It is as if the mind relieves itself of boredom by dwelling on the remote past, that is more enthralling.

On the way, too, there are triggers of the past. Passing troops always stir in me memories of my days in battle as a general. Indeed anything to do with the army always has some deep significance for me, even discarded objects: a broken chariot wheel, a torn banner, shreds of uniform, pieces of bamboo strip, a disused tent. In my eyes these hold military lessons on strategy.

Just like a doctor knows the condition of his patients from feeling their pulses, so must a strategist hold conversations with the ordinary people so as to gauge the depths of their sentiments. Even though I consider myself no longer actively concerned with society I am still fascinated with anticipating change. Such a journey is therefore as essential for renewing my interest in strategy, as a bath in summer is needed to refresh the body.

Strangely, I draw lessons on strategy ever more sharply from the mental replay of the past. This despite the fact that I am merely sitting here listlessly on the cart. Also, often an unexpected meeting with a long forgotten face unlocks memories.

One highly perceptive soldier who trained long under me once asked me during my youth a simple but profound question: 'How can one, if ever, be certain of victory?' And in the ensuing dialogue I had then probed deeply into the specific contexts that favour victory.

I keep reflecting on our talk over and over again.

To put it simply, there are five keys I believe to be instrumental to victory. Why five and not more? Well, too many may cloud the mind. It is better to specify five and have these truly implemented than list a hundred that are merely memorised. Our hands have but five fingers each and yet they nonetheless have the dexterity to handle the most complex of tasks: writing, carving, tilling, riding, fishing, hunting.

The *first* finger I will count on is *timing*: there is a time to fight and there is a time *not* to fight. A fight should be initiated as far as possible by oneself under the most favourable circumstances. One should avoid being drawn into a fight contemplated by the enemy unless victory is assured from the most assiduous analysis.

In war there are occasions when the actions of the enemies – sudden departure of core troops from a walled capital, for example – provide unique opportunities for calling for a battle that is certain of victory. Then in such contexts one must act decisively to seize certain victory.

With the *second* finger I will recall the importance of skill in using forces of contrasting *sizes*: large and small. Victory is certain for generals able to combine effectively the deployment of both small and large forces. To secure ultimate success in war, a variety of military actions, some involving complex, intricate manoeuvres, must often be conceived. Some of these are better implemented through using small forces.

To create havoc in an enemy's camp through fire is more likely to be accomplished by means of a squad of soldiers with special talents. On the other hand to cow an enemy into submission behind a walled city requires deployment of large forces. And as a battle situation is fluid the general must be skilled in adapting the formation of his army – dividing or combining his forces – to capitalise on the enemy's weaknesses and avoid their strengths.

A *third* point is to retain a continuing sense of *unity* among soldiers from different ranks within the army. For an army that acts as one is difficult to beat. An arrow is easily broken, but not a dozen united in a bundle. In war the situation is never static: a festival of wines may be turned into a blood bath. A close victory may become a rout when the enemy unexpectedly send in massive reinforcements of their elite troops. So the wise general will ensure that officers and men are bonded together by a deep sense of brotherhood, so that the army may weather the vagaries of war.

7   4

The *fourth* precept I hold on to is *prudence*: never act rashly and if possible capitalise on the carelessness of the enemy. An arrogant general may be induced to act recklessly through a series of feigned defeats. Enemy troops may, through achieving these easy victories, regard themselves as invincible and thus become increasingly bold and less circumspect.

So if the enemy soldiers begin to behave in a reckless manner, then a detailed scheme should be worked out to lure the entire army in the enemy's camp into a place where it will be easy to kill them. For example, cause the enemy's troops to wriggle along a narrow path between two steep sides. Boulders, boiling oil, spears, arrows, rolls of burning grass can then be directed at these soldiers once both the exits are sealed. A wise general must be watchful of himself, lest the enemy should deliberately hurt his pride so as to agitate him into rash actions. I always ask generals to remember that human anger may subside but dead soldiers can never be revived.

And finally, with the clasping of my hand I mention the *fifth* precept: to keep the king from interfering with military affairs when an able general is in charge. And I remember hearing the onrush of waters as I spoke. For I recalled an ancient tale of how an impetuous young king, on ascending the throne, ordered the army to abandon border fortresses and take the shortest possible route – crossing a deep and dangerous waterfall – back to the capital city.

This despite the fact that enemy troops were already amassing themselves at the border. For he wanted to inspect the army troops personally. Since those who were late would be severely reprimanded, the general had no choice but to order the soldiers to brave the rapids. And it was as if Heaven were trying to warn them of their folly that thunderous rain fell as the soldiers tried to cross.

Danger

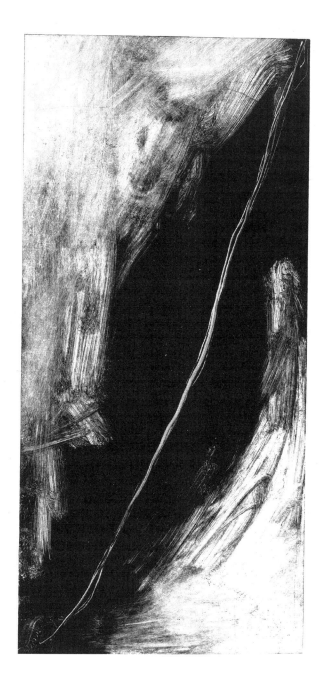

Many in the first wave were drowned in the attempt, together with the country's most precious warhorses. So distraught was the general by the loss that he rescinded the order. The army was disbanded. Many of the soldiers became bandits and rebels. And so a kingdom lost an entire army by virtue of the king's interference with military affairs.

Victory is more certain to be within grasp if all the five considerations prevail. I recall meeting this perceptive soldier again in his old age: the encounter rekindled in me further enthusiasm for seeking and testing principles that govern why some wars are won and others lost. With the passing of the years I feel myself decline physically but my powers of analysis still remain strong.

7 ▨ 5

I can hear somebody at the door. The usual noises accompany the old driver of the cart as he brings greetings of the season. His face is wrinkled with cheer, a cheer that comes from being contented deep within. From the glow in his eyes I know he too looks forward eagerly to the journey. And from our conversation I learn how flowers have sprung up along his way here. There is nothing more pleasing to the eyes than seeing carpets of blossoming flowers. A riot of colours reminds me of the banners that flutter in the wind when an army is on the march. Knowing that it is time to begin my journey, I hope it will not be too long before I turn to these records again.

4

1

I AM GLAD to open up this new array of bamboo strips collected throughout my travels across the border. I can smell their freshness and feel their smoothness. I always find the bamboo plant something to marvel at. Its surface is a pleasure to stroke with one's fingers. My thoughts flow better when I lay my brush on their strips. I often choose to record my deeper thoughts by carving characters on them. Because of their sturdiness I feel certain that my thoughts will be preserved through the ages. I hope future generations do not repeat the costly mistakes we have made in wars. I therefore record my thoughts, distilled directly from my own experiences, reflection and deep thinking on these little bamboo strips. I earnestly hope that future generations may study and benefit from these records.

In these mountainous regions, I often find giant trees which have been viciously uprooted in stormy weather. The scene vivid in my mind is of the ruptured roots of an old, majestic-looking tree lying on the ground. These resemble the entrails that spill out of an abdomen, as when a once grand and highly revered general had a curved, twisted blade driven through him. The bubbling muddy waters surrounding the roots of the old tree gush like fresh blood. A grand old tree in the forest is as glorious-looking as a general in the field. The richly green foliage of the tree resembles the banners that accompany the general as commander-in-chief on the battlefield.

I see in my mind's eye how a storm is also similar to the scene of battle: its images are metaphors for battle. The cries of the winds and the slashing of the rain are like the battle

Flexibility

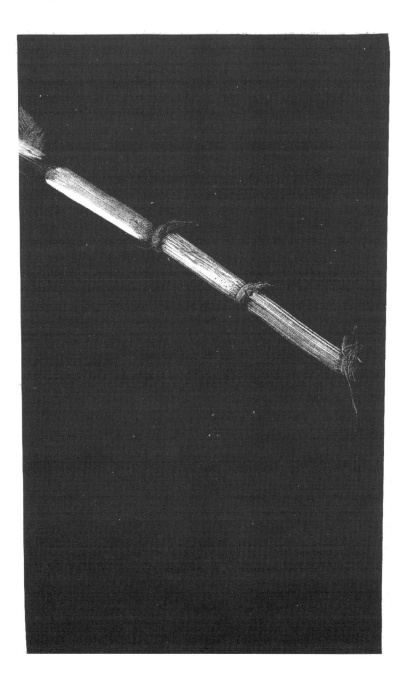

cries and flashing of swords. When mass upon mass of soldiers clash in combat the sounds, heard from a distant mountain, are like the mad swishing of leaves and branches. These branches often appear twisted as the gales build up into a fierce tempest. In the same way the bodies of soldiers slain in battle are contorted beyond recognition.

1 2

I have yet to see bamboos being uprooted, even though some of these plants are often just as huge as trees. Their resistance to the torrents of wind and rain is even more awe-inspiring when they are sited on the windward side of a mountain slope. See how these bamboos flex backwards, accommodating themselves to the rush of the storm, and readily rebound when it subsides.

It is like an army that retreats in a planned and organised manner when the attacking enemy forces are simply irresistible. And the moment the enemy tire themselves out and are resting, the army resumes its posture. Such an army is able to survive through acquired flexibility: it avoids being routed by a vastly superior enemy force by skilful withdrawal – like the bamboo bending backwards without snapping. Whilst the enemy troops remained strong, the invincible army lies low, remaining hidden deep in the woods.

The instant the enemy forces tire themselves and are resting, the army launches surprise counter-attacks – these actions remind me of the bamboos flexing forwards. Just as the bamboo endures stormy onslaughts, the army preserves itself from annihilation. The bamboo flexes forwards wherever and whenever the storm is weakening. And an army advances on enemy troops only through gaps of weakness. Such forays are successful precisely because they are made in moments of an enemy's vulnerability.

1 3

These insights were gained as a result of my assiduous observation of the bamboos. This is something that has long intrigued me ever since I began the study of the art of war with a concerted effort. So whenever possible I observe (as I did during my last journey) how these bamboos are able to survive the bitter onslaughts of wave after wave of torrential rain that keeps slashing at them unabated. I am amazed at the flexibility of the bamboo: it has no difficulty in yielding to wind and rain driving at it in full force. But without fail, the torrential waters and winds slacken, and it flexes quickly forward.

Only when lightning strikes directly do I find that the bamboos succumb and are then razed to the ground. Just like the mighty army which is destroyed when their camp, hidden deep in the jungle, is ambushed by the enemy archers. In this situation any army camp is an easy target for archers, who simply rain arrows tipped with fire on the camp. Yet even in these circumstances, the wise general of a truly invincible army is able to devise a plan for escape.

A typical tree in the forest, like the typical army, often lacks flexibility. In a storm, the tree is locked in direct confrontation with the howling wind and rain. Though such courage is admirable – the giant tree fighting against the whipping rain and wind, or the army stubbornly defending against all odds forces far larger than its own – the end is one of utter sadness: an uprooted tree; and valiant troops lying unceremoniously as dismembered corpses.

The general who seeks ultimate victory must try to preserve the army: no number of acts of bravery in battle ever amounts to the final outcome of winning the war. The general must constantly search for those qualities in an army that make it invincible. I often ponder deeply about those qualities that enhance an army's durability despite having to wage many battles. In the search I find studying bamboos provides useful insights.

1 ⚔ 4

So what are those unique features of the bamboo that may usefully be emulated when a general seeks to enhance the invincibility of an army?

Interestingly, unlike the common tree, there is a hollow – an emptiness, a void within – that runs through the length of each bamboo plant. I often see usefulness in a void: in what is not there rather than what is! Imagine living in a house without windows. And in the case of a wheel, it is the hollow in the centre that renders it useful. In conversation it is often what is *not* spoken that is significant.

The hollow in the centre of the bamboo must have contributed to its remarkable pliability.

So an army must learn through its training to be flexible in formation. Also the army must be trained to blend into the shape that is most appropriate given the enemy troops that it encounters on the battlefield.

There is another quality. To the uninitiated, the bamboo must look from the outside just as solid as any tree. Thus at the same time the army, besides being pliable, must know when to assume the appearance of being solid – even when in reality it is 'hollow' within! Can this really be done?

Yes. Clothe soldiers in grass to deceive the enemy about the numbers when seen from a distance. Drag wood over grasslands to simulate clouds of dust that suggest large numbers. In the darkness of the night use soldiers to carry bundles of flaming sticks. These are some devices for creating the appearance of a large, formidable army.

A close study of the bamboo 'tree' will quickly reveal that it is not a tree as such but more akin to a cluster of reeds growing together, that appears to the distant observer as one giant tree. Their manner of growth means that bamboos are able to disperse the concentrated forces of nature: the wind and rain are 'broken' into almost independent, disparate currents through the bamboo 'tree'.

The consequence of this is dilution of nature's forces. Likewise a general, when encountering a concentrated force, must devise a means to disperse the enemy into smaller, independent forces. And the forces of nature – gales, torrents, mighty winds and rain – in meandering inside the bamboo tree find no 'targets' at which to direct their force to uproot. The general must so organise his army that the enemy troops, though superior in numbers, can find no substantive targets to attack. In this way the enemy troops are frustrated in their attempts to gain a crushing victory.

This is due to the way the bamboo 'tree' is structured – independent reeds are bundled together. To be invincible an army must in time of need be easily bundled together as a single fighting force, closely clustered like the bamboos. The secret therefore lies in how effectively an army is organised.

1 ≡≡ 5

A general must learn to distinguish between invincibility and being victorious. Invincibility depends very much on the individual qualities of each and every one of the soldiers in the army. These qualities may also be modelled on the lines of a bamboo reed.

This brings in yet another feature of the bamboo that ought to be noted – the qualities of the individual bamboo reed. Each is as formidable as another. And the bamboo reed has so many uses: in writing, in farming and cooking imple- ments, in weaponry – spears and arrows – in laying of traps, and for food (bamboo shoots).

In the same way each soldier in an invincible army must be trained to contribute as wide a variety of skills as the various war situations demand. War is never static, and so tactics must be adapted to changing situations. To be effective soldiers themselves must be highly skilled in the operations demanded of them.

Little wonder that I so admire these little bamboo strips, as I record my inner reflections on aspects of the art of war.

The first day of the eighth moon – another occasion for me to reflect and seek the roots of my thoughts on strategy in writing *The Art of War*.

How often do people think deeply about the *lack* of constancy in life, assuming things will remain as they are? And based on my own encounters with strategists, I doubt that many really ask themselves seriously about it. Or even when they do, it is often too late: change in its flow has already overtaken them. Whilst it is true that change is often unpredictable, it is essential for strategists to observe the nature of change in the broader context of life.

In my prescriptions to strategists, I often used to emphasise the critical role of *timing* in determining military success. There is a *right* time for everything. But to be able to assess whether it is an appropriate time to act in a particular instance, the strategist must make it his habit to be constantly alert to the flow of change in nature.

My belief in this principle of war is derived from my constant observations and reflections on the nature of change itself: for I consider myself an eternal student seeking to understand this phenomenon. Human society is not immune; it is part of change as it evolves over time. Indeed, I often see human society as an integral part of a larger scheme of things in nature.

In any given situation it is necessary for the strategist to weigh up those factors critical to success and determine how they are evolving in the course of time. For nothing – be it the weather or human relations – remains unchanged and thus, by being always alert to change, a strategist is more likely to succeed. The strategist must nurture in his mind an ability to perceive change in the nature of things.

This is what I will turn to next: fostering awareness of change. I hope by capturing these fleeting thoughts in writing to encourage future strategists also to cultivate such a habit. All that is needed is a constant sense of alertness to things around us, beginning with what is happening closest to us.

Futurity

I often try to grasp the essence of change in the flow of things in nature. Every day, I see the alternations in brightness and darkness as the sun rises and sets: the gradual brightening of the day and its progressive darkening. Such brightening and darkening have implications for the strategist in deploying troops.

The strategist must appreciate how the progress of a day may affect the mood of the soldiers. In the morning, after a night's sleep, they are fresh and reinvigorated – their morale is also at its peak. As the day progresses, the soldiers begin to tire. Following the rest after lunch they are again refreshed. But as the day drags on they become wearied by the endless round of duties. As night falls, they begin to feel the need for a good rest. Thus a strategist should consider these factors when planning the timing for initiating specific military actions.

Military actions must be planned so that the basic need of soldiers to be revitalised through sleep is taken into account. There is an inherent cycle of action to be followed by inaction. For an army needs to recuperate after each major battle. Just like the sun that shines in the day and disappears in the night.

Each night, I find subtle changes in the continuous cycle of waxing and waning of the moon. According to a regular cycle, the moon goes through birth, growth, maturity, decline, death and rebirth. Like the soldier who, after being born, grows to possess a fine physique, matures with battle experiences, declines in bodily strength through old age, then dies, to be reborn.

Another related aspect is the need for the strategist to time battle moves after considering the cycle of change in the moon. For under a bright, full moon, soldiers are better able to see into the distance. On a moonless night enemy troops may launch a surprise attack under cover of darkness. Crossing rivers may be ideal on such moonless nights.

Some of the stars seem to take part in this cycle of ever-continuing change, shifting their position across the night sky from time to time. More interestingly, I often ponder at length on the appearances and disappearances of stars, the jewels of the night sky. They seem to be subject to the natural flow of change – birth, growth, maturity (hence their brightness), decline (dimness), death (disappearance) and rebirth (reappearance).

Our ancients long believed that the stars signalled change on earth. Perhaps the changes in the stars do carry with them portentous messages: the dwindling light of a royal star seems to correspond to the weakening of imperial rule on earth. Reading the stars is, however, a highly complex and difficult skill to master.

I have heard since I was young of how, when the stars streaked across the sky, something terrible would happen on earth. I have long contemplated the essence of the relationship between heaven and earth – the heavenly signs, are they truly predictive of earthly events? For if I could uncover these secrets, it would be of great use to anyone formulating military strategy. But it may be a mystery too deep to uncover within a single lifetime.

2 ▰ 4

Through a lunar year, I experience the seasonal changes of spring, summer, autumn, winter. The pleasant, cool weather (spring) giving way to the heat (summer), then cooling off to be comfortable yet again (autumn) and then sliding into the depths of coldness (winter). The length of a day varies with each season: shortest in the winter and longest in summer. Correspondingly the night is longest in winter and shortest during summer.

And for each season, I observe that the sun appears to follow a certain path through the sky. The moon seems to set a different course within each season when crossing the night sky. The stars too adapt to seasonal change. As must the strategist adapt his strategies.

2 ▰ 5

The winds also change their pattern, along with the seasons. Although the winds are invisible, their changes may be keenly felt, depending on the direction from which they flow, their strength and degree of coldness.

The effects of wind direction are clearly visible in war. The army that is charging against the onslaught of strong, biting cold winds is in a less favourable position than with cool winds driving behind it. It is worse still for an army ordered to charge uphill against bitter, cold and strong oncoming winds.

Arrows carried by the winds go much further, and thus favour the defending army encamped on the mountains. Conversely an army charging uphill, but backed by very strong winds, has some advantages. These strong winds will be blowing in the faces of enemy archers and thus affect their aim – the arrows they shoot will be less accurate. Imagine the sand and dust being blown in the faces of archers: how can they aim properly? Even if the aim is unaffected, arrows that fly against strong wind often travel far less distance and have reduced impact. Indeed, from my battle encounters, such arrows may never even reach their targets. Arrows falling short will demoralise the archers but stimulate more fervour among those charging up the hill towards them.

There will be added momentum in assaults reinforced by the wind when it is in the attackers' backs. Pushed by the wind, soldiers are likely to feel physically that the charge up the hill is less strenuous than anticipated. So if the army that is attacking sufficiently outnumbers those defending, then the odds – in these windy conditions – are clearly in favour of the attackers.

2 ⚎ 6

For the strategist, it is the interplay of a wide range of different forces of change that has to be factored into a military situation. As regards the weather conditions, the strategist must consider the sun, moon, season and wind along with many other factors in shaping a military action. Thus an assault up a hill may be favourable as follows.

On a moonless night in winter, amass the troops at the bottom of the hill. The lack of visibility can be exploited to create the illusion of large numbers – simulate large numbers by the use of fires and drums – attacking the enemy encampment on the hill. The direction of the charge should be such that the howling wind is behind the troops. Fire-tipped arrows should be used to set ablaze the enemy's camp: the strong winds will carry the arrows much further than usual and spread the fire far quicker. The timing of the assault should be early dawn when the soldiers have rested and are now eager for action. Enemy troops will be given an escape route and will not be pursued – the main objective is to seize the camp. Having an escape route means that enemy troops are less likely to fight to their deaths. It is anticipated that when the camp is captured, the day will be just breaking: the sun will provide the necessary light for consolidating the hold on the enemy's camp.

In the art of war the strategist must always be conscious of the flow in things. Indeed change is central to the way I shape strategy. Wars too have their cycle. There is a time to attack and a time to defend. For timing is everything in waging war – factors may change to advantage. The art of war is to preserve oneself until things of nature change in one's favour. So do not attack when weak but defend until the situation has changed in your favour. Then, when your strength is in abundance, you should attack. In attack leave your enemy with no possibility of recovery. Uproot to completely destroy the crops – otherwise when the winds next blow, your enemy troops may blossom again.

Today the flowers in the garden are blossoming. And it will not be long before I see apples falling from the trees. In time, I shall find little apple saplings springing forth in the garden.

From these observations of nature, I realise an important principle in strategy formulation: the power of transformation in an ever-continuing stream of change – flowers into fruits. The fruits are intended by nature to be eaten and, when discarded, the apple seeds are dispersed. Such activities ensure that the cycle of life continues, with the seeds growing into little plants.

This is the natural flow of things in life that strategists should be constantly alert to and be aware of. For this – the power of change – must be utilised by the strategists in formulating plans. To be able to see the obvious is not, however, the acme of skill for a strategist. Any ordinary person is very conscious of these natural sequences in things such as flower–fruit transformations.

The ability to anticipate accurately possible future scenarios from given situations is essential for any strategist who wants to excel in the art. The true difficulty lies in being able to 'see' how the future is likely to evolve given the present. For besides the changes that emanate from a single source, there is in war the need to consider also the interactions between a variety of sources of change: nature, people, weather, methods, ideas, society, country and so on.

Here, as before, I search for the sources of my thinking on this aspect of the art of war.

It is likely from my keen observation since youth of insect life in the garden that I realised how some worm-like creatures may be transformed in time into beautiful flying objects. In particular I am talking about the caterpillar that transforms itself into a butterfly after a period of long sleep or inactivity. Whilst the caterpillar crawls, the butterfly flies. Yet one is formed from the other. The two contrast in so many ways: one is ugly, the other so lovely. The power of change seems already inherent in the caterpillar. All that is required for

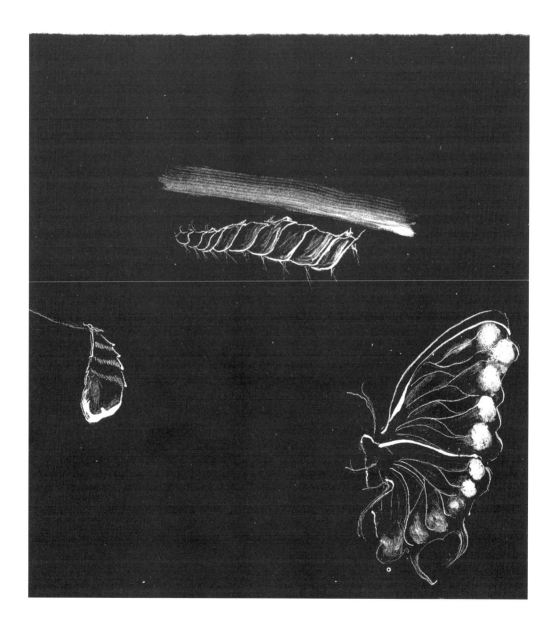

such transformation seems to be time and a period of meditative inaction.

Although I ponder why this is so in nature, it is the ability to recognise such transformations that truly matters for the strategist. Knowing such tendencies the strategist may be able to take necessary actions at the right time – neither too early nor too late. Thus if I wish to have a butterfly instead of having to chase for one in the jungle, all I need do is to find a caterpillar and let it transform itself as part of the natural process. This I find intriguing.

Such possibilities of transformation are not only inherent among the plants or insects; they may apply equally to human and especially military situations. A strategist must be able to recognise possibilities for bringing about such transformations when waging war: weak, ill-disciplined youths may be transformed into tough, fearless fighting soldiers through a period of intense military experience and training.

The strategist often finds it necessary to seek new resources so that the state may be able to continue the war effort. Such resources may *not* be available in an obvious sense. Efforts are needed to transform what resources can be found so that they may be utilised in waging war.

3 ⚏ 3

A regular army that is engaged in several long military campaigns often needs to be revitalised through fresh intakes of troops. As the war drags on it becomes necessary to consider new resources to continue these efforts. One of the sad consequences of waging long wars is the utter depletion of resources. As young men continue to be absorbed into the army that wages war at the battlefront, only the young, aged and women will be left behind to tend the farms. A time will come when human resources will also become scarce.

In time, to continue with the war, it may even become necessary to consider 'transforming' the less fit into soldiers: aged males, married and young women. In this lie the true skills of a strategist. In the past there have been stories of how ancient states in the last stages of war had to resort to using the weak – their aged and female – to defend the capital city.

For the regular troops then guarding the cities had to be despatched so as to reinforce the army at the front. Once skilfully transformed, these 'weaklings' had been known in the past to repel onslaughts by regular armies. The strategist must never ignore the possibilities of such transformations.

I was once challenged by a king to demonstrate my skills in the art of war. I was asked to shape a formidable fighting force out of dainty, playful, young women. Anyone seeing them playing in the palace field was most unlikely to entertain any thought of them as fighting soldiers. In this I was, however, successful. I started by instilling discipline, and had to put to death one of the king's favourite concubines. This of course displeased the king greatly but was necessary in my efforts to mould a fighting force.

Through tough training, the women were transformed into formidable soldiers whose duties were to act as the king's bodyguards. So if this is possible with young women, how much more is possible when a strategist is given raw youths! So the strategist must train his eyes to see the possible given the actual.

It is the same with materials required for wars: the possibility of transforming cooking and farming implements such as pots and cooking knives into swords, halberds and spears. I remember how a cluster of villagers transformed themselves into a fighting enclave, with every available day-to-day metal implement transformed into weapons of destruction. And with intense training in arts of war, the farmers became fearless fighters. The invaders, who were accustomed to raiding and bullying these villagers, were themselves stunned by the transformation.

3 ⚔ 4

By cultivating such skills, the strategist in waging wars will be able to perceive threats long before they surface. Actions may then be taken to eliminate the threats before they manifest themselves. For although men tend to record for posterity the bravery of generals who fought victorious battles, these men are not masters in the art of war. Indeed, the true strategists of the past may never even be mentioned, but it is they who truly function at the acme in the art of war. They initiate strategic actions to prevent wars from ever occurring, removing threats long before they appear on the horizon, and taking steps to prevent warlike tendencies from manifesting themselves.

For I heard during my youth how the wise strategists of old, who foresaw the potential dangers of war in the ambitions of young kings of the powerful neighbouring states, began implementing strategies to quell such tendencies. There are many possible counters to war, such as forming strategic alliances among the weaker states, but sometimes what is most effective is to counteract directly the personal tendency of an ambitious king by exploiting his lust for women.

One strategy is therefore to encourage ambitious kings in self-indulgence through wanton pleasures of life. Women have played key roles as part of grand strategies but their contribution often goes unrecognised. For unlike warriors, who bloody themselves in the act of war, these women live luxurious lives entertaining vainglorious kings. So history continues to glorify the generals even more than those who lay down their lives fighting the enemy!

I could say that one beautiful woman who successfully fulfils her role in countering a king's ambitious designs is more than equal to an entire army. Why? She, by her talents alone, is able to prevent a state from being attacked. If she did not contribute in this way the resources of an entire state may have to be wasted in wars with a powerful neighbour. For these peerless beauties, when presented as gifts to the power-hungry kings, are often able to distract them from military affairs. Other gifts – pets, artifacts, games – are also intended for the purpose of distracting the young kings.

Often the king of a weaker state, foreseeing possible threats or dangers, may form a blood alliance with the king of the stronger state by offering his own daughters as brides. So the strategist must be alert to more than one possibility of averting wars.

133

3 5

I have seen grasses that, though destroyed in a fire and lying dormant, once again flourish when the winds blow over the plains. So even though fire may seem swift in its destruction of the grasses on the plains, this destruction is incomplete: the roots still remain buried in the ground. So the ground may yet again be quickly transformed into grass plains.

Ask any hunter and he will tell you that tiger cubs are as lovely as human babies when young but they are a source of danger in the future: they will grow into fierce tigers. When fully grown these tigers will be difficult to kill. Such 'cubs' have in them the potential for change, to become serious threats to villages. Strategists should develop the skills of recognising the dangers inherent in situations or metaphorical 'cubs' and take early steps to prevent such threats from manifesting themselves in the course of time.

Thus the slaughter of entire families may seem brutal in wars but these actions are compelled by the foreseeable future threat that the young offspring present. These young witnesses of brutality committed as acts of war against members of their families – parents, brothers or sisters – are likely to grow up to be very determined to exact revenge. They are the very material from which to build teams of vengeful, fearless and invincible soldiers. For them war is a personal mission of seeking to right whatever wrongs have been inflicted on their families.

3 ⚌ 6

I have heard from the ancients about the strange behaviour of animals immediately before the coming of earthquakes. Even though such signs are there, those aware of them are defenceless against the destruction wreaked by these earthly forces.

The idea that strikes me from observing such phenomena in nature is the latency of power: something that lies dormant and yet is capable of springing into an awesome display of strength. Against such forces there is no possible escape from utter and total destruction.

So in *The Art of War* I prescribe the strategy of placing soldiers lying concealed and then bursting into sudden action in surprise attacks when enemy troops traverse their paths unexpectedly. Those who excel in defence are masters of the art of concealment, and can conceal themselves to such an extent that they seem to lie in the ninefold earth. So in stillness be like the mountain – immobile. Yet be capable of trans-forming into an unstoppable force when attacking. For those who excel in attack move as though they are from the ninefold heaven. Be like the lightning in flashing out power that scorches whatever lies in its path. Many a mighty tree have I seen in the forest, felled by lightning strikes.

Secrecy

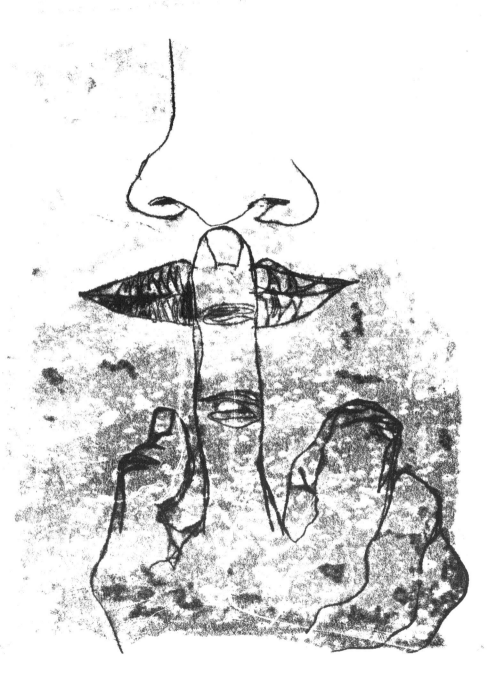

4 🎋 1

I am flipping through this collection of bamboo strips upon which I record the flow of my inner thoughts on strategy.

Sometimes I wonder if the world will ever really know the true stories of strategists working behind the scenes to avert wars. Most of these manoeuvres are done in the utmost secrecy. So few people through history will really be able to appreciate the dexterity with which these strategic acts are implemented. Often steps are taken to conceal such actions, even to eliminate *all* those involved in highly secret manoeuvres. But this may at the time seem justified to prevent a worse evil: that of an entire population of a state being trapped in endless and brutal wars.

So even messengers, once their tasks are done, are knifed in the back right in their own backyards. *Why?* The fear is of any leakage of information by those involved which may lead to discovery of the intricate 'machinations' behind the scenes.

One typical 'machination' is to use substantial rewards to get key people – especially disgruntled ministers, generals, even princes – in a powerful neighbouring state to be willing allies. The strategy is to arouse their sympathy with the national cause.

4 🎋 2

The task of constructing such a wide network of contacts in high places is painstaking and expensive. But through building this network the king of a weaker state may be able to learn in a timely fashion of any ambitious, covetous designs of a powerful neighbour. With such early warning he can forestall any military initiatives.

If thwarting the ambition of a king is not possible – the neighbouring king may be too consumed by glories from military conquests – it may be possible to take steps to redirect such covetous designs towards other neighbouring states. In this way time can be bought to prepare for possible counteractions or preparations.

Other stratagems can be advanced to placate the king or redirect his energy to more pleasurable pursuits. Clearly if such manoeuvres are ever discovered as a result of an unfortunate oversight, then the people living in the state may be plunged into years of toil and suffering as a result.

4 🕮 3

I recall writing extensively in *The Art of War* about the use of secret spies to counter the enemy. The fundamental idea is to ensure timely flows of reliable, though highly sensitive information. Codes are sometimes used instead of words to convey secret messages.

The role of spies in preventing wars is most important. When the news received is of likely worsening developments towards war, the strategist must make early counter-moves. These may be as brutal or cruel as military actions seen in wars.

But these acts are often shielded from the eyes of the ordinary people. Indeed, some of the fiercest, if I may say, 'shadow fighting' is unseen and undocumented, much of it taking place deep inside palace walls.

Such schemes may involve ingenious methods of kidnapping. Torture is often necessary to compel information from the sealed lips of people in the know. For those that give away information during torture also fear for their lives. Their own masters will surely punish them for revealing the truth.

A few innocent details are often critical in a silent, bloodless war, for example, the specific location of the room or concubine the king is going to withdraw to on a given evening. Such information enables spies to be sent to eavesdrop on the king's conversations, or the named concubine to be approached to divulge strategically useful information.

Killing, which is often part of the scheme of things, can be bloodlessly gruesome. For instead of swords, arrows and spears, other weapons are used: poison, ropes, sharp knives and other ingenious devices. Or people may be thrown off cliffs, into deep rivers, or buried alive.

For a long time I have been told stories of heavy bribes being paid to buy the loyalty of the servants of ministers of war. These ministers often see wars as a means of advancing their own personal interest. They campaign for the king to enlarge his kingdom through conquests. These servants, once bought, are expected to administer poisons to the minister's food. The story does not end with the murder. To cover up the conspiracy, the minister's servant too has to be exterminated.

Although these acts seem cruel, the resulting death toll is negligible when compared with the millions of lives that may be lost if states are thrown into wars. From the desire to avert wars many stratagems are coined, tested and refined through replication.

Secretly diverting the king's ambitious designs from one state to another is a ploy often used by the master strategist. But to do that requires spokespersons who are skilful in arguing the case. Another common strategy is to brew conflicts through exploiting the personal rivalries and jealousies among the ministers within the king's palace.

Insider news of palace developments is highly prized for its value in helping the strategist formulate effective strategies: which minister or general is fostering such ambitions of the king? Who are the strategy advisers? Who could be bribed to advance the interest of our state?

Kings, ministers and generals often have their own strategy advisers who explore possibilities, test ideas and suggest alternatives. It has been recognised since ancient times that it is valuable to test one's ideas or stratagems against another mind. Such interactions help foster multiple perspectives which later converge to produce a novel strategy.

Besides strategy advisers, a range of people is also critical as part of the machinations behind the scenes. Thus eunuchs, despite their lowly status, are as crucial in this palace infighting as generals on the battlefield. As I have earlier recorded, the use of beautiful women is one stratagem.

Besides that, treasures, gems, fine horses, rare swords,

139

gold – whatever is precious – are bartered for favours to be done in the interest of the state.

All wars have a cost.

Again the amount of money spent on these gifts is a paltry sum when compared with the cost of cities destroyed as a result of war. What about the mental agony, suffering and deprivation? Surely some value, albeit intangible, should be put on the experiences that peasants have to go through in the event of war. Besides, when cities are lost in wars, their treasures will certainly fall into the hands of the enemy.

So for a state waging war, to have peerless beauties, reliable informants, eunuchs and influential spokesmen is as crucial as having able generals.

4 ▆▆ 6

It is only natural for human beings to be prone to admire those who fight long and hard battles. Easy victories seem less glorifying. Yet the true strategist never wages a war unless victory is already certain. But wars easily won are often remembered less by people – perhaps painful sacrifice is part of the glory of a long fight that is finally won. And so throughout our ancient records, acts of remembrance are performed only for those who died fighting wars – especially wars in which the sufferings of the people were intense and acute.

So, inevitably, if history is used as a basis for assessing the skills of strategists, the truly great strategists are likely to be glossed over or even entirely ignored. Many are already forgotten with the passage of time. Many a brave general wages wars that from the outset will mean certain defeat. But these generals are often admired and loved because, by virtue of their extraordinary and raw courage, they have been able to turn the tide.

Should these persons be counted as great warrior-strategists?

The answer is, simply, no. They often choose to embark on a war despite the fact that the odds are stacked high against them. Yet history remembers them for their bravery. Bravery may itself become a fetish among men. So one must always be on guard even against those who by their nature are daring and brave.

The truly great warrior-strategists are most unlikely to gain any title for bravery. Through their strategic thinking, they ensure that a war is won even before it is fought – they do not count on acts of bravery to prevail in battle. Such strategists often take up positions which mean that they never suffer defeat in enemy attacks. So how could they ever be recognised for bravery?

And when waging wars, true strategists do not embark on costly military campaigns unless they are certain of easy victory: they fight wars that are already won. In other words they only do battle with enemies already defeated. Again, in such circumstances, there is no opportunity for displaying acts of bravery.

True strategists are unmoved by passion for bravery. For them, every victory has to be a calculated one. Winning is but a natural outcome of what is already predestined in their scheme of things.

On this note, I shall retire to bed.

141

I woke up this morning with the mist receding, and again I am going to take a walk of specific length to a distant hut visible on the other peak. This reminds me of another principle that I should emphasise in the minds of strategists: the central role of measurement in waging successful wars.

I always make it a habit to test my skills in judging distances by sight. I estimate the number of footsteps needed to reach a certain point and thus derive its distance. I then undertake the journey just to determine how accurate I have been. Another measure that I often use is to estimate the distance in terms of the number of days needed to cover a journey.

Also I make a point of determining distances between known destinations. I often ask in terms of the number of days required for travel by foot and by horse. So over the years I have accumulated a knowledge of distances between major cities, towns and villages.

In addition I would want to know of any special difficulties or dangers likely to be experienced when a journey is made, for instance, whether marshes or deep ravines are to be found along the paths; also whether on these journeys the paths are wide enough for carriages.

I take note of the actual ground conditions: whether flat or undulating, sloping upwards or downwards, hard or soft, shaded or open. Such information is most useful too when formulating detailed military manoeuvres.

Also I am keenly interested in how far a particular site is away from the river. Water is an essential commodity required by troops on a daily basis. Besides being a source of water, the river can also act as an obstacle. This is especially so over those stretches where the river is fast-running or its depths are unfathomable.

Over the years I have been studying the terrain; I am now familiar with places where river crossings are possible. Some of these crossings are impossible during certain times of the year. This becomes critical when I am asked to devise a route for immediate withdrawal.

142

Whenever I have to advise on military strategy over ground which is new to me, I will spare no effort in making exhaustive and detailed enquiries. Often I plot the ground on a map using a piece of cloth. On this I mark key features: towns, cities, forests, roads, paths, vegetation, crossings, dangerous or slippery ground.

The measurement of distances is basic to the art of war. For such information is needed to determine how quickly troops may be deployed between two given localities. How quickly the troops are able to cover the ground will also depend on the type of march that is ordered.

143

For troops to fight well, however, sufficient time has to be made for rest. It is unwise to order tired and exhausted troops after a long, forced march to do battle. Longer and more difficult journeys will mean that the soldiers will require more time to be in peak condition for battle.

Troops wearied through long and difficult journeys become easy prey for the enemy. I often study how long, difficult marches may affect the morale of the troops. I am reluctant to pitch weary troops against an enemy that has rested properly.

Of course the tougher the soldiers, the less weary they are after a long journey. Certainly age is one measure of the soldiers' physical stamina on the battlefield. But another factor is the quality and type of training which the soldiers have undergone. I prefer to utilise men on the battlefields who have undergone thorough training in effective use of weapons.

Soldiering is a difficult profession, requiring tenacity, toughness and a will to win. Whilst some of the king's expert troops may be able to march for days and still prevail over enemy forces, the ordinary soldier is often so exhausted after long and hurried marches over difficult terrain that a period of rest is necessary. Also time is needed to condition the soldiers psychologically.

As a strategist in devising military strategy you must have some measure of the quality of troops *vis-à-vis* the task at

Map

hand. Some questions may help direct the mind to key issues.

How long will these troops take to reach a given destination? Are there scouts able to chart a path through the dense forest? What will be the condition of the troops after making the journey there? And so on.

In war, another aspect of measurement is important: relative measurement. As a general-strategist in the field, I would always make detailed investigations, comparing my own troops *vis-à-vis* those of the enemy. Even in peace-time, I would compare the readiness of our troops as compared to that of others.

For these investigations I used to go out into the field incognito. I would test my own intuition based on my own observations, with information gathered from spies. I would frame questions to elicit the essential information for strategic analysis.

5 ▬▬ 4

Besides the soldiers I would look at the types of weapons in use: their length, sharpness, lightness, tautness (of bows and arrows). Often I would personally test out this weaponry when making comparisons. Also, I used to study the qualities of the horses: their differences in endurance and speed.

Only if such details are attended to can the strategist formulate meaningful strategies. So I had bows and arrows used by the enemy tested, and compared the results with those used by my own troops. I would draw the bows and test the strength of the strings used, look at the arrows in their flight paths, study the sharpness of the arrow-heads. As an example, apart from the technical aspects, I would also investigate how training in archery differs between the two armies.

I would seek to answer questions. Are there specialist archers? How many of them? What are the assigned roles of the archers? Where are they likely to be deployed? How accurate are they when in combat? What is their effective range? What about the training received in archery by the average soldier?

The strategist must make this constant enquiry a habit of mind. Besides the physical endurance and technical capabilities, strategists must also measure the qualitative attributes of the soldiers, such as which side is more committed to the cause for which they are fighting. Unlike distances, these may only be determined subjectively and are impossible to measure directly.

5 ▤ 5

After each battle, I would obtain details of soldiers wounded or killed – how many archers, foot-soldiers, special forces – so that I could better redeploy those who are still fit. So after each major war, I would need to reorganise the army into new formations.

Another measure is the rate at which different supplies – water, food, weapons, chariots, horses, uniforms – are consumed in the process of war. Since the costs of war can escalate easily, the strategist must devise cost-effective means of attaining the same military objectives. So I emphasise keeping a detailed inventory of the different items used in war and keep a constant eye on their adequacy.

For whilst wars may have to be fought, the strategist has the moral obligation to reduce their cost and ensure minimum wastage. For the costs of war are ultimately borne by the people. Wars inevitably impoverish people of the warring states, so the strategist must devise plans to minimise the deprivation and suffering inflicted on the people.

5 ▤ 6

I used to seek alternative *non*-military solutions to achieving objectives. I would devise my own measures for estimating the costs of war – men, materials and equipment – and constantly test the reliability of these estimates through actual military operations.

Thus I would set about in secret to study the configuration of the enemy's defences – city walls (height, construction and structure), the troops (skills, morale, weapons, deployment), supplies inside the city – and then calculate the quantity and quality of troops required to conquer the city. I would estimate how many days a military operation is likely to take, given the resources available.

Another measure that I would often try, based on available information, is to estimate the probability of success of each possible alternative course of action. Just as when an egg is cast against a rock, the outcome is immediately foreseeable, so, when waging wars, the strategy is to cast rocks against eggs!

Outcomes of war should never be left to chance. Instead every conceivable measure should be taken to seize victory. There is little purpose in sapping a country's resources unless there is certainty of victory.

So when formulating strategies, the strategist utilises whatever means may possibly be derived from the circumstances to capture the different factors critical for success in war.

147

Force

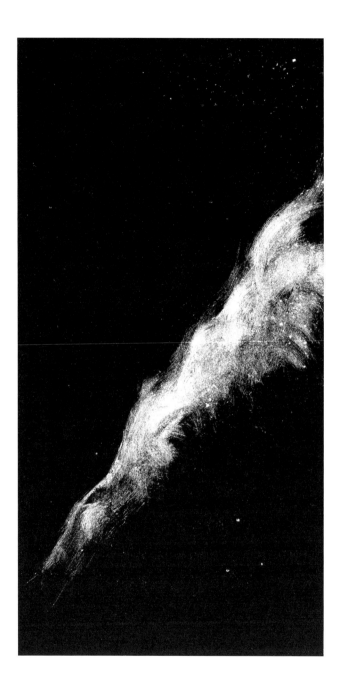

6 ⬛ 1

Spring, the beginning. I recollect how as a young man I derived the principle of irresistible force from quiet observation of the mechanics of a waterfall.

It was deep, freezing winter when I retreated to stay in a friend's house next to a waterfall. I was then recovering from wounds sustained in a long pitched battle. I needed a quiet, remote place to recuperate. And as I rested on the window sill of the little hut that overlooks the waterfall, I observed day by day how, with the coming of spring, the ice melts into water.

As my eyes witness the gradual increase in the flow of water, my ears are alive to the sounds of the falling water. The music of the waterfall rises in a crescendo until the fullness of spring brings forth the rush of water that transforms the atmosphere. The trickles are now overflowing like waves. The air around the hut too is freshened by the moisture.

Although I had recovered fully from my injury I stayed a little longer to contemplate the meaning of this natural phenomenon. Sometimes I followed a long and winding path up to the very top and edge of the waterfall. On reaching the top I just had to hold my breath. I remember exclaiming:

"How steep the water must fall to reach the bottom!"

No wonder that the water strikes the pool below with a such mighty force. The water that falls must have in the process gathered so much momentum from the downward dive!

6 ⬛ 2

The sight awakens me to the possibility of troops emulating the force of water. I then begin to see masses of soldiers as waves of forces, just like water in action. Indeed, in many ways the human bodies that comprise the army, in charging forward resemble the waves of water at the waterfall.

I recall how an army is able to charge through a gate although it is aflame. The soldiers seem to be driven by an emotion that is beyond the ordinary. The soldier is no longer acting as an individual as such but becomes part of a greater entity. The momentum of the charge is not unlike the water rushing down the waterfall. Just like water, that is indifferent to height, so the soldiers can be blind to the dangers of the roaring flames when storming through the city gates. Many a victory rests on a sudden upsurge of energy from the soldiers fighting as one whole.

I recall vividly the sight of soldiers in motion seen from afar. From a hill-top I stood to observe the battle scene: the armies in action are like waves rippling along the banks of waterfalls. The sand clouds that churn and stir in the air are like the foam of water bubbling at the very bottom of the waterfall.

Even more memorable are the scenes of generals leading the charge of an army. The mighty general with his banner fluttering in the wind forces the lines of enemy troops to open and unfold. The scene is reminiscent of waves breaking and unfolding when confronted by rocks jutting unexpectedly out of the riverbed.

The officers behind the general, who follow through with the charge, model themselves after him in cutting down enemy troops, so that gushes of fresh red are visible even from the distance. Enemy troops are simply shocked almost into inaction to see how their lines, consisting of their finest and bravest, are so easily forced open. They panic.

6 ▰ 3

Some begin to flee from the battle scene. Other enemy troops follow suit and a stampede results. Faces tell a thousand tales: those frightened, panic-stricken faces of soldiers who simply abandon their weapons to save their lives. Nothing so spurs the courage of soldiers than seeing enemy troops fleeing in a mad rush, with their backs exposed as easy targets. The archers simply rain their arrows down, scoring many hits on the backs of those who try so desperately to flee.

In such dire circumstances a rout is beginning to take shape. For it is often said that every battle has its decisive moment. A single brave general may be all that it takes to turn the tide in his side's favour.

But what is it that enables one general to be so capable of arousing in soldiers the courage to storm like waters dashing through high, dangerous rapids? Soldiers can be so inspired that they can scale some of the most formidable and impossible mountain passes in the west.

6 ▰ 4

I recollect stories of soldiers who braved impossible mountain passes to help their wounded general escape from the clutches of enemy troops. Despite the bitterly cold winter blizzards, with their bodies leaning against icy, high mountain edges, they soldiered on, carrying the wounded general on their backs.

The mountain peaks were so high that they seemed to float in the blue sky. There was also little vegetation around. What pushed the soldiers on and on was their determination to break free from the enemy troops. Their crossing of one cliff to the next often demanded feats of outstanding courage and skill. For to bridge between cliffs where the gap might be more than three bodies' length the soldiers needed to devise a very risky method. Ten able-bodied soldiers organised themselves into two columns, each consisting of five soldiers piled one on top of another. The human columns then fell towards the other side to form a bridge. As the soldiers stared down into the abysmal depths below, the severely wounded general was carried across the human bridge.

Why were the soldiers so dedicated and loyal to the general? What qualities did the general have that these soldiers so willingly throw away all concern for their own safety?

The soldiers continued to scale heights which have long been thought inaccessible. The general too, despite his wounds, kept his own flagging spirit alive. He was absolutely determined not to disappoint his own soldiers whom he regarded as his children.

Crossing a divide in such a dangerous fashion is but one of the many feats the soldiers had to muster simply to survive.

On occasion the soldiers had to contend with other equally impossible hurdles. For example, they had virtually to claw their way, using short knives and carving out little ledges on stony surfaces in their climb up a gigantic boulder. This mountain of a rock simply jutted out, blocking the path forward and rising steeply into the clouds.

The strongest among the soldiers had the general tightly roped to his back as he strenuously and carefully pulled himself to the top. His hands groped the polished surfaces for anything – little ledges, carved niches – upon which to fasten his grip. The soldiers watched as the limp body of the general slowly inched up.

Every breath of the icy mountain wind was keenly felt on the skin of these soldiers. Even a moderate wind seemed able to toss the coupled body of the general and soldier off into what seemed like an abyss below. Soldiers who failed to make the climb shouted at the top of their voices as they fell off the boulder into the unfathomable depths:

"I regret not having the good fortune to be able to serve the general. But I shall in my next life...".

There was no hint of fear, only of deep regret, in the echoed voices of these fallen soldiers. Such deaths only made those who were left even more dedicated to struggle on, powered by the belief in their cause.

The body of the general was a symbolic representation of the cause to which they had committed their lives. Their belief in the cause was so strong as to sustain them as they soldiered on in the thick of this wilderness where few human beings ever venture.

There is a lesson here for the wise strategist. Men are often prepared to lay down their lives for lofty causes to which they are committed. In this instance, it was the preservation of their homeland against foreign, invading forces. For their homeland signified for them a way of life that was unique, a culture and ideology that they cherished.

As I was later told, these soldiers arrived at a quiet faraway, place entirely out of reach of the clutches of the enemy.

6 ⚌🎋⚌ 5

Again there are other memories of stories told of the simple raw courage of ordinary soldiers who braved the elements of nature in their fight for a cause that they believed in; of how a battalion of special guards, led by a loyal general, accompanied the king in his flight from usurpers of the throne through the passages that lie deep beneath the surface of the earth, where only darkness reigns.

Only a handful of the king's best guards remained to prevent entry into these underground passages for days on end. An entire army of enemy troops was assigned the task to pursue and eliminate the king, the general and the guards. For entry into these sunken passages was possible only through a narrow slit at the foot of a mountain.

Although the usurpers were finally able to force their way through, they found it simply impossible to continue their hot pursuit in a maze of utter darkness. Also by that time the loyalist guards were already far too deep inside to be tracked down. They were so driven by the desire to preserve their king that they were blind to the dangers lurking in the dark as they made their way through the labyrinth.

They wandered in pitch, total darkness and dead silence, hoping to find the trail that was said to lead to an opening somewhere in the thick of the forest. In the pitch darkness, some lives were simply snatched away. So quickly was it done that it seemed to be the act of spirits dwelling beneath the earth. Perhaps they were angry about such a massive intrusion.

One member of the vanguard slipped and fell into some unknown abysmal depths in the dark. Again there was no cry that betrayed any fear; only expressions of regret at not being able to continue to serve the king. Another fell and was drowned in an underground lake, unseen at the side.

When the soldiers finally made their way out after many days and nights wandering in the maze they looked so pale and white, with dark, red, sunken eyes. Many a villager thought they were ghosts coming back from the other world.

The king was fortunate to have in his service a master strategist as general. He had long ago mastered the fine art of training and inspiring people to fight. So able were his guards, fighting in unison, that their thrusts forward resembled those of waters plunging into abysmal depths. Through his leadership a new army was raised deep in the forest that later swept the usurpers out of the kingdom.

5

1  1

SUMMER – IN ITS very early beginning.

Strangely, I am beginning to yearn for the quieter wintry days. Perhaps it is the deeper stillness of my mind during winter that I look forward to. In *The Art of War* I have distilled my reflections into basic principles. Here I am recording my search as deep as is possible within me for the sources of my thoughts on the art of strategy.

I often emphasise that strategists must try to perceive the key principles that explain changes in a myriad of things; to observe keenly natural phenomena and draw from the cosmic patterns of change lessons in strategy.

How does nature organise itself in continual change? Is there a strategy in the natural scheme of things? Or are events in nature purely random occurrences?

My observations tell me there is a Way of Heaven that I may call the *Tao*. Despite appearances there seems to be an overarching design in the natural scheme of things. I see patterns, cyclical movements in things that imply a certain order within nature, yet inherent within this order lie the seeds of disorder.

1  2

So whilst the seasons have a pattern of *re*occurrences, no summer in my own experience is exactly like any one I have experienced before. There are always some aspects of a summer that differentiate it from those that I have encountered before – too hot, too wet, too dull, too early or too late.

When I advise on organisation I allow for an element of the unpredictable. It may be better to be conscious of the possibility of the unexpected or unexpectable than to try to allow for every possible contingency.

The army is but an aspect of the natural scheme of things. Indeed, all human beings and their affairs are an integral part of an ever-continuing process of transformation and change. Since all soldiers – whether those of the enemy or your own – are human beings the strategist must seek to discover an underlying order in the scheme of things. Human behaviour is but another aspect of nature.

1 ≡⚁≡ 3

For the strategist there are some aspects in the organising of soldiers that should be investigated in greater depth, for example, why are some generals better leaders in motivating soldiers, so that they obey them willingly?

In contrast, there are generals whose only means of ensuring compliance is to throw the military code in the faces of the soldiers. In the course of routine military affairs, the outcome may seem to be the same – things still get done whether the soldiers implement the orders willingly or not.

There are, however, some circumstances when the very survival of an army hinges on whether these soldiers are true followers of the general, for example, when the battle is lost but the army is not yet crushed and is in retreat. Or when the soldiers themselves realise that only by sacrificing their lives can the army be salvaged. They may have to hold the line of defence resolutely so as to enable the remnants of an army – including the general himself – time to escape.

In these exceptional circumstances success depends on whether the soldiers themselves admire, respect or even love their general. If a general is hated by his own soldiers, the outcome in such a situation is likely to be very different. Soldiers may abandon their posts and return to civilian life. Or worse, the officers and soldiers may turn the general in so as to appease the enemy.

The quality of the relationship between the troops and

their general is therefore of deep concern to the strategist. What he must try to master are skills in strengthening the bonds between the ordinary foot soldiers and lancers and their general.

1 ▆▆ 4

Related to insight into human behaviour is another skill required of master strategists: the ability to read the minds of those present in conferences held to discuss military affairs.

Often, I scrutinise their facial expressions. The unspoken is often more instructive than the spoken. Or in a conversation or speech what is left unspoken may be equally informative as what is spoken.

Another task is to search for the deeper motivations or the true intentions of those who speak – why certain words are used and how these are emphasised in the process of speech.

I also try to detect bodily changes – eyes, faces, posture – when words are spoken so as to probe into the true dispositions of those present. Whilst lies may be uttered, the eyes often betray the true intentions of the speaker.

Other skills I try to sharpen are in predicting the likely reactions of human beings to given events. Although different individuals may respond differently to the same event, the true skills of a master strategist lie in being able to anticipate accurately the course of action an individual will most probably embark on.

Thus I often put myself in the position of that person and ask what actions are open to him. To be able to do this properly, the strategist requires reliable and detailed information about the specific circumstances confronting the enemy.

The skilful strategist should be able to structure events so that a specific person, given his predilection, may be anticipated to act in a particular way.

1 ▆▆ 5

Having an in-depth knowledge of human behaviour – individual, group, and mass – is essential for any strategist who is

Expressions

advising the king on military strategy. Understanding people – their motivations, concerns, fears, tendencies, desires, weaknesses – is the basis upon which the fine art of organisation is to be mastered. Organisation is no different from doing other things.

Thus, whenever I was assigned by the king to advise on how best to deploy a specific army, I would immerse myself in their midst – chatting, drinking and relaxing – and was able to get a good grasp of the current situation: their morale, attitudes, problems.

What I valued most through involvement in these interactions is the possibility it afforded me to infer facts about the whole from study of a few. Just as the farmer is able to tell the quality of rice from a farm when he is given some grains, so should the strategist be able to discern qualities of an army from some of its soldiers.

One must of course be careful, like the farmer selecting those few grains: one must ensure they are taken from the right plot of land. In order to ensure the reliability of what I am trying to discover I try to mix with a wide cross-section of men from a given army.

These conclusions often influence me in determining how I implement a strategy. Thus, if I discern that the army, though loyal and enthusiastic about engaging the enemy, is poorly skilled I will not entrust such an army with border defence. Instead I will convince the general of the need to reskill the soldiers in the art of weaponry.

1 ⚎ 6

Principles relevant in organising a squad as a fighting force should be equally applicable to the running of an entire army. The fundamental concepts for controlling human behaviour ought to apply. But in controlling a large number of soldiers certain devices may be required. For instance, to bring the squad into a certain formation, all you need do is merely raise your voice. But to coordinate an entire army, drums may be needed. Such drums may be used to stir up courage as well as alert the soldiers about the actions to take.

More sophisticated commands may be conveyed through the use of differently coloured flags and banners.

Banners tell the troops which general has their command. Different groups of soldiers may be assigned different roles. But one must be alert to the strategic implications of organising in this way: the enemy too may be able to gain useful information from implementing such devices in his army.

This brings me to the question of organising secret military operations. It is very difficult for an army to conceal its operations. The enemy is likely to have spies infiltrated into the ranks or to have the movements of an army closely watched. For covert operations smaller squads or even a single soldier may be far more effective. Code words may then be used to convey secret messages from one squad member to another.

The use of night fires on hill-tops to convey urgent messages has long been practised by our ancestors. Fires may be lit at army posts far out into the border areas when there is imminent danger of attack by enemy troops. In some circumstances, I may use well-known and established practices in organising to deceive the enemy. By not making fires, I am able to convince the enemy forces of our lack of awareness of their planned attack. I may instead use men on fast horses to forewarn my troops in the rear.

Similarly, different coded signals may be implemented just before battle to coordinate movements of the different sections within the army. But for such coordinative changes to be successfully implemented there must be a very thorough and detailed briefing.

1 ▰ 7

Another issue that concerns me deeply is: should there be differentiation of functions within the army? This would mean greater specialisation in military skills. One possibility for specialisation is by type of weapon used: archers in use of arrows, lancers in use of spears, cavalrymen in control of horses.

Personally, I still prefer that the role of soldiers remains as fluid as possible. So I emphasise that soldiers be trained in a range of weaponry skills. Their role should depend on the mission that is being undertaken. I may even reorganise the entire command structure of an army specifically for a particular mission if that is necessary.

The idea is to obtain the best fit between the army and the assigned mission. The tendency of generals is to be quick rather than deliberate when engaging the enemy in action. So often the soldiers are unnecessarily exhausted after having been made to traverse long distances, only to be left there idle.

Organising and reorganising troops is often necessary so that the army is always optimally formed for any given mission. The size and composition of the force should be what is most appropriate for the task at hand. Indeed, I often require that soldiers sharpen their skills in the specific weapons that are critical for the success of the mission. Thus if accurate archery skills are essential in a given mission, all soldiers will be drilled in them.

So much for my reflections on organising – a fundamental skill for the strategist.

Unorthodoxy

2 ⚏ 1

The winds this morning are bitterly cold – and this in summer! With very light clothes on I was caught totally unawares. I can remember being surprised regularly enough to suspect that it may be nature's deliberate doing. Nature seems to contain within itself the elements of the unorthodox.

A sudden upheaval of waters can cause villages to be submerged within a very short space of time. I recall vivid scenes in my mind's eye of water, water, water everywhere. All that villagers could do was stay perched on the rooftops.

Shattering rain of icy stones falling from a clear, cloudless summer sky. A strange phenomenon that goes beyond all comprehension. Many people rushing for cover – under roofs, trees, sheds, whatever.

Whirlwinds that appear out of nowhere and disappear just as mysteriously. I remember howling winds that blew out of nowhere as I wandered in search of herbs. For what purpose? From where? And to where? Nobody really knows.

There is even more that is unorthodox in nature.

2 ⚏ 2

The transmitted records of our ancestors tell stories difficult to visualise – of how the peaceful earth that supports all life suddenly moves, shakes, divides and swallows. Whole cities, if not an entire civilisation, may have been wiped off the earth in a few movements.

What counter is there then to such unorthodoxy? Human beings are so accustomed to the notion of an unmoving earth. Our whole lifestyle as farmers is based on that notion. So when I occasionally till the soil, I remind myself that what lies below may be an entire civilisation! Lost to an unorthodox act of Mother Earth.

Even more astounding are tales from the travellers that come from faraway places: of mountains that spout boiling, bubbling, molten substances from the very core of the earth. They call the molten liquid 'lava'.

There is no fury quite like it. Anything that stands in its way is simply obliterated. Again human beings have no way of countering such an unorthodox change in how a mountain behaves. So sacrifices are offered to the mountain gods. But there must be more to it than simply anger on the part of the gods.

Is it not nature's way of alternating the orthodox with the unorthodox? The book that has survived through thousands of years from our ancestry has *change* as its central theme. The alternation of orthodox and unorthodox is but part of the ever-evolving phenomenon of change.

The unorthodox has such a force that it simply smothers all resistance in its path.

The unorthodox simply overpowers.

2 3

Among the animals there is too an appreciation of the principle of unorthodoxy, as manifested in many varied ways. For example, in the unanticipated, twisting and sweeping movements that enable an eagle or tiger to gain its prey: the swift dive downwards or the sudden leap of the body. The predator that survives seems to have understood and later mastered intuitively the principle of the surprise move that shocks. Such sudden, surprising and sweeping moves may have so shocked its prey as to freeze it into inaction.

Another form of unorthodoxy lies in altering appearance: from the usual to something that shocks.

Across the path of the forest I saw a most unusual scene: that of a bird fluttering away from a caterpillar. I then realised the tiny caterpillar's secret of self-preservation: it had transformed itself into a most scary-looking creature. From my own enquiries I learned it to be the larva of the elephant hawk-moth which has mastered the unique art of self-transformation: lifting its head to reveal the 'eyes' and thus look like a snake.

The same notion underlies the success of the frilled lizard in scaring off enemies. For on many occasions I have seen how the little lizard is able to frighten off many a predator by displaying the flaps hidden in its neck.

So here deep inside the forest little insects too have mastered the principle of unorthodoxy.

Even in the natural course of things, the unusual occurs within the routine.

Rain. In normal rainfall, there is the familiar rhythm, but when unorthodoxy prevails the falling of rain is transformed into heavy downpours, accompanied by roaring music – thunderous sounds and dark clouded skies with quick flashes of blinding light.

Wind. The common caressing breezes of nature contrast starkly with the roaring bursts of sudden energy – tearing off roofs, uprooting trees and striking fear deep into the hearts of all present.

So the strategist who is a keen observer of nature deciphers in these phenomena a principle relevant to the conduct of war: engaging with the ordinary but deploying the unusual and extraordinary to win.

Everyday routine has accustomed many to certain expectations as to the ordinary course of things. Therein lies a cherished principle in striving for victory: strike relentlessly into the unprepared. Weave the extraordinary into the ordinary.

2 ≡📖≡ 5

So it is in pugilism: teachers who have evolved certain powerful bodily movements (punches, kicks, blows) are often most reluctant to impart – even to their most trusted pupil – the final and most destructive stroke in the sequence.

Some only make this stroke in their very last breaths of life. Still others think it better to take such secrets with them into the next world. And I hear stories of how these masters, perhaps to preserve their art within the realm of human beings, would then manifest themselves in the dreams of their favourite pupils. Through these dreams teachers would instruct them in the most secret doctrines or the last step in a sequence of pugilistic moves.

Why are these masters so secretive about the last step in the sequence?

I have thought long about this and I realise that they too understood that to prevail over your enemies, the element of surprise is vital.

How then does one put all this together to explain why the intermixing of the unorthodox with the orthodox helps an army prevail over the enemy during warfare?

All actions originate from the mind. So the unorthodox must act on the minds of the enemy troops. It surprises them so much that in the extreme case they are simply frozen, shocked or paralysed into inaction.

The minds of the enemy troops are so amazed by the unorthodox that they often or momentarily lose their composure. Surprise is a fundamental reason why unorthodoxy is critical to an army's success .

In warfare to attack the enemy directly is orthodox, but surprise attack is unorthodox. As direct attacks are unsurprising, victory is less often obtained in this way. Victory comes more through the use of unorthodox approaches that contain an element of surprise.

When an army is structured, there should be, besides the soldiers performing normal functions, those skilled in the unorthodox arts of war.

Like the waves of the sea that never cease in their undulating flow; like the sun and moon in their alternating appearances, the skilful general must be as infinitely resourceful as nature in the use of the unorthodox in the conduct of warfare. Special training is called for when developing officers and troops that are to be skilled in these ways.

Soothsayers often explain unorthodox occurrences such as natural phenomena – be they swelling waves or scorching heat – as heaven's displeasure with men on earth. These signs are read and interpreted for the benefit of generals to better interpret events on earth.

Such soothsayers believe in the intimate relationship between heaven and earth. Thus the signs in the sky are seen in the light of corresponding earthly events. This seems inherently logical since, according to the wisdom of the ancients, all things are but one.

So the night skies are studied for signs of unorthodox

happenings: the dimming of once bright stars, the disappearance of stars, the emergence of new stars. Ominous signs are often read in the stars that shoot across the night skies.

Each star is said to mirror the fate of a specific general in the struggle for power on earth. If the star of the general is declining then the soothsayer tends to read in such a sign adverse developments. Conversely, if his stars are becoming brighter, this bodes well for the general concerned.

Then there is the fear of the sun being completely consumed by an invisible dragon in the morning sky. Because of this fear, drums and gongs are beaten, for farmers fear that if nothing is done the whole earth may be condemned to an age of utter darkness.

Not only the signs in the skies are read but also any unorthodox occurrences – the sudden snapping of the general's banner despite the light winds that blow. The sudden perching of the large, black crow on the general's chair: for many this seems a bad omen. Or the general might have a bad dream, such as being bitten by a wild boar, with blood flooding the bed. Such bad dreams are read with shivering lips as suggesting the doom of the general in forthcoming battles.

Ghostly encounters by troops – especially those of the souls of dead enemy soldiers – are said to be even more foreboding.

But is this always the case? I often wondered, sitting here alone.

2 🙣 8

For is it not possible that things may be reversed too: earthly events may foretell what is going to happen in the night skies? But whatever the truth, the reality is that human beings are prone to act according to such beliefs. The strategist should therefore work on the fears or hopes of soldiers, being human, about any unorthodox occurrences. He can use the idea of supernatural occurrences to advantage in conducting war.

Thus to boost the morale of soldiers fighting a one-sided battle, the general may falsely declare his dream of riding victorious over the dead bodies of enemy troops. Panic and fear may be caused in the enemy's camp by circulating rumours of the supernatural: of ghostly appearances of soldiers returning from the dead to warn them of imminent defeat.

Or through heavy bribes he may deliberately cause bad omens, such as the 'accidental' breaking of the general's banner. These are unorthodox tactics that may be applied by the strategist to influence the outcome of war. The strategist must in his turn be alert to possible machinations by the enemy working on the irrational fears of men.

In addition, there remains the critical role which the supernatural *may* have in determining war outcomes. To the signs of heaven the strategist must be attentive. The ultimate strategist is one who neither believes entirely nor disbelieves altogether. Such signs are but strategic factors that go into his reckoning of how to wage a victorious war.

No war is static and there are no fixed rules – except to win.

3 📖 1

A moonless, windless night, around midsummer. Life: simplicity within complexity.

I often find that to succeed a strategist must be able to grasp the essential principles from evolving scenarios. As no two scenarios are ever identical, the strategist must accurately perceive how different dynamics could be operating within each.

Past experience is undoubtedly useful for the strategist but he must never be bound up with it to the extent of failing to perceive emerging trends. Also many a seasoned strategist has faltered on account of failing to recognise a fundamental change in circumstances. These are as variable as is a shift in the loyalty of the people towards a king or the general level of combat skills of an army.

The physician, who diagnoses by feeling the pulse, must maintain an open mind when seeking for possible causes of a patient's sickness. The strategist must, like the physician, attack the fundamental causes as indicated by the presence of symptoms.

Essentially I believe that the strategist has to see the complexities that underlie change. He must penetrate to the point of being able to identify the principal forces driving those changes. To do this he must reduce the complex to the simple.

3 📖 2

I sit here reflecting on a mass of floating images. My mind is flushed with floating scenes of forests, rivers, mountains, cities, palaces, markets, people, food, music, birds in flight and much else.

I often wonder if there is something common that underlies the multi-faceted nature of life. Like a jade piece so finely cut as to reflect multiple planes, so must the mind of a strategist be so finely tuned as to be able to take a multi-faceted perspective of every situation.

I remember my wife's dress, worn during our wedding many years ago, that was so finely woven with pictures of dragons, trees, phoenixes, peaches and so on. Yet these

Timing

images, interwoven in such a complex way, were derived from just simple threads, woven from only a few strands of colour: red, white, blue, yellow, black and green.

Through the resourcefulness of the weaver, myriad images of the living world were captured: birds, animals, mountains, streams, and so on. Despite their complex textures, at the very core were simply differently coloured threads. It was the resourcefulness of the weaver that made the complexity. The ultimate source of the creativity so evident in the dress was the ingenuity of the weaver – in her mind. The few coloured threads were but the means for the creativity to flourish.

So must the mind of the strategist be as fluid as that of the weaver. His mind must be able to lace together intricate patterns of stratagems, stratagems that flow in tune with the ever-changing situations of war.

3 ≣▮≣ 3

According to the *Tao*, all things on earth and heaven spring from nothingness – what is called the great void. And this emptiness or nothingness becomes one. One transforms itself into two. By an ongoing, creative process the myriad things of the world are brought forth.

I remember always that despite the innumerableness of worldly things, their root source is nothingness. The *Tao* teaches that all phenomena, including what we see, hear, touch, taste and feel, are at their core empty. So I nurture my mind through quiet meditation on the void.

The most ancient and revered book – the *I Ching* (the *Book of Changes*) – draws on just two basic elements, represented simply by broken and unbroken lines – the *yin* and the *yang* respectively – to construct an eight-by-eight matrix resulting in sixty-four hexagrams.

The system of hexagrams constitutes a mental model, within which is conceptualised all possible worldly situations: sixty-four in total. Through the use of simple yarrow sticks, it is possible to divine which *one* of these sixty-four applies in a specific situation. In addition the model suggests how this *one* is likely to evolve to become another of the remaining sixty-three possibilities.

The model has been applied since time immemorial to unfold the deeper meaning of changes as perceived by our senses. By its construction the model seems to enable the enquirer to connect himself or herself with a deeper intuitive consciousness – perhaps the great void from which all things originate. Thus the mind of the enquirer is all-important as he or she utilises the yarrow sticks.

I marvel at the simplicity of its conceptualisation. The *yin–yang* principle is consistent with the natural order of things: all animals that I had come across – horses, sheep, pigs, dogs, cats – have their complementary male and female counterparts. Through sexual intercourse between the female and male pro-*creation* of new life is made possible.

Yin is reflective of the female principle and *yang* the male. The *yin–yang* interaction is symbolic of the deeper creative forces and processes at work within nature. I have deep reverence for the creators of the *Book of Changes*. For it must have been a daunting task to mirror the forces of nature within the confines of a book.

Also deeply ingrained in the thinking of the ancient *Book of Changes* are the five basic elements that may be abstracted to represent things of the world: wood, earth, metal, fire and water. From their interactions the ancients were able to draw inferences about the nature of change in the world.

3 ▰ 4

In everyday living there are examples of how what is seem-ingly complex is constructed or built from basic elements.

Foods, despite their wide variety when analysed in terms of taste are found to comprise essentially basic flavours: sweet, sour, bitter, salty. And then these categories will seem inadequate when all flavours are blended into a meal.

As I tend the garden and so remain close to the soil, I know that despite the innumerable varieties of small plants in the forest there are elements common to them: roots, leaves, flowers, seeds. All the roots of plants are alike in that they tend to flourish below the soil.

The ancient farmers must have learned from observa-tion and reflection that it is only through the little seeds that new growth is possible. Trees, despite their wide variety in the forest, share the same basic configuration: stem, branches, leaves, fruits.

The same is true of things constructed by men. Pieces of music played in the courts may sound different, but are all derived from the playing of the five notes. Musicians tell me that the number of tunes possible is simply endless even though there are just five notes. And so is it for colours that beautify the world.

As for cities, the strategist sees that they share certain common features: walls, roads, buildings, wells, markets and so on. The ordinary men living there may simply be too engrossed in the daily hassles of city to realise this.

Yet if one knows well the basic elements that comprise a particular city, then it is possible to use such insights to plan the defences for any other city.

The strategist must be able to see and interpret all these basic elements in things of the world.

3 🕮 5

Another insight I gained from working intimately with nature is that of seeing processes embedded in the flow of time. Indeed all lives are subjected to change through processes.

There is birth, growth, maturity and decline. This applies to human beings as much as to animals and plants. See how my children are born as babies, grow up to be young men and women and how my wife and myself have matured and then aged.

The strategist is alert to the cycles of process in things. In wars there is the usual beginning of battle where the morale of men is running high. Then physical fighting ensues. When the dead start to pile up and fresh blood washes the battlefield, many are going to feel disillusioned.

In the evening when strong winds bring the stench of human carcasses lying strewn across the battlefields, there may even be desertions. The first to desert the army in such situations are the conscripts. Then as more soldiers become weary of the endless round of fighting, even the regular troops may abandon their arms.

The strategist must understand the interrelationship between the different stages in the process of war and their impact on the morale of soldiers.

To predict how a strategy may work out in a given situation the strategist must gain a deep insight of what motivates people. Despite my experience of war situations, I have yet to encounter two situations that are identical.

So the strategist must always be thinking of new ideas, stratagems, methods and solutions. Through the creative use of extraordinary and ordinary forces he must generate limitless combinations. For war is another aspect of nature where success and failure often depend on the creativity of the strategist.

Winter is coming.

The rare white eagle from the distant, northern holy peaks is again seen roaming the skies with eyes glued to the ground for its prey. I once witnessed the effortless efficiency of this magnificent King of the Birds of Prey, when it dived from out of the deep blue sky for prey: a young deer grazing on the steep mountain slope.

How swiftly and precisely the King of the Birds of Prey can kill! One swift action, wielding those giant claws, and the once lithe body of the deer became limp, lifeless. The deer had no possibility of being forewarned: the usual predators come from the sides, never from the skies. Even if it had been warned, unlike the rabbit, it had no burrow to escape to.

The dive was so smooth. The eyes of the deer were downcast, fixed on the grasses. I doubt if it ever had the chance of knowing that its killer was the kingly eagle.

Another simple flap of wings, and the king now with its prey seemingly strapped to its claws, soared skywards. In a moment it disappeared as a mere speck amidst the thin air of the cloudless sky.

I was stunned, more by the nonchalance and perfection of the act than the fact that it had happened. Killing executed as if it were a natural part of a dance movement. It was as if a heavenly choreographer had composed this kingly dance.

It was all over. Even before I blinked my eyes.

From this observation I derived precious strategic insights into the art of fighting: *momentum* and *timing*. The acceleration gained through the dive as the body propelled itself down on its prey had enabled the majestic eagle to muster magical force. Just one simple sweep, and the claws were sunk deep into the slender neck of the deer.

Even from the distance I was awed by the precision of the striking claws. The surge upwards seemed to be powered by some divine force – the carcass gliding along in the vastness of an empty sky.

Another scene that reminds me of the critical importance of

Eagle

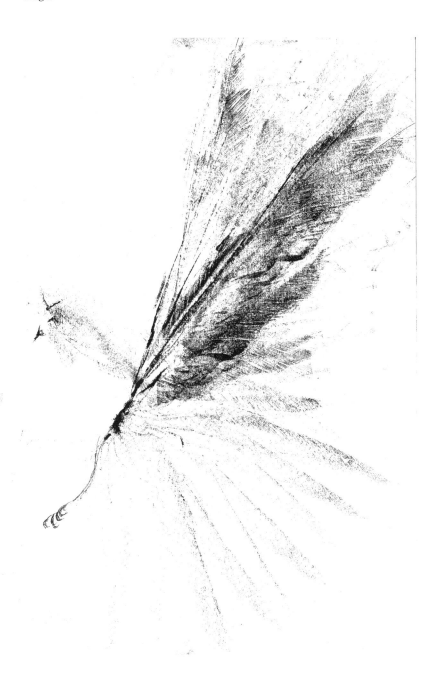

momentum and *timing* – I can hear the roaring waves even now – is the onrush of waters of the Yellow River when it overflows.

The scene reminds me vividly of how torrential rain – a watery onslaught – can so easily move huge, rocky boulders. Giant, rocky pieces that had long – and as far back as the villagers could recollect – rested on those earthly sites.

Again the explanation must lie in the precise *timing* of the onslaught and the *momentum* gained by waters rushing down the embankments. Ordinarily it is impossible for me to imagine that water could wield such mighty power. These mountainous rocks seemed so immovable.

Similarly, it is unimaginable for a bird to slice a dead deer so effortlessly. What is it that enables the white eagle to have such a mastery over precise timing?

Is there internal stillness in the mind of the eagle?

The secret ought to lie in the momentum gathered and its application at precisely the right moment. These principles the strategist must learn to master.

This may be true for the mastery of any art. In cooking there is a precise moment when the fire is ready for stir frying the fish. The precise moment is different when frying vegetables or meat. This knowledge constitutes the secret skills of the master cook. How does the cook know the *right* moment to stir fry?

In farming, those who are truly skilful know exactly the right time for planting the seeds. How do they know?

The connoisseur of tea, he who has mastered the skill of producing the tea perfectly brewed – how does he know the precise moment when a particular type of tea is ready to be drunk: the moment when the tea leaves exude their best fragrances?

Can such skills be taught or are such talents innate in the person or living thing?

4 ▆ 3

For the same reason an arrow propelled from a fully drawn crossbow carries with it extraordinary powers of penetration: it can pierce through even heavy armour. As any experienced archer will tell you, it is the precisely timed, yet effortless release of the arrow, that gets such remarkable results.

As the old soldier guarding the city walls will tell you, no city gates are inviolable. It all depends on the momentum the soldiers are able to build up when charging at the gates. So the strategist must master the essential principles of momentum and timing when attacking cities.

Indeed these principles may be the very key to victory. Imagine the awesome powers of an army that may be released by the strategist if only he is skilled in this way.

Great is the general who is able to lead an army in total disarray to victory. To do this he has to nurture their morale, rebuild in them the confidence to win when they resume fighting. He has to maintain the momentum of the forward march of an army till final victory.

4 🔲 4

This time of year is precisely the moment for the strategist to observe in his early morning strolls how the plum blossom brings forth hope: fresh flowers sprouting out of embattled branches – knotted, twisted, distorted – of seemingly dead trees.

These scenes call to my mind recollections of the past: how even soldiers badly battle-scarred – emotionally and physically – may be revitalised for war. Just like after a period of rest and hibernation during the deep winter, animals are once more eager to welcome spring.

Similarly, the soldiers who, after a period of rest and recuperation in isolated plains, may once again be eager for fresh engagements with enemy troops. The general must utilise *time* as a strategy for nurturing in his down-trodden, embittered soldiers the spirit to fight fresh battles.

Then fresh banners, like the plum blossoms, may once again emerge from the tired, withered army.

I remember trotting along admiringly as the army marched down the grass plains. The momentum was maintained through the constant blowing of the wind. These winds shored up the morale of the soldiers, especially those who had been beaten into retreat.

No longer do these soldiers lament the loss of their bodily parts, be it a finger, ear, eye, hand. Instead they had a triumphant glow on their faces and wore these deformities like war medals for bravery. Such scars may be more precious than imperial jade pieces – for nothing was more telling of a soldier's brave, glorious survival from the evil depths of war than these scars.

4 ⬛ 5

As the cicada regenerates itself, the army was revitalised by the ritual of the long march down the plains. The marchers moved to a silent rhythm: a rhythmic flow that could be sensed but not heard.

The army had become one. Like a sword being made, this army had been welded together by the flames of countless battles – the last of which was the most brutal and disastrous. The villagers stood in awe as the army swept through the valley. For with renewed energy and vigour the glorious army was such a contrast to its old defeated self.

Massive injuries were sustained after many ill-fated, badly timed, bloody orgies waged deep in the valley – and so many were killed that the villagers called it thereafter the *Valley of the Dead*. The river, yellow since the beginning of time, remained for many days a strange orange from the blood that oozed out of the floating corpses.

This army rose from disastrous defeat to great fame. These successes were attributable to the general, with his mastery of the art of momentum and timing. In the desolate plains, he learned the secrets of the power of these arts. His attacks against enemy strongholds now resembled more and more the way an artist wields his brush and makes bold strokes on paper. Each stroke of attack was so smoothly executed.

The momentum of his army in action was much like the dive of the white eagle. The attacks were like the strike of the eagle claws. The enemy's city gates simply tore open – like the skin of the deer – when assaults were made by troops storming at them with heavy logs.

Even double-lined walls caved in, unable to withstand the continuous onslaught led by the general's elite cavalry.

From afar could be seen the enemy troops scurrying away from their defences into houses inside the city like frightened rabbits seeking their burrows.

The army was elegantly coordinated, like the waves of the mighty, overflowing rivers that caused rock-based walls simply to fall over.

Such a sight struck me deeply as a young boy and now amazes me even more as a retired strategist. That is perhaps why despite the many intervening years of wars these images are still the most vivid in my mind.

5 ⟡ 1

Deep into winter. I am writing during wintry blizzards. My mind is invariably drawn again and again to the turbulence of war. Rather than consciously resisting it, I let my spirit explore the contours of my inner consciousness. In such a situation, my unconscious gradually becomes immersed in the vast dreamscapes of war.

Outside, the violent, chilling winds are penetrating through thickening snow. Through the thickets of churning whiteness, I can see that the distant, once silent and still forest is suddenly imbued with life. It is as if there has been an awakening of its spirit.

Standing here in the courtyard I watch how the tops of leafless trees dance against the background of monotonous grey skies. There must be a heavenly choreographer behind all this. The dancing movements of the trees are synchronised with the melancholic howling of the wind.

Or perhaps it is just Heaven's way of awakening inside me the chaotic aspect of war. Chaos is an inevitable facet of war.

The astute strategist however, sees such *dis*order as integral to war. In formulating his strategy, he allows a role for the chaotic. Just like water shaping itself to the inner contours of any container, so the strategist is mindful constantly to configure his strategies to ever-changing circumstances.

5 ⟡ 2

The shackled, wooden gates are slamming wildly against the walls – '*pang! pang! pang!* . . .'. I stumble out into the freezing cold. The roaring noise of the wintry storm is so intense that it seems to penetrate deep into my very being. Flurries of snowflakes hurl themselves mercilessly at my old wrinkled body. Oh how these winds seem to dance in concentric circles!

Edging my body against the blinding winds, I slowly inch myself forward so as to blot out the noisy disturbance.

That I can still do despite my aging frame. But the turmoil that unfolds in my mind is quite another matter. There is no escape from what is buried deep in one's heart. Indeed, far from fading, that inner vision seems to be made more clear with age.

Chaos

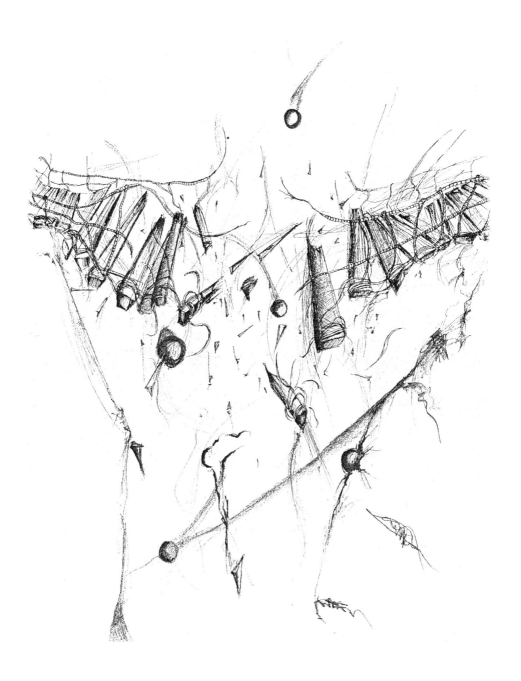

Memories sunk deep in my unconscious unfold to show many scenes of war. The wintry storm outside stimulates replays of many past visions. Some are so vivid and real, despite the passing of time. Others float quickly past. Still others are illusory and dream-like.

Now the howling of the wind resembles cries of soldiers. The crescendos of '*hooo...*', '*wooo...*', '*ahhh...*' resonate within me. Each sound seems to have its own distinctive tonal quality. At times, for some strange reason, these sounds are distinctively identifiable with individual soldiers, some of whom I witnessed perishing in the thick of fierce combat.

A battery of cries – '*ahhh! ahhh! ahhh!*' – suddenly echoes deep within me. I am drawn into memories of the brave young soldiers who sacrificed their lives shielding me, as their general, from the flood of poisonous arrows with their unarmed bodies.

Sounds of wars waged long ago in the distant past are finding their echoes inside me – *re*-echoing and *re*-echoing.

Could anyone possibly bury for ever these morbid sounds?

Faces simply spring up from nowhere to come before my mind's eye. Long forgotten, forlorn faces with downcast eyes that seem to stare into nothingness. Wars may be over yet may never be forgotten – at least not by me.

5 🕮 3

The winds whirl round and round inside my room as I try to write on these strips of bamboo. The winds appear to whirl around inside my mind too – stirring and stirring relentlessly.

I must have fallen into a quiet slumber.

Or did I?

Whatever state I was in, I then felt myself transposed back in time and space. The cacophonous sounds of war are becoming more distinct. Images are becoming more and more focused. I am beginning to feel myself right there as the scene of war replays itself.

The view I have is so strangely familiar to me. Is it some war that I directed? I can see soldiers below me milling round in a circular fashion, fighting every inch to advance up a military tower.

Echoes

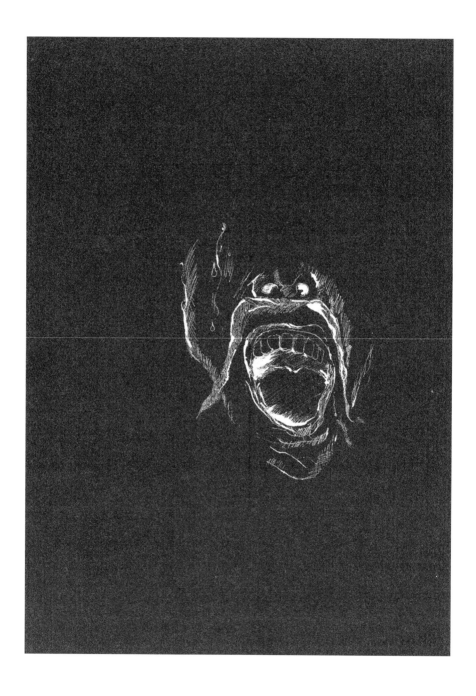

'Oh yes, I do remember!' I exclaim to myself.

I had called it the *Tower of the Dead Soldiers*. I even ordered that it be burnt along with the dead bodies – so loathesome the stench of so many rotting dead.

The steps leading to the enemy's command centre at the top are already heavily carpeted with dead bodies. Oddly, though, I seem to see fresh blood seeping out of the very walls of that doomed *Tower of the Dead Soldiers*.

Is that possible?

What remains of the once glorious army are the very elite troops of the general: the best-trained, toughest and the most brutal – the Special Guards – those schooled in the belief in fighting gloriously to the death.

For the ordinary footsoldier in the enemy's army, the war has already been lost. What could possibly occupy the minds of these ordinary soldiers, locked in such dire circumstances? They simply want to get out of the maze of a city ruined by war, out of this utter madness.

For the Special Guard, his ambition is to realise what he has been always told is his life's only duty: to fight to the death defending the *Tower of the Dead Soldiers* – that is if it is ever under siege. For the general, this is his castle, his last bastion of defence.

But who is really the wiser – the Special Guard or the foot-soldier?

I think the ordinary footsoldier. A judgement of courage or cowardice should depend on circumstances. Greater courage is needed to retreat, preserve one's life and seek an opportunity to regain victory. In fact the simple way out is to die a seemingly glorious death!

I see little purpose in dying gloriously. It is like the destruction of a hill through the burning of growing trees – all for a moment's glory. But with death and destruction all hopes for victory are dashed.

So the general, though defeated, should continue to lead what remains of his army and people out of the city and avoid certain annihilation.

Instead I see him positioned at the top of the *Tower of Dead Soldiers* surrounded by his personal Special Guards, still looking majestic in his armour and totally unperturbed by the slaughter below.

I remember offering the general an opportunity to work out the terms of surrender. The city is strategically located and I wanted it for its site. A prompt surrender would enable me to achieve my goal without spilling blood.

But it was not to be. Despite being surrounded, he remained too proud to want to admit defeat. He was too drunk with pride to think clearly. Till the very end he fought – but how admirably! – all alone on top of the *Tower of the Dead Soldiers*. With a white cloth tied round his head and with his silken white hair flowing over his shoulders he looked the sage-general.

He was able to hold back the advancing soldiers through expert wielding of his mighty, specially cast halberd. The countless forward thrusts of my soldiers were thwarted by the ferocity of the way he cut with the sharp edge of his weapon – many headless bodies were due to his actions alone.

But in a moment of respite, a stray arrow shot from the ranks below and penetrated the back of his neck. He stumbled, and almost on his knees, gasped for breath.

In that split second of vulnerability and despite his early display of ferociousness, the soldiers were suddenly enboldened to charge forward. He then most unexpectedly released a shout that rocked the air: '. . . *arrrrr!!!*'. Some of the soldiers were so shocked by the scream that they backed away and fell off the *Tower of the Dead Soldiers*.

A hundred spears rained down upon him, with many piercing his body. Instantaneously, yet another hundred followed. To the ordinary soldier, better than the spoils of war is the memory of having dealt the final killing blow – even if yours may be one of hundreds – on such a general. He was widely reputed to be invincible.

Oh for what purpose this fight to the ultimate end? I often ask when recalling the scene.

Only a green hill with trees can continue to supply wood for fires, not one that is itself totally engulfed in flames.

5 ≡📖≡ 5

The city defences have already collapsed. Logs once used to ram the gates now lie there abandoned. Bodies, arms, heads, pieces of human flesh, broken arrows, wheels, banners lie floating in the moat.

How wasteful!

Yet a little distance away, inside the fallen walls, the cacophonous music of battles is heard again – screams, cries, yells, shouts. The tonal quality of this piece is however a little different from that heard at the *Tower of the Dead Soldiers*.

On the horizon, streams of defeated officers, soldiers and residents – the aged, women, children, babies – are crushing themselves, trying to squeeze through the city's constricted back gates. The people that finally ooze through fan out towards the open wilderness lying beyond.

To those uninitiated in the art of war such scenes appear so confusing. Yet such disorder is necessarily part of the process of waging physical wars.

5 ≡📖≡ 6

I see in my mind's eye the triumphant strategist – the young me surveying the aftermath of a city ravaged by war.

I recall now my orders to the soldiers not to pursue those who had fled – I believe in allowing, if not secretly creating, the opportunity for the enemy to flee.

But why? It helps to dampen the enemy's will to fight. As part of my strategy to avoid wanton killing, I had before the start of the war declared to the city dwellers that they would be spared the agonies of war only if the general, known for his ruthlessness, was bound and handed over.

For I knew from secret sources that the people in the city simply hated him for his brutality and cruelty. If it had worked, many lives would have been spared. Unfortunately it did not work out as I had devised.

The general had kept such a tight rein over the city dwellers that those who so much as muttered a word on the matter were arrested and tortured inside the horror chambers of the *Tower of the Dead Soldiers*. The brutal man himself died a savage death.

The city had therefore to be taken by sheer force: at the cost of 10,051 lives with close to a thousand or so severely wounded. That is the price for strategic control of a city lying in a prime site, at a crossroads.

The storm too has died down.

A hot, dry summer and too little rain.

Even the moon's heat seems unbearable. I walked to the stream to fetch some water. The fishermen too had gone upstream, laying traps. How ingenious these bamboo traps! But to lure the fish baits have to be used. In laying bait the fishermen are illustrating a principle that strategists may emulate – the art of creating advantageous situations. To succeed, the strategist must observe the situation so as to derive strategic benefits. Like the fisherman the strategist learns what can be used to bait the enemy. He must appreciate the strategic potential within given situations.

I explore my reflections through the following themes: earth, fire, wind, beauty, supernatural, vegetation, potential for growth, decay, banquets, gifts, site, unorthodoxy, arrogance and counter-strategy.

Earth. Its form, height and contour. The strategist must learn how to use the ground in properly deploying his forces. Thus tactics are configured so as to be appropriate for the ground, and to take the best advantage of it.

Thus a log, when pushed, will roll down the slope of a hill and gain momentum as it descends. Soldiers charging up the hill will find it impossible to resist a log that is rolling down from the hill-top. The strategist exploits such potential so as to prevail over the enemy.

Fire. A major weapon in war. The good cook knows how to manipulate the fire in the stove to the best advantage. Thus for stir-frying meat glowingly hot flames are required. But for simmering food, a low constant heat must be maintained.

As the nature of the fire depends on the type of firewood being fed into the stove, the cook also has to learn to distinguish types of firewood. The master cook has an intimate understanding of fire strategy. He can almost judge the strength of burning fires by a mere glance. He knows exactly what types of fire are needed for cooking a particular dish.

Wind. Direction, strength and duration. Here the idea is to exploit the strategic potential that the wind has to offer. There is often a prevailing wind on any given site. So the strategist must learn from where the wind blows, how strongly and for how long. This information, coupled with

189

Strategic potential

knowledge of the ground, will come in useful when strategies are to be formulated.

Thus, knowing when the wind changes direction has distinct advantages, especially if the other side is unaware of this. So if the enemy believes the wind to be blowing strongly in an easterly direction and plans to charge uphill in the same direction, the enemy troops will be less worried about the use of fires against them. But if the strategist knows there is to be a reversal in wind direction during the time of an enemy's attack then a fire strategy may be devised to foil the attack successfully.

Beauty. Just as worms are bait for fish, so are beautiful women for generals. These women are powerful lures that may be used for many purposes. One is to divert the attention of the general. Another is to gather information on his strategic intention. Better still is to influence the enemy's plans. Further, to sow discord or disharmony among the general's trusted officers.

Supernatural. The strategist appreciates how the irrational may work on men. So to cause panic among men, the strategist creates fear among them of the supernatural, for instance, by circulating stories of ghostly encounters with dead enemy soldiers who warn of impending defeat. In the depth of darkness he may use eerie sounds to frighten away enemy soldiers, or create ghostly screams, howls or cries – all these weaken the will of the enemy to fight.

The strategist understands the hold the supernatural has over the minds of ordinary men at war – the power of the subconscious. He understands how soldiers' minds may easily be manipulated! Soldiers who believe they are doomed are more easily defeated, for they lack the determination to fight ferociously. Those who are convinced of their divine right to win wars are the most difficult to overwhelm.

Thus the enemy general, if he is unduly superstitious, may be shown 'heavenly signs' that foretell of impending defeat. Or persons may be paid handsomely to act as soothsayers to thwart the plans of the enemy's generals. Soothsayers may be asked to convey messages of certain victory if a specified course of action is taken.

Vegetation. The astute strategist appreciates the nature of the vegetation. In a period of drought such as is now being experienced, it is easy to raise a fire in the dry grasslands,

particularly if there is a strong wind blowing too. Occasionally the strategist takes advantage of specific vegetation –
marshland, dense forest, dangerous labyrinths – when
formulating strategies to deal with the enemy. So the
strategist studies the contextual factors before deriving
stratagems for waging wars.

Potential for growth. Another factor for the strategist to
take into account is the potential for growth in any particular
situation. A baby tiger is easily killed. But if it is left to grow,
the day will come when it becomes impossible to handle. Also,
even though the hilly plains may now be clear of vegetation
by the action of wind and through the passage of time, new
shrubs and grasses are likely to grow. The strategist must
allow for the manifestation of potential.

Decay and decline. Conversely the strategist should also
be aware of the onset of decay or natural decline – in some circumstances such a tendency may simply be inevitable. So
when the ruler of a friendly neighbouring state is aging and
bed-ridden with illness, the strategist must coin stratagems to
ensure that the likely successor will continue to favour his
own state. With the death of the ruler some changes may certainly be expected. The seasoned strategist is alert to such
possibilities.

So the mind of the strategist is often heavily taxed with
contriving stratagems so as to influence who is to succeed as
king. For rather than leave it to chance, the strategist will
plan to influence the outcome. If the stratagem works countless lives may be saved, but if an overtly ambitious person
succeeds to the throne, many more wars may be expected on
account of the new king – especially if the kingdom is a powerful one.

Banquets and feasts. As a court strategist I often had to
accompany the king to banquets and feasts. No banquet that I
attended was without some schemes or plots being put forward. I used to spend much time analysing the situation and
trying to determine the true reason or purpose behind an
invitation to a banquet.

Is the enemy planning to entrap us?

I am also alert to the possible effects that wine, good
food, women or gifts may have on men. In such a context,
one's guard is often lowered. Yet it is precisely in these situations that a sharp, strategic mind is most needed. For one

must interpret the true intention behind the use of certain words. Also, sometimes what is left unsaid may be of greater significance than what is spoken. Facial expressions often betray true attitudes and feelings.

There are tales of how heads of kings and generals are just as likely to be lost during banquets and feasts as during heated battles! Skill in the choice of words is as valuable as the handling of swords in such contexts. Some words flatter and ease tension whilst others may inflame passions. Wars may be averted by equally careful use of words as swords.

Gifts. Also important is the right choice of gifts made during banquets. A king known for his fondness for rare green jade may be enticed through such a gift to allow the giver of priceless pieces of jade temporary occupation of a city. In some cases a king may even sanction the use of his own troops for a specific expedition.

So kings must beware!

Oh, the bargains that may be struck during such feasts! And an entire city may be lost through the exchange of a piece of rare jade – a silly bargain struck by the king impulsive to own a rare stone.

Can a toy ever be worth a city?

Site. Since the principle is to seek strategic advantages from given situations, the choice of a site for battle is crucial. The strategy devised must be appropriate to a given site. Just as water conforms to the contours of the ground, so must a strategist act flexibly.

Unorthodoxy. An enemy adept in strategy is also likely to act strategically. In this case there may be scope for the use of surprise and unorthodox manoeuvres contrary to the known rules of the art of war and to the expectations of an enemy schooled in strategy.

Thus when an enemy expects an ambush, we must deliberately avoid making one. When the enemy expects us to use logs, boulders and fires as they cross the narrow path between two hills, we deliberately abandon these methods. Instead we surprise them in the open fields.

Arrogance and frustration. Another principle is to lower the enemy's guard. This may be effected by deliberately frustrating the enemy, hungry for action, by avoiding any engagements. And if there is an unexpected meeting in the fields, feign defeat.

In this way the enemy is likely to grow ever more arrogant. A time will come when the enemy can easily be lured into a trap. Indeed, just as victories are necessary to boost the morale of one's own troops, feigned defeats are required to induce arrogance and carelessness on the part of the enemy. Frustration, arrogance or impatience are the states of mind that should be deliberately fostered in the enemy.

The mind of the strategist has to be flexible. Besides tapping the strategic potential of any given situation, the strategist also seeks to read the strategic design of the enemy – anticipating and testing out possibilities.

Thus before allowing the army to pass through a narrow path between the hills, the strategist is likely to send men to scale these hills to see if enemy troops are already hiding there, possibly equipped with boulders, logs and arrows. Then the strategist can avoid such a route.

Counter-strategy. Sometimes, the strategist acts to counter the working of enemy stratagems. In some situations, this may be extremely difficult – for example, convincing the king to refuse gifts of beautiful women from a neighbouring state. Men are easy prey for beautiful women, with alluring charms and promises of love sparkling in their eyes. To counter such moves the strategist may need to find women with even more striking features so as to gain the attention of the king. Men – especially kings – are often ruled by the heart rather than the mind!

I shall continue writing, despite the heat, tomorrow.

Yesterday I explored ideas about deriving strategic benefits from given situations. Again the weather is still hot and dry. But despite the heat, I shall write. I shall continue with the same theme.

What really excites me is to exploit the hidden, latent power in any given situation or context. That is why in *The Art of War* I devote an entire chapter to the role of the ground – with its different configurations – as it provides the strategist with different opportunities as well as risks when waging war.

For me, the symbol reminiscent of the theme I want to investigate further here is the tremendous power behind round boulders as they roll down mountainous heights.

Heavy round stones sitting on hill-tops are potentially powerful weapons: the military officers must know how to cause them to roll off the slope in order to be effective.

I remember witnessing how an entire regiment of cavalry – the most formidable in an army's fighting unit – was simply crushed at the bottom of the hill by stones that crashed down so heavily on them.

Like pelting snow that easily penetrates ill-constructed roofs, these boulders easily crushed and flattened chariots and other carriages. After that the cavalry troops simply had to abandon their mission of acting as the vanguard in assaulting the steep hilly slopes. In that episode, the attack had simply to be called off.

I realise that there are three principles involved here: the sheer weight of the stone, its roundness which enables it to roll downwards, and the momentum gathered by the stone as it rushes downwards.

Essentially, the same principle of momentum must apply to the water that comes rushing down the hills in such a mighty fashion – just stand under any waterfall and you can experience its sheer power.

In perhaps the same way arrows tipped with a little sharp stone or piece of metal can, after gaining momentum,

195

Momentum

pierce through even the strongest of armour – especially if the arrows are shot from strong bows and carried by the wind.

Similarly, soldiers leading the charge forward, such as the cavalry, seem always to be imbued with so much energy and drive. In contrast the defenders appear lifeless with their stoic expressions and hollow eyes staring into the distance.

Is it possible that the attacking soldiers are transformed simply as a consequence of pure movement?

7 ▰ 3

I now recall a tale from antiquity about how a wise, retired general persuaded the entire people then living in the valley – including the aged, young and women – to retreat into the hills. He set up the defensive base so as to avoid plunder and certain annihilation by the enemy. The enemy forces consisted of the most savage troops then known in the ancient world.

This wise general fully understood the principles of strategy and applied them appropriately for the protection of his homeland, every corner of which he was so familiar with. He could even describe the fragrances found in each part of the forest!

As the people retreated into the hills the general devised ingenious stratagems for dealing with the enemy. He anticipated their likely lines of advance, given the site of their chosen base.

The most able and the toughest of the people were divided into small bands and made responsible for operating the traps to be built inside the thick forest.

For one rectangular stretch of dry grassland, he studied the wind direction. He had his men ready to ignite fires on all sides but left one obvious route for possible escape. That route incidentally led to a long wooden crossing over a wide river. His idea was to leave an obvious escape route.

After the enemy troops had 'escaped' to the other side his men were to destroy the wooden crossing by burning it at one end. This would prevent the enemy troops now stranded on the other side from reinforcing the attack. The river was so wide and deep – even during low tide – that there was no possibility of them ever wading across.

For those enemy troops that were just able to escape the booby traps set deep inside the forest, the general had planned that they be finished off by cold-blooded slaughter by his selected small bands of elite soldiers.

These soldiers were dressed in leaves so that they could in a moment blend into the greenery of the forest. These small bands of specially trained soldiers were to harass the enemy's troops at the side. The slaughter was to appear gruesome so as to instil fear in the enemy troops. Under no circumstances were these bands of soldiers to engage in full battle with the enemy. His was a hit-and-run tactic.

He knew too well the might of this terrible foe: hardy herdsmen from the north who were used to barbaric ways of living. They were easily angered and often acted hastily.

Once the work had been executed these bands of soldiers would swiftly melt into the depths of the forest.

7 ⚎ 4

And indeed the enemy troops did come from the directions anticipated. As the wise general regarded these enemy soldiers to be wild animals, he devised many types of bamboo traps and laid them along the paths through the forests, thick with bamboo trees.

Sharp bamboos, their edges smeared with poison, were made to jut out of deeply dug holes. These cavities of death were so well camouflaged with dried leaves, mud and debris of the forest that not even those experienced in the arts of warfare could detect them. Only those who built them would know where they were laid.

Any person falling into these traps would die instantly – there was no possible escape.

Here the principle of momentum was also applicable – falling human bodies gather momentum before they land on the bamboo spears. The clumsier and heavier the fall, the deeper the wounds. These northern barbarians were tough but, given their huge and bulky frames, such traps were most appropriate for trapping them.

At other vantage points, arrows and spears made from bamboos – again all poisoned at their tips – were made to fly the moment certain strings were tripped. These were placed so as to rip right through the hearts of the wild enemy soldiers.

Besides these traps on the land, nimble young men also manipulated traps from the tree tops. The general knew that the barbarians were less agile and completely inexperienced in climbing trees. How could they be otherwise, having led their lives in the grass plains?

7 ⚎ 5

Boulders were strung up in the trees, encased in nets that could be cut when the enemy's troops – especially the armed chariots – were below. The falling boulders so crushed the chariots that they were immediately rendered useless.

Having observed where the wind was blowing from, the general decided on the precise place to establish the base. By careful allocation of men he ensured that his base, comprising mainly the aged, young and women, still had an adequate number of able-bodied men. These men were to help counter any enemy soldiers that might finally charge up the hills.

The site was chosen so that those coming uphill faced the wind blowing very strongly in their faces.

The general had ordered that many huge rolls of dried grass be made. These were all stocked round the sides of the hill-top. There was a quiet but determined preparation for the inevitable war. Everybody was eager to counter the fierce onslaught by enemy forces. Obstacles on the slopes were cleared to ensure that these rolls of grass could go down unhindered.

Those who escaped the fires should be buried by heavy boulders. Thus a search was made far and wide for rounded boulders. These were heaved up the hill and again placed at vantage points around the base camp.

In addition, lessons were conducted in the art of firing arrows tipped with fire. Given the strong wind, even arrows fired by weak arms were able to traverse the required distance before landing with the momentum needed to wound the enemy soldiers.

Needless to say, the northern enemy were close to being annihilated. Also they were completely frustrated – they did not get the chance to fight a 'real war', but instead found that their numbers dwindled through devious 'hide-and-seek' actions in the forest.

Then more of their numbers were lost through the 'fire bath' in the grasslands. Some of their tribes were lost for ever. They were forced to begin their lives anew on the other side of the Yellow River.

Those who were compelled to charge uphill – under severe threat of death from their officers – simply dragged themselves up. These were acts of desperation and futility. Having seen how their fellow soldiers were so brutally slaughtered they imagined that the base camp must hold even more terrors.

Many simply chose to abandon the army, to become wanderers seeking new homes. So when the rolls of wild fire came chasing after them, these soldiers just turned and ran for their lives. Even the officers fled.

6

1 ⚔ 1

EARLY SPRING AND the atmosphere is one of interesting transition, from the white quietness that is so bleak to the warm emerging green. The change of season brings with it changes in the dominant colour of the surrounding scenery. Living up this mountain the changes strike me immediately.

Colour has always had profoundly symbolic meanings for warriors too. White has been associated with stillness, death and the idea of surrender. When the army is in full fighting spirit, colourful banners with the names of their generals are carried by soldiers riding on horseback.

Red is universally the colour of the living and the joyous. For death in war is often brought about by loss of that colour – loss of blood due to open wounds. Young babies who are healthy have a reddish glow on their faces. But the faces of the dead are pale and white. Not surprisingly white is the colour of winter, signifying lack of life and activity.

Since time immemorial ancient warriors, when mourning their beloved generals killed during war, have always chosen white for symbolic representation. Over their military uniforms, they wore white. The canvas of their camps is white. Even white banners are seen fluttering in the wind.

I am not able to recollect when the practice of wearing white headbands started. But it has become a tradition that when soldiers are marching out, determined to exact vengeance for the cold-blooded murder of their generals – especially those beloved by officers and soldiers alike – they wear white headbands.

With the awakening of spring, plants, insects and animals are once again alive and there is a stir of activity.

Some of the early principles contained in my writings in *The Art of War* are derived from my constant study of how – especially in the fresh air of early spring – the hunter, both man and animal, is able to capture prey for food.

Like myself, the animals too must welcome the spring. Simple hunger forces them to come out of their hiding in search of food. I too have to replenish my own supplies.

As I understand from the *I Ching* all things in the world are derived from an all-embracing Oneness – for want of a better name. If that is so then the fundamental principles in *The Art of War* – essentially of how one force prevails over another – must also be embedded in the ordinary, everyday happenings around us.

Are these principles I have derived from constant observation and daily reflection so universal as to be timeless?

I often wonder.

What, then, causes one to become the prey of another? First, of course, one has to be noticed.

Since it is impossible to be hidden forever one should strive to be as unnoticeable (as distinct from invisible) as is practical. One has to learn to blend with the environment so as to become an indistinguishable part of it – become 'one' with it.

Second, one has to be overpowered or be rendered powerless.

The long period of hibernation during winter must make such a contrast with the flurry of activity during spring. Yet in movements out in the open there is the inherent danger of being noticed.

A rabbit that lies hidden inside its burrow avoids capture by being underground. It is impossible to see the rabbit from the skies. But one that is outside, hopping around and nibbling at the young sprouting shoots of spring grasses can quickly be spotted by the hawk circling above.

The other reason why the rabbit ends up as a meal for the hawk is that it is can be easily overpowered. A larger, more powerful animal like the wolf need not fear being noticed by the hawk. So in waging war the power to overcome an enemy is another factor in success.

1 3

The essence of crafting a stratagem that works to trap prey is the inner hunger that drives the prey to the trap. In the rabbit–hawk example, the open grasslands may be viewed as a 'trap' for a rabbit hungry for luxuriant, tender grass shoots *vis à vis* the sharp-eyed hawk towering above.

So the wise rabbit that is fortunate to escape quickly learns to peer at the skies from the safety of its burrow before emerging. To survive the rabbit must also learn to hide itself quickly at any early sign of danger, such as a moving speck in a cloudless sky.

Just like the rabbit burrowing for protection, the army builds walls round the city as defences against attack. At the appearance of any sign of possible danger of an imminent attack the gates are immediately pulled shut.

Banquets and feasts where the best of foods and wines are served have been used since ancient times to entrap generals and kings. For a person becomes most vulnerable once he is a guest inside another's walled city or armed palace. So I would always advise the king to be on his guard whenever he is invited to a feast. The next invitation may well be his last meal – like a tiger straying into a hunter's trap of a tied goat.

How does a strategist sense that a particular configuration of circumstances may be a trap?

1 4

I become suspect whenever I see a lure in a contrived situation. For instance, I remember a general who had been so successful in the defence of the country at the northern borders that he incurred the jealousy of the minister of war himself. The minister worked on the fears of the king that this general had perhaps become *too* successful – he might one day usurp the throne.

Entrapment

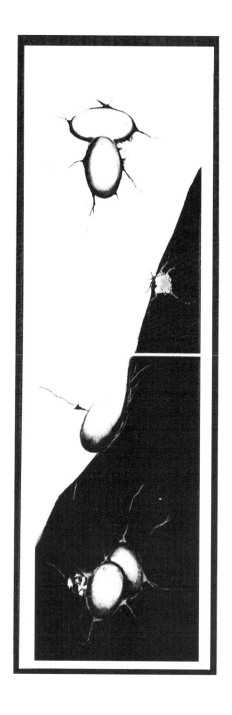

He was tricked by the jealous minister to venture out of his 'burrow' – despite clear signs of danger – through a ploy to confer on him an imperial title. The title was however, to be received personally inside the king's palace – a place where the general had to disarm himself and enter without any of his own personal bodyguards.

In that moment of exhilaration caution was thrown to the winds. Perhaps he could have been more circumspect. One must be alert to the dangers of being noticed. For ironically, that is often the beginning of trouble – one ends up as a prey to one's own success.

The general could have excused himself, on grounds of the tension at the border, from receiving the imperial title in person. Another ploy is to feign illness. Time is needed so that the general may probe to see if there might indeed be a ruse behind all these unexpected honours.

Like the rabbit that is safe inside his burrow, the general is protected within the border town by his own army. But the moment he makes a move there is possible risk of danger.

I am hardly surprised to find in the forest that just as the tiger seems to owe its survival to its speed and power in killing – it has sharp claws with the power to rip open bodies – the large tortoise must owe its survival to its unique capability to stay always within its protective shell.

205

1 ⬛ 5

A favourite stratagem of mine in war is to lure the enemy into a trap by configuring circumstances that appear to promise a quick, early victory.

Which general or soldier does not enjoy the triumphant feelings that even small victories bring?

A series of such staged easy-to-win victories often induces the other side to become less cautious in the next encounter. Indeed, after some time the officers and soldiers may become so drunk with pride from easy wins that they become even more reckless.

At the same time our own soldiers will become more

and more restless to show their true mettle. When the urge to fight becomes irresistible then the time is ripe for the final showdown.

The strategy is to so shock the other side completely – accustomed as they are to winning with ease – so that they may never be able to recover from the nightmare of being utterly defeated.

For in all strategies, time plays a fundamental role. Drawing on this principle, the strategist must be able to devise lures so as to cause *movement* by the enemy.

Movement often brings a greater dispersal of forces. When made to move heedlessly around the ground, the energy of an individual soldier is dissipated. Also there is likely to be greater consumption and wastage of resources – things may be abandoned to sustain the momentum of a move. When dispersed the enemy forces also become more difficult to coordinate.

My idea is to conserve the strength of the army and deplete that of the enemy. My army watches like a hawk that rides on the wind high up in the skies. Let the enemy be like the rabbits, enjoying their easy nibbles on the dewy morning grasses. Then in one perfectly timed and contrived encounter, the army sweeps down like a hawk. The enemy is finished off, like the rabbit, in a single swift killing action.

1 ⬛ 6

I would often formulate counter-moves to foil enemy strata- gems, such as avoiding baits and lures, forgoing what may seem to be advantageous, and never needlessly tiring the sol- diers. But in turn I would apply constant pressure on the enemy: to weary them, destroy their supplies so as to starve them or, better still, to feed off them, goad or force them into making hasty decisions.

2 ⚏ 1

Towards the end of autumn. I am preparing myself to embrace the cold again, sitting here simply reflecting. That's the beauty of being alive: experiencing the subtlety of change. How often I long for the quietness of winter so as to restore my spirit, the inner *chi* – the flux of energy inside me – through undisturbed and calm sitting.

Yet the end of autumn inevitably brings with it a twinge of sadness: I am witness to the closing of another cycle, another year. I hope to be moving one step nearer sublimity. For in old age, every passing season means that the physical self becomes ever more rigid and heavy, and the skin wrinkled and coarse.

Like a tree that ages, the body gradually loses its nimbleness. I hope through meditative practices to refine and purify myself and perhaps attain an exalted state of being.

Like the casting off of old soiled uniforms for clean garments, I try to cultivate within me a new purified body. The mysterious, deeply secretive *Taoist* path to immortality has long intrigued me: the sublime processes of purifying oneself through deep, quiet meditation and refined breathing till one finally attains immortality.

But is that really possible?

I often wonder. I have, contrary to *Taoist* precepts on preserving one's vitality, exhausted myself in my youthful years by being very actively involved – mind, body and soul – in the practice of waging war.

I did not then fully appreciate the importance of abiding by the *Taoist* precept in nurturing one's spiritual essence. The precept is deceptively simple: keep the mind blank and sit like an uncarved block of wood.

2 ⚏ 2

Often when I sense the beginning of the transition from autumn to winter I ask myself:

Should I remain indifferent to the change in the seasons?

Surely it is only human to feel. The ebb and flow of

feelings – fleeting though these may be – renders one truly a human being.

Does the boulder lying on the path that winds up to my hut experience any sensations during this transition?

I doubt it.

What about the trees?

Perhaps. For soon the trees will begin to shed their leaves and become bare. They too adapt to the change of season. Without foliage the forest looks stark and almost devoid of life. Look at a denuded forest after the evening snow, set against a background of the full moon – feelings in awe of nature are so easily evoked.

Do animals feel?

The horse that I would ride into battle certainly has feelings. I know my white horse intimately – I can quickly sense the changes of mood. I communicate my finer reactions through the sensitive use of my fingers – besides the usual riding signals given through the reins – and the horse seems at times so human as to appreciate my more subtle feelings.

Over the years I have become able to understand the neighs of my horse better. Often I wonder if my white horse may, in a previous existence, once have been an officer within the cavalry. Nothing seems to excite the horse more than seeing the cavalry in action – I could sense when riding it the intense onrush of blood through its body.

The horse seems able to respond quickly in battle situations – on some occasions even saving my life. I am fortunate to share such a good understanding with the horse – and out there in the field we would function as one.

2 ≡🏇≡ 3

Substantial as the rocks may appear, many are easily washed away from their sites by something that seems insubstantial – water. I have witnessed this when the banks of the Yellow River are ripped apart by overflowing torrents.

This brings me to recall how effective mist can be in slowing the onslaught of an army. In these mountainous ranges I often study the formation of fog – how it clings to the surface of paths round these mountains.

These misty scenes are so graphically etched on my memory that I can easily distinguish one from another. The varying types of scene, with their different shades of haziness, are painted vividly in my mind.

A touch of mistiness often makes a place all the more entrancing. The sun's glow through the mist may transform what is a simple mundane dwelling into an abode for some heavenly being.

At times the fog is so thick that it is just too dangerous even to walk along a well-trodden path. At some edges a wrong turn may lead one to fall off the cliff.

I remember being told the story of how an invasion by the tribes living in the northern wilderness was repulsed.

The invaders were led by an ingenious but notoriously brutal warrior – nicknamed the Butchering Warrior of the North – with an insatiable appetite for plunder and slaughter. Many days of fierce fighting had been continuing at the borders. The royal troops held back the advance by fending off the attacks from behind double-layered walls.

The northern army was finally forced to withdraw when the fog – so dense that one had to strain the eyes just to see one's fingers – from a nearby lake began to set in. The fog came and surprisingly, despite the wind, lingered around the protective walls of the border city.

'Did anyone invoke divine powers?' many city dwellers asked.

It did not take long before offerings were made to Heaven. From afar the approaching fog seemed like some divine monster called upon to attack the invading army from the rear.

How the scene transformed itself! Looking at one moment like some benign heavenly deity, all of a sudden there was a demon-like creature with long tongue that seemed to spout furiously poisonous fumes. The tribal warriors were scared by the approaching fog. Even the Butcher of the North feared the fog for he took it as heavenly displeasure with his acts of violence, especially now that the fog faced his army head on.

Mystery

So, as the story goes, he ordered the full withdrawal of all his tribal warriors. And for years thereafter the border city enjoyed unprecedented peace.

Oh, how something so insubstantial as the fog can be so effective!

2 ⚌ 4

I learnt from this story lessons about the possible roles for things that are as subtle and insubstantial as fog. For instance, there must be various possible uses of smoke.

There is art in the creative use of a wide variety of types of smoke in different circumstances. Indeed during various wars I have ordered smoke to be used to full advantage.

I was once pursued by an enemy force many times the size of my own. I escaped encirclement and certain annihilation by using thick smoke to cover our route of escape through the forest.

The strong wind, that blew in a favourable direction, was of tremendous help. The wind blew thick smoke into the faces of enemy soldiers, choking them and making their eyes water.

Just as I had devised a system for the use of fire on hilly peaks at night as a means to convey messages over long distances, I found heavy columns of smoke effective to signal warnings over long distances during the day.

When enemy spies were known to be hiding inside some dark caves up the mountain, I ordered that smoke be used to ferret them out of their hiding.

2 ⚌ 5

So I wrote in *The Art of War* about the importance of mastering the fine art of being subtle and insubstantial. The outcome of war does not simply depend on brute strength, though that is one factor. So when waging war I would emphasise the capability of an army to remain soundless, and mysteriously so, especially when making surprise moves.

How can this be accomplished?

A few precautions can be taken to ensure the silent movement of troops. Soldiers are ordered to bite on a piece of wood between their teeth so that they will not even whisper when moving.

Another precaution: the hoofs of the horses are bound with pieces of cloth when moving out of a city steeped in darkness. Or soldiers are asked not to ride the horses through the dark streets but simply to lead them.

For an army to remain subtle and insubstantial requires of its general the ability to evade the main thrusts or counter-thrusts of the enemy. Such elusive tactics often frustrate the enemy forces, goading them to make strategic mistakes.

How does an army remain unwearied despite long marches?

By journeying through places *without* encountering the enemy. Soldiers implementing the strategy of deliberate avoidance – despite the lack of actual combat activity – are contributing as much to final victory as those locked in hand-to-hand combat inside deeply dug trenches.

As an analogy, are windows useful precisely because of their voidness?

Sometimes *not* fighting is just as important as being engaged in fighting. This is something which often goes un-appreciated. There is a tendency to glorify only those soldiers who are involved in the actual fighting with the enemy.

The general must master the art of defence, by defend-ing those places that will *not* come under attack.

How?

This requires a deep intuitive understanding of the art of war. For the general must be able to fathom the mind of the enemy, anticipate their expectations and therefore predict their likely moves. Or better, make it impossible for his side to come under any attack. And conversely, in attacking, to hit where the enemy least expect it and therefore do not defend themselves or offer only weak resistance.

3 ⚔ 1

Another of the many dull wintry nights – endurable only because it affords me the rare opportunity to catch the rich flow of my thoughts on the art of war, enriched by the cumulative experiences which I have gained since I first wrote *The Art of War*.

Perhaps because of my advanced age, my writing has become more reflective and less prescriptive. These writings I am embarking on are unlike any of the thirteen chapters in *The Art of War:* they are discursive rather than focused.

Maybe age is the reason why there is so much rambling in the way I write. Also my desire is to capture the multifaceted aspects of mastering the art of strategy.

The strategist has to be very observant of everything around him, not only in seeing but also in using his mind to penetrate to the very essence of things. Essentially the mind of a strategist is that of a deep thinker.

Also I want to reflect on the processual aspects. For I am still attempting to mirror in my current writings the mind of a warring strategist. I am sure that for thousands of years to come we shall continue to see wars being waged.

3 ⚔ 2

There will emerge intelligent, scholarly men whose skills lie mainly in helping kings and their generals to formulate effective strategies. In time there may emerge the profession of court strategist, a person whose major function is to advise kings on matters of strategy.

During my time, I functioned both as commander-in-chief and often as court strategist. So for me strategy formulation is integrated with implementation. But this need not necessarily be so.

Given the many possibilities of waging war, there must be value in having the best minds in the kingdom available to explore alternatives before committing so many lives to taking military action – this is often little appreciated by generals hungry for glory on the battlefield.

Rare indeed is it to find within the kingdom persons having both the qualities of a warrior – able to endure the sheer physical hardships of waging war – and at the same time those of a scholar, in possession of a fine mind.

So the roles of the 'formulator' and 'implementor' may in the future become divided rather than integrated in a single person.

3

Like the heavenly painter trying to capture the depth of feeling evoked by the scenery before him: the floating clouds high up in these mountains, the flight of birds in the skies, the flow of waters in the streams – I too attempt to capture the inner workings of the mind of a court strategist.

How am I able to predict – and, in the eyes of some, how can I *divine* – the moves of the enemy?

How am I able to draw a line on the ground and the enemy will simply be unable to breach it?

How can I mark the spot where the enemy's general will be shot dead and *divine* the precise year, season and even day and time of it happening?

How am I able so miraculously to divert the attacking force coming headlong towards a city?

There is no magic in my strategic skills.

I hope here to dispel such nonsensical notions that I possess any *divine* powers. What appears to be magical is the result of my devotion in mastering the art of war.

4

Anyone studying *The Art of War* diligently will improve in the subject. I must admit, though, that some are naturally more talented in the practice of strategy than others.

If my skills are indeed seen by others to be far superior it is simply because they are more finely honed. The skills of a strategist become sharpened through practice.

Perhaps I spend more time thinking deeply about these things, whilst others tend to rush into battle simply on the spur of the moment.

I hope my writing has the same power as the paintings that I have seen in palaces. The master painters record the marvels of the scenery high up in the mountains – with the mist and clouds – and their paintings simply have that power to arouse deep feelings. Some capture so well the subtly changing effects of the mountain light.

Living here I have come to realise that no mountain scene really remains unchanging. In fact to the keen observer a mountain is always changing subtly; so is the situation when waging a war. The situation in war is fluid and the astute strategist must be attuned to change.

War by its very nature evolves continually. I would often immerse myself in the circumstances of my opponent – the general I am fighting – so as to fully appreciate the issues that confront him and the options open to him.

Every little detail about the opposing general is sought relentlessly by me. For since I want to be able to anticipate his every move I must become him – empathising with his style of fighting, strengths and weaknesses, inclinations, temper, preferences, likes and dislikes, habits and so on.

Whatever I am not certain about I find out through designing simple experiments to test my assumptions. I watch carefully every detail of his reactions to these experiments.

To test how the opposing general is likely to respond to certain military manoeuvres I deliberately get the army to change formation.

There is, however, little need to conduct many experiments just to validate a certain fact or belief about him. I know the taste of the river water by taking a small sip – there is no need to drink many cupfuls. But for water from a different river, lake or stream, the experiment must be repeated.

The idea is to gather all available information necessary for detailed formulation of a strategy by simple yet effective means: these I have alluded to in *The Art of War*.

But accurately reading the mind of another is a technique difficult to impart – perhaps it is a talent that comes naturally to one skilled in strategy.

Only by truly understanding your opponent can you make him divulge his plans or lure him out of his secret haunts. Do not overlook the little details about a person, for they too tell a story.

A few brushstrokes reveal the level of accomplishment in a painter. The moves that a general makes in a skirmish are indications of his competence in the military arts.

Immersion

Paintings reveal to a trained eye the style and personality of the painter. So a seasoned court strategist should be able to decipher an opposing general's grand strategy from a series of coordinated military moves executed by him.

3 ⬛ 5

I study for days on end the demeanour of the man with whom I am fighting. Often I spy on him. I hang his portraits in my study as I empathise with him. Needless to say, I gather every little bit of news about him.

I was often impressed when I was inside the king's palaces by watching shows or plays. The actors, despite their painted faces, were able to enact the roles of characters in a given play.

Years of training, I am told, go into perfecting that single role – the actor is assigned one major role for his entire life. Laborious effort is required to master every single gesture to perfection.

Every day the actor becomes more and more the person he is to play on the stage. His face is so thickly painted that there is no way one could tell who he really is. Such a process ensures that long before he is on stage the actor has so subdued his own personality that he often becomes the man he is portraying in the play.

It is not surprising that, after years of immersion in the chosen role, the actor's original personality may be transformed. I have seen men who have played major female roles in drama and are now so changed that they are more feminine than any woman I know.

When confronted with an opposing army I first try to immerse myself in the personality of the general that leads it. Ridiculous as it may sound, I do on occasion sympathise with my opposing general. I see the man – his strengths, weaknesses, difficulties and constraints as well as his follies – whom I am so supposed to fight against!

I never allow myself to be moved by anger, hatred or envy in respect of the enemy's general. For outcomes of war are like the game of Go – there is little room for emotions on a board of black and white stones – and so it is on the battlefield.

Before conceiving of a major military mission designed

to eliminate the opposing general, I first test how well I know the man. As I have said, I create situations – military experiments – and watch how he reacts.

In other words, I test my beliefs about him. From the series of experiments I may then be able to validate my beliefs about him. If I can read his mental processes perfectly – his mode of strategic thinking – then I ought to be able to anticipate his very next move.

3 ▰ 6

Despite the wilderness and the occasional bird or two for company, I find this little hut – hidden away in the mountain – ideal for deep reflection.

One should set aside time to engage in an internal dialogue with oneself. It is only then, as I have found by retreating up here to reflect and write, that the deeper insights are revealed.

The mind has a way of storing within itself a wealth of buried insights. Looking back in time, I realise how differently I react as compared with the other generals when confronted with a given war situation.

Many – at least in my time – were simply too impatient: they craved immediate victories through vigorous action in the field. Thus often the response, when my opposing general felt he was being humiliated, was to act quickly. He would rush his army out: the gongs would be sounded and the drums beaten – the goal was to seek to overcome the enemy by fighting, and this despite the often enormously difficult conditions in which to wage such wars.

History has a strange way of rewarding such vainglorious, physical feats done in moments of bravery – even when many lives are needlessly sacrificed! The strategist who devises stratagems that avoid risking lives is often left unmentioned. His contributions of saving so many lives through strategy are buried only in the memories of those dead and gone.

Thus many a general hungers for that promise, sometimes elusive, of having his name remembered eternally. Many sacrifices are made just to achieve greatness through victories – even if it means fighting desperately in long pitched battles. That he could be lured out from behind the high walls to cross deep moats to fight.

I try to master this art of 'becoming' the enemy and thus be as precise as I possibly can in predicting his next moves. Knowing intimately what the enemy general treasures and loathes, I am able to manipulate him.

I cause him to act according to my will. Like mastering the art of puppetry: the skilful manipulation of strings that causes the puppet to behave as I dictate. The better I am in 'becoming' the enemy general the more incisive are my strings of control over him.

A hot, cloudy, starless, windless night – so still that I can feel the movement of the thinly sliced moon crusading across the empty sky. I ought to be in my little dwelling high up in the mountain but here I am still sitting here in my city home. It is essential however that I occasionally call on my fellow kinsfolk.

What transpired during our long meeting I must record on these bamboo strips before it escapes me: the mounting fresh evidence that the prescriptions on the art of war are yet again being validated through practice.

I am told that now many more young military officers are seeking a copy of *The Art of War* – the work I completed so many years ago.

Many have been trying to obtain an accurate hand-made copy for their own study. So my own kinsmen have been kept busy by a continuous flow of requests: to make duplicate copies, often on freshly bound bamboo strips.

My nephew has done it so many times that he is even able to recite *The Art of War* from back to front. And from what I have heard, some aspiring young men even commit every single word I have written to memory.

I ask myself: is it useful to commit these precepts to memory – word for word?

Surely there must also be an evolving, creative dimension to the art of formulating military strategy. All that has been written in *The Art of War* has been derived from my specific war context, one which may change fundamentally in the course of time.

What changes might there be?

New weapons for killing. Different means of transportation. Defences that are novel. And so on. New designs for building cities: moats, dug-in but covered trenches. Use of different animals in war: armed bulls dragging along wooden boards stacked with sharp, pointed daggers. The range of war devices is as limited as the ingenuity of man.

4 ⚏ 2

I hope that whenever young men read *The Art of War* this possibility of change and adaptation will be kept in their minds.

In other words, there is an implicit contextual presumption underlying these precepts or any rules for waging war. Thus in a changed context even I, as the author of *The Art of War*, may prescribe differently.

I am of course happy to learn that some generals are even insisting that my work be studied by all officers in the army. But I hope such learning is not undertaken simply in a dogmatic fashion. Nor that the precepts are followed blindly.

If it is indeed true that so many are now applying *The Art of War* precepts on the battlefield then I must now start thinking of new strategies to counter such blind, unthinking application of my doctrines.

If a general adheres too closely to a given set of stratagems – even if these are drawn from *The Art of War* – and repeats them all the time, then his military actions will lack that vital element for continued success in waging war: surprise!

4 ⚏ 3

I am not denying that I am pleased that my work has not been in vain, that what I recorded on a few strips of bamboo is becoming (surprisingly to me) so widely known and practised.

Oh, if only I were young! I would continue to test these precepts through the thick of battles and through the process refine and sharpen my military ideas and thinking.

There are, however, some very fundamental precepts in *The Art of War* that are so basic to any conflict that they are likely to continue to be valid despite the passage of time.

This must be elaborated.

From last night's conversation I am more than pleased that one general currently responsible for the north-western front has declared the he always abide by a principle advocated in *The Art of War:* know in advance the detailed deployment of the enemy forces but deny the opposing side any such knowledge.

So he builds up an intricate network for the gathering and dissemination of information among the tribal peoples of the far north.

Assuming you are a general, one possibility is for you to feed the enemy with false information about future deployment. However, for this to be believed by the other side, you may also have to mislead your own officers.

It is only realistic to assume that there are spies among the officers and men. Besides, the enemy too will test how reliable a piece of information is. You must independently confirm whether the enemy have discovered your scheme, and moved their forces in anticipation of your planned deployment.

Let the enemy be irretrievably committed to such counter-strategies before making any new moves. If they are locked in these counter-moves, then you should without any advance notice immediately reconfigure your forces and quickly implement your actual strategy.

You must *never*, in the interest of ensuring that your true strategy will succeed, alert even your closest comrades-in-arms. Success often lies in you yourself maintaining the utmost secrecy about your strategic plan.

4 ▄▌▄ 4

Just like the well-known prescription for kings who want to reduce the odds of being assassinated, have a number of different possible rooms to sleep in and announce only the actual room that very evening – and do the same every evening!

For although the king's personal bodyguards and servants may be thoroughly screened before being selected there remains the possibility – no matter how remote – that they may be bought by the enemy's heavy bribes.

So, as a precaution, all these rooms are prepared and the king only decides that very evening where he wants to sleep.

Although trust is necessary, it is even better to institute tight controls to reduce the chances of an assassination ever succeeding.

As another precaution, no servant is allowed to work more than a year at a stretch in the service of the king, even though the actions of these servants are already being closely watched by the king's spies. And even among the spies, some are assigned to watch over another!

So it is in selecting the consort with whom the king plans to spend the night. The king is to be provided with a bevy of beautiful women from whom a choice is to be made: this is done again in the interest of the personal security of the king. With such a procedure the enemy must bribe each and every one of the consorts – something which is very difficult to accomplish in total secrecy.

The extent to which security measures are required depends on the popularity of the king. Even for a king who is popular there may still be some of his own people who may be bribed to assassinate him. Of course, if the king is widely hated by his own people, then far tighter security measures will be necessary.

But if the hatred of the king grows unabated and is very widespread, then there comes a time when even the tightest security measures will not prevent the inevitable: the assassination or removal of a person widely hated by the people. As the ancients would say, Heaven has by then taken away his mandate to rule.

4 ▰▰ 5

So it is for the general: the ultimate test of whether he succeeds depends on how well respected and loved he is by the very soldiers he is leading.

The general able to exploit the element of surprise through having a complete knowledge of the enemy's every deployment is more likely to win battles. With a growing stream of continuous victories, there is likely to be a deepening of respect among the troops for the general.

Conversely, a general whose officers and troops are continuously disappointed or shocked by surprise attacks successfully launched by the enemy will begin to lose faith in him as their military leader. Some, seeing the turn of events, may harbour thoughts of abandoning their posts or even switch sides.

4 ≡🕮≡ 6

One rule which I believe will stand the test of time in the context of any military warfare: deny the enemy any early warning of the *time* and *place* of an encounter. The secret is to sustain the pressure and initiative through surprise moves.

The size of an army alone is not necessarily a decisive factor in determining an outcome of war. Consider a hundred thousand troops that are ill-disciplined and poorly trained, and have low morale. They are battling against ten thousand highly skilled and motivated soldiers: *which side do you think will finally prevail?*

I am inclined to choose the latter. For, by virtue of its large size, the army may be more difficult to control, co-ordinate and motivate.

To fight such a large army successfully, the secret lies in avoiding the whole but engaging its divided parts. Arrows when bunched together in a batch are difficult to break, so never lock your small army in a pitched battle with one much larger than yours. Remember: a single or a few arrows are more easily broken.

So the wise strategist will devise stratagems to entice the opposing general to divide his whole army into smaller parts. Better still if the parts are so far flung apart as to make it impossible for one to reinforce another.

Wear down the main core of the enemy army through sporadic attacks by small elite squads. Sometimes suicide squads are sent to penetrate deep inside the enemy's camp and create havoc.

The objective of these 'hit–run, infiltrate–wreak havoc and shock, then withdraw' moves is to throw the opposing army – at its very core – into total confusion. If put in a quandary – right at the heart of his camp – the enemy general is less likely to be able to think strategically and act rationally.

4 ≡🕮≡ 7

The strategy is to use your whole army in surprise moves against each of these smaller, subdivided parts – one at a time – choosing those that are most vulnerable first and vanquishing them.

But the enemy must never know which camp is to come under attack. If that remains unknown then the enemy is compelled to defend in so many different places as to be weak in most – it is like shattering a boulder into a thousand pieces. Each piece is easily picked up, as compared to a whole boulder.

Build up the morale of your own army by accumulating little successes. The series of defeats will certainly dampen the morale of the enemy troops – may even cause them to lose faith completely in their own command. The idea is to cause your enemy officers, along with their soldiers, to abandon their general.

For this reason the moral purpose behind the war is crucial. Men are far more easily persuaded to rally behind noble and just causes than those pursued for selfish reasons alone.

Efforts must be made where feasible to reintegrate the enemy troops that now choose to fight under your banner as your own men. Thus as the size of the enemy's army dwindles by the day, yours swells and grows in strength.

I find it worthwhile to repeat, before I retire for the evening: *never* allow the enemy to dictate the time and place of battle.

Now I am back here in my little retreat up in the mountains. The coolness of the evening air contrasts sharply with the heat of a city night. I am glad to spend my summer days here.

Memories of the rest of the conversations I had during my stay in the city – as yet unrecorded by these wrinkled hands – are flooding my mind. Visions of the past too appear before my mind's eye.

I often experience this inner urge to complete my life's work by setting down my thoughts on strategy – not just the prescriptions, but where possible feelings, judgements, hunches, guesses, intuitions, fears, doubts and aspects of me that are only human.

Writing energises me.

These memoirs capture the more evanescent thoughts that surface as I reflect on *The Art of War*. In my old age, with a body too stiff to ride a warhorse to battle, I can only reflect on the past. As I grow older too I find that I sleep less and less. So writing is a relief from insomnia.

Conversations are useful as these trigger deeper reflections. So my conversations with my kinsfolk in town revived scenes of the buried past.

5 ⚜ 2

How fast time escapes us all! In my twilight years I feel such a sense of urgency to reach the future generations. I want to convey what I have learned through a life devoted to winning wars through strategy.

It seems like yesterday that I wrote the brief *Art of War*, yet decades have flowed past and through me since.

Time.

I am beginning to be concerned about things that troubled me little when I was younger. Such as whether a reader of *The Art of War* in the distant future   whether an officer, general or even a person in everyday life – will ever realise how extensively these precepts so neatly recorded in the thirteen chapters of my book are grounded in my own experiences.

I seek the truth from facts: universal principles of

strategy derived from observations and reflections on concrete war situations.

An illustration follows.

5 ▆▆ 3

My belief that victory does not depend merely on the size of an army is derived largely from my personal encounters through a war with the state of Yueh.

Their large army was prevented by me from being deployed effectively. I deliberately made it impossible for them to know the time and place of battle.

Sometimes I misled them.

Due to their formidable size I could only engage a *part* of the Yueh army at any one time – very often a minor part. I would smash a specific segment of the Yueh army with my entire force, summoned to appear at a specific time and place.

As I waged such overwhelming, surprise moves against a tiny part of the Yueh army it was only natural that we always won. My choice of the specific time and place for engagement was never made arbitrarily but only after very careful deliberation.

For my success depended on surprising the enemy: thus the battle had to be fought *when* and *where* they least anticipated it.

So although Yueh's standing army was awesome in size they were rendered impotent through my strategy of avoidance.

For whenever I was warned about the full mobilisation of the entire Yueh army in a concerted effort to defeat us, I would quickly alert my men. Although the soldiers under my command were often widely dispersed through the land they would stay in close touch with military headquarters.

I would order them to disband immediately, withdraw into hiding and await further orders. The idea was for the soldiers to melt into civilian life – to remain still, never to act but to simply observe, to blend, in short.

On the other hand, in Yueh's capital city, grandiose rehearsals and displays held sway. Crowds were awed, some cowed into quiet submission as they saw new chariots, cavalry, archers, glittering weaponry, sharply pointed spears and so on.

Unnoticed and mingling among the Yueh multitude were some of my best soldiers – ordered temporarily to become civilian – clothed in farmers' attire.

The Yueh army looked majestic and formidable, with their banners fluttering vigorously in the morning wind as the soldiers marched out of the capital city's gates. Cheers of victory were shouted out loud by the onlooking crowd. Everybody expected the mission to lead to a crushing victory.

Little did they realise that I had deliberately ordered my men to avoid any engagement. My base camp was completely abandoned; we expected the Yueh army to raze what remained to the ground.

Many of my men returned to farming. Others to fishing. Some have ended up climbing the mountains in search of rare herbs.

It takes two to fight.

By withdrawing I denied the Yueh general his coveted prize – a crushing victory. Even the sporadic search and kill missions yielded little. Nothing concrete was achieved: no slaves in chains, no captured chariots, horses or weapons. Yueh's army returned late one evening with soldiers despondent, frustrated, dejected, disappointed. Their banners with the general's name dangled on the poles. Riding through the city gates the general's solemn face seemed to express that 'it was all for nothing' look.

The eyes of the city dwellers betrayed their disbelief: how could an army the size of Yueh's return so quietly? And nothing to show for it.

Silence demoralises as it haunts.

Many unanswered questions filled the capital city of Yueh. Doubts appeared in the faces of its citizens. Indignant voices were heard on city corners:

"How could an army the size of Yueh's march out in broad daylight with such grandeur only to crawl back on a dark night in such a lacklustre fashion?"

More voices:

"Something is very wrong with our command!"

An indignant echo:

"Somebody should replace this useless general and his lackeys."

An insider spoke:

"Does the king know of this insult?"

A minister had been overheard:

"What a fiasco – and our army is so big!"

And so on . . .
Voices grew ever louder as the people drowned their anger with pots of flowing rice wine, served by my soldiers turned waiters.

Inside Yueh's army – as I was told – dangerous, dissident whisperings were heard even among the rank and file.

A disgruntled officer:

"Grandiloquent speeches by the general and officers but we see no concrete action."

Another:

"As always we have been outsmarted."

The king, keen to silence the murmurings inside and outside the army, quickly had the general removed.

5 4

This information came from my army, still there watching the enemy!

Stillness is as critical as action in war.

Empty spaces enhance a painting – adding deeper and more profound meanings to a work of art; so does stillness in the art of war. A room is useful precisely because of the empty space enclosed by walls.

Through stillness I was waging war at a more fundamental level – chipping away at the Yueh soldiers' confidence

Fluidity

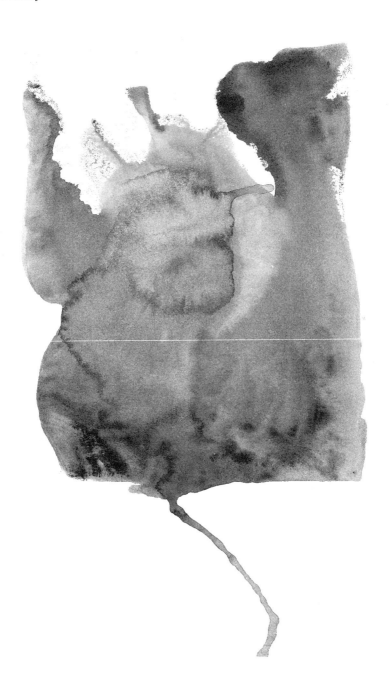

in their military leaders. I created doubts in the minds of the Yueh people on the capabilities of their large army.

Keeping my own army intact and still, I caused the people of Yueh to begin to whisper doubts and to raise concerns about their army.

As my strategy unfolded these noises grew louder to become a chorus that would eventually cause the downfall of the general. In time even the king would be endangered. Another general was appointed, one even hungrier for quick results.

'What an excellent prey to my scheme of war!' – I remember exclaiming upon receiving the news.

I like nothing better than to have an opposing general who is easily angered and impatient for action. Whenever there is a change in command I begin my testing of the new general's strategy, or his way of waging wars.

I re-activate my spy network – the general's past, personal relations, connections, weaknesses, strengths and so on. Every detail reveals a fresh side of the new general.

I must test to determine how truly accomplished he is in the fine art of war. I ask myself:

"Does his art of war mean fresh opportunities, new dangers? How must I reconfigure my strategy to wage a winning war against him? What are his most vulnerable points?"

And more such questions for me to think through.

My own strategy requires that my soldiers be able to 'swim' as swiftly as the fish – with the grasslands their sea.

Fluidity.

This principle, derived from my observations of the world, is tested through my military encounters. Its efficacy, and that of other principles, must be validated through results.

I stress in *The Art of War* the need to test any preconceived ideas about the enemy's battle strategy: incite the enemy to take action so that their deployment of troops reveals their wider strategy.

As I have also said in *The Art of War*, configure the formation of your troops differently and study the enemy's immediate responses. From how they respond – time taken, types of troops being mobilised, where reinforcements are coming from, weapons used, formations adopted and other factors – it is possible to draw conclusions about their strengths and weaknesses.

This, I am told, is now being quite widely advocated and practised, especially by one general in a southern state.

5 ▰ 5

The testing of any preconceived idea or assumption is just as relevant in our ordinary lives. Every wise farmer, before planting his field with the seeds from a new strain of crop taken from afar, will test these in his backyard.

When presented with a new, tamed horse I often asked for it to be tested in my presence – any horse taken from the wild must be sufficiently tamed before I could safely ride on it. Also, before I rode it to faraway places, I needed to test its strength, speed, stamina and endurance through rides over shorter distances. Through these I gained useful insights into the characteristics of the horse.

A reader in the distant future may even find these principles relevant to other spheres of life – whenever there is conflict and competition apart from the purely military.

6 ≣🦋≣ 1

Mid-autumn: a season of change and transition: the autumnal scenes are the most memorable for me. Sometimes it seems as if the changes in the seasons are wrought by these breezes, gently blowing winds that whisper of a time for change. Walking through the forest I am captivated by the rustling music of falling leaves.

Winds.

Each leaf moves differently towards Mother Earth: one rushes, another glides, the other tosses, this circles, that flutters, the next lingers, none is the same, but every one of them reaches the earth.

Earth.

So many, many lives are sustained by earth: in the forests, mountains, deserts, cities, villages, camps, rivers, skies, streams, hills, seas – everywhere there is life.

As I stand there watching I realise there is another distinctive feature in my practice of the art of war: unique, non-replicative, fluid, indefinable movements.

In the leafy dances in autumn, each leaf has its own unique variation in movement even though all eventually come to rest on earth. An ordinary person experiencing the autumnal scene may find nothing unusual except for fallen leaves on the ground.

It is the same when scenes of wars are visited: a person sees dead fallen soldiers strewn across the battlefield. Yet each leaf charts a unique path to the earth.

So for each fallen soldier his fight to the death is uniquely his own: one fell due to a stray arrow, another from a deep cut by a thrusting sword, the other from a spear stuck in his body, in the distance a head is lopped off – and in many other ways a soldier may fall to the ground.

6 ≣🦋≣ 2

For me there are many and possibly countless variations on how I may wage a war. So too there are limitless variations on how I configure the army for any confrontation, even though I keep to central, left and right forces.

The composition of each of these forces – types of

Uncertainty

soldiers allocated and their tasks – will vary from battle to battle.

A major determinant of how I reconfigure my army is contextual: characteristics of enemy forces (size, skill, morale), strategy pursued by the enemy, terrain, weather, weaponry in use, supply lines, nearest rivers and wells, living conditions of people – are they starving and tired of fighting? – and so on.

By constantly varying my strategy I am able to shock, surprise, puzzle, frustrate and rush the enemy general.

6 📖 3

In order for me to be able to flex the forces under my command I must stay in very close touch with my men.

Since effective coordination is critical I devote my energy to devising an intricate network of contacts throughout the country, extending beyond mountains, over rivers and lakes through the depths of forests – no village is too remote for the reach of my men.

So when I need to amass my men I can do so in no time. If certain specialised skills – such as expert administration of all kinds of poison – are needed as part of implementing my strategy, I can easily reach those who seem to be happy just eking out a living in the remotest corner high up in the mountains situated to the far west.

The most vulnerable to my *twists* and *turns* in strategy is the typical uncouth general – scarred, hard as metal, loud-mouthed, daring in exploits and fearless even in face of personal danger.

What is typical of these generals, who have often risen in the ranks from footsoldier right up to a full-fledged field marshal commanding generals, is that they are full of brute strength but little learning and do not appreciate the works of fine artists.

Even though the general often has an adviser he does not take advice easily – especially when what is proffered runs counter to his temperament, such as advice to stay inactive.

So his retinue of advisers often offer what generals want to hear – to fight without delay. To such tough soldiers wars only mean the massing of soldiers on both sides of a dividing line – perhaps even mutually arranged in advance – and one side storming into the other.

The soldiers then participate in an orgy of shouting, knifing, spearing, cursing, cutting, struggling, panting, riding, yelling, sweating, killing, slaughtering, screaming, butchering – and for those destined to die – dying: many very quickly and for the less fortunate slowly and painfully.

Still others leave the battlefield with less glory than when they first started – the crippled, frightened, blinded, maimed, mutilated, shocked, scared, deaf, dumb – for those that cling on to life many end up as beggars limping in the streets, forgotten and forsaken. The glorious banners they were once so proud to be serving now abandon them for ever.

6 ▰ 4

For me as a war strategist my 'soldiers' are not limited only to regular armed men in uniforms. As I always fight on the side with the strong moral purpose or just cause I can easily muster resources – often offered voluntarily – that my opponent finds difficult to obtain through bribes, compulsion, torture or threats of death.

I have 'soldiers' who are invisible but whose effects may be experienced: the scorching sun, fog, mist, haze, wind, rain, thunderstorms, lightning, clouds, whirlwinds, earthquakes – to use these I need only the skills to correctly interpret the ancient weather chart.

Some of my 'soldiers' are hardly soldierly, as the following examples show.

A young lad who spends his time roaming the streets but whose senses are as sharp as the eagle's, able quickly to sense a change of mood among the citizens.

The family of a beautiful and innocent girl who has been massacred by my opposing general: they would gladly seek revenge by any possible means.

The herbalist living in the very depths of the forest, who is able to concoct potent drinks with predictable effects.

The hermit cultivating the path of immortality up in the mountains, who is skilled in consulting the *I Ching* and reading the night skies for signs of earthly changes.

Even the most sought-after courtesan in the city, who is frequented by high-ranking officials – generals, ministers and even princes – but who is deeply dedicated to our cause: I count on her to eavesdrop on their conversations.

The old man who, when young, was devoted to helping city dwellers tell the time throughout the night using a clanger: I rely on him to inform me of any strange activities in people's homes.

The thin and cheerful city messenger who runs errands and often asks to deliver letters to distant places in secret: he alerts me of anything suspicious and even on occasion delivers a false letter ordering the return of a general later captured by us in an ambush.

The disgruntled officer bypassed in several promotion exercises but still serving inside the enemy camp.

And so on.

6 ▆ 5

But of course my 'soldiers' include too the very ordinary helpers who serve the court in the palaces of the state I am opposing.

So I said in *The Art of War* that my army has no definable shape – it is simply *shapeless*. Precisely because it is shapeless it is impossible for the enemy to effectively counter or eliminate it.

I count as my soldiers not only the farmers who toil the land but the womenfolk as well – they have their roles at different stages of a war against the enemy. So the true size of my army is limitless.

I am equally concerned about the welfare of these farmers: that they are well fed (taxes being kept reasonably low), and treated with humanity and respect, as are the regular soldiers that guard the city gates. The farmers till the soil daily and as such are kept strong and healthy – healthier perhaps than those who do nothing else but sentry duty!

To transform farmers into soldiers is less difficult than may at first appear. In the case of farmers, the muscles are there already through hoeing the lands. What needs to be changed is the implement – replace the hoe with a spear or a halberd, a battle-axe or even a sword.

The most difficult task is to instil in the farmer the will to fight. Often the enemy supply this through their unreasonableness in making impossible demands or through their rampageous behaviour.

But farmers are an obvious source of soldiers. In addition I tap the least expected sources: concubines used for pleasure in the royal court.

6 ⬛ 6

I once built a military garrison composed entirely of the king's concubines: there the difficulty was to instil in the young, dainty ladies of pleasure the military code of behaviour.

I achieved this at the cost of the life of the king's favourite concubine – she had to be beheaded to demonstrate the seriousness of the undertaking. Even the king's protests were of no avail – a military order is an order.

Sparing her life would endanger the command: nobody would ever take orders seriously, and that would be a major threat to the whole system.

That head purchased for me a garrison of formidable troops who served as the king's personal bodyguards. I doubt if the king ever forgave me for the loss of his prized concubine, but my actions had to be consistent with my own principles contained in *The Art of War*.

Since my conception of 'soldiers' is so different from that of other generals, it is not surprising that they find it impossible to fathom my thinking.

7 ▦ 1

Another day of continuous rain. The farmers must be feeling relieved by these rains. For many feared that after this lovely spring there may yet come a long, dry summer.

Farmers have always depended on the weather for their livelihood: as a young general I was always impressed by their stoicism – quiet optimism in the midst of severe hardship.

Tolerance. Their tolerance of unreasonable demands enables them to survive the impossible deprivations brought about by war:

- conscription of their sons into the army;
- their harvests being pillaged by hungry soldiers;
- their womenfolk raped and abandoned by marauding bandits;
- confiscation, in desperation, by the military of their hoes, cooking implements – anything metal to sustain the war effort;
- in dire circumstances anything made of wood: the house, roofs, chairs and tables are sacrificed.

The farmer, despite such turmoil, remains ever more determined to keep tilling the land – with his bare hands when his farming implements are confiscated – no matter how trying and difficult things may be.

As a last-ditch attempt to defend the kingdom, the farmer, despite his years, often volunteers to go into the city to defend it.

The city survives only through the farmer's sweat and often his tears in keeping it well-fed with grain from the soil he has tilled. Now he answers the call to contribute his life and blood to ward off the invading army.

A farmer's burdens!

7 ▦ 2

The extreme poverty that I have seen, which is typical of the farmer, is beyond any city dweller's imagination. Oddly I see more smiles than frowns among those living in the village than I do in the city.

Now I have the chance to experience the other side of the farmer's life: brooding pessimism despite the plenty promised by the fine weather. Farmers anticipate that the future may become difficult even though they are now enjoying the good times – a bountiful harvest as a result of fair weather.

And they are preparing themselves mentally to cope with this anticipated change for the worse if, or rather when, it comes, as change is simply inevitable.

Unlike the nobles and city merchants who are insulated from the vagaries of nature by their granaries, wealth and bestowed titles to land, the farmers are directly and immediately affected by droughts and floods.

Nature has instilled in them such qualities as resilience, discipline, adaptability, tolerance, acquiescence, simplicity, plain living – more remarkably a deep philosophical outlook on life. There is a sharp contrast between the qualities of the farmer and the city dweller.

Using words to portray the city dweller: materialistic, sceptical, money-minded, servile, sophisticated. The contrast in physical profiles is equally striking. For the farmer is often lean, tanned and wrinkled, whilst the city dweller is likely to be less lean and to have fair, smooth skin.

The farmer always keeps himself attuned to change in nature. For him, knowing the time – to the precise day – when the season begins to change is crucial.

7 ▦ 3

The image of change – a circle like the moon and the sun – as recorded in the ancient *I Ching*, must surely be reflective of the farmers' deeply rooted sense of continuum of change that underlies the universe.

Farmers are more aware of the wide expanse of the universe through having to work daily under the blue sky and resting, gazing at the star-studded sky in the night.

Thus the farmer is far more intimately sensitive to the relationships between changes in the stars – their dimming and brightening, stillness and movement, or even appearances and disappearances – and earthly events: the demise and rise of kings, generals, lords; of wars, crises, famines, droughts.

Living close to nature the farmers are more likely than others to experience the oneness of nature. Indeed some farmers tell me they can feel the pulse of the earth as they till the soil – and know that the earth is alive. Living in their huts, their feet stay rooted to the soil.

7 ▨ 4

I remember when I first saw the symbol of change in the classic *I Ching* – within a large circle the tiny circle of white in the black half, and on the other side the black dot in the white half – and I grasped immediately a deep intuitive understanding of the meaning of change in nature.

It is simply impossible to convey my grasp of the essence of this change in words. As a tool words have their limitations. The symbol of change in *I Ching* conveys the message that, inherent in any system, lies the very seed of its own destruction. Or that in every *con*struction lies the very seed of its *de*struction.

Thus one dynasty rises as another falls.

The symbolic explanation is there too: any system rises to reach its zenith (white signifying brightness or glory) and at that very moment things begin to turn in the opposite direction (hence the presence of the black dot).

That is what the farmers feared after having enjoyed such a long period of good weather: things *by their very nature* may change for the worse.

The stoicism of the farmers in the face of the utmost difficulty may be grounded in their belief that when the dark forces (black) have exerted themselves to the extreme a return to better times (white) should begin.

Such sensitivity to changes in nature is to be expected from farmers, as they must decide for themselves precisely the right time to plant the seed.

Some of them could still, though very vaguely, trace their ancestry to wandering nomads but they themselves preferred to remain dedicated to the land they farm – even when this does not belong to them. For many there is only the memory of the ceaseless ploughing of land.

Oneness

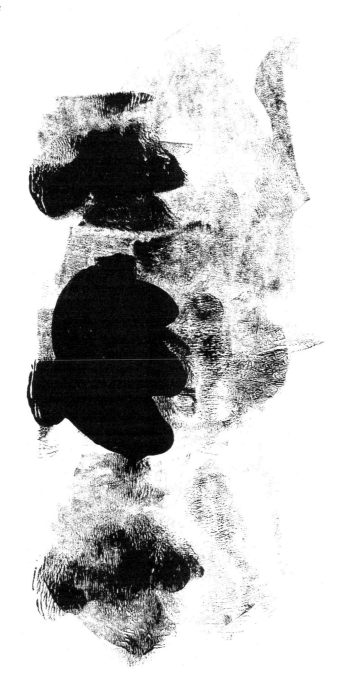

7 ⚏ 5

Change.

The lines in the *I Ching*, when consulted on changes, are also symbolic of the transformation of things: the *yang*, the unbroken line, changing into the *yin*, the broken line. For after the *yang* line has reached its zenith it will begin to weaken, and eventually break and become *yin*.

No season lasts for ever.

When winter reaches its extreme of bitter, icy cold then the moment has come for the beginning of a return to warmth.

Thus deeply rooted in the minds of the farmers is their belief that systems in nature have embedded within them the quality of *cyclicality*. Every evening the farmers see the moon ceaselessly waning and waxing. Every season has its turn and the cycle continues – spring bringing summer leading to autumn and returning to winter.

Then how can a war be any different?

In war the conditions are always changing so the strategist must watch the situation closely. Even the days vary: some are long and others short.

7 ⚏ 6

I chose to retire from the service of the king once I had secured victories for him over his arch enemies. For I too am no different from the farmer. I was wary that after having enjoyed the blessings of the king for so long I might finally come under his censure.

What could possibly cause such censure? Victories often bring about jealousies in the court. It was better that I retired than become the victim of intricate schemes coined by eunuchs, who often have nothing better to do than plot so as to while away the time.

I was wary too of the ministers who had become ever more fearful of my growing status and influence. The king himself may have wanted to reduce any possible threat to his position – I had become so widely regarded as the man responsible for the string of victories.

At the time I was basking in my military glory I decided to retreat voluntarily. I had reached the very pinnacle of a long career in the generalship of the army.

I was also following the *Tao* when I chose to retire; the task of gaining the king his kingdom had been achieved.

7   7

No wonder the farmers remain so stoical in the face of change. For nothing is more constant than change. Even the war conditions, as I have also emphasised in *The Art of War*, never remain unchanged. Indeed they are continuously changing.

As I grow even older I perceive how the farmer – unlike the city dweller – has a finer grasp of the relationship between man and earth. And also of man's relationship with the eternal. From the farmers too comes the realisation of the need for men to care for Mother Earth who nurtures us, and to whom we return at our life's end!

I recall how the century-old farmer living below these mountains always speaks of his return to the soil.

Return.

Through his daily meditative approach in farming he must have experienced that sudden realisation of the ultimate – for he is no ordinary person. He seems to have experienced the sublime and returned to the *Tao*. His eyes have that distant look, even though he may be standing right there before you.

Rain.

I am always reminded of the pristine qualities of water on seeing rain – falling as if from heaven. With wood, fire, metal and earth, it is one of the five elements of nature.

I have in my writing of *The Art of War* and in these memoirs often reflected on strategy using the analogy of water: ever changing yet remaining unchanged!

7

1 ⚏ 1

VERY LATE IN the afternoon. The sky and distant land a sheet of creamy whiteness splashed with an unmistakable yellowish tinge. The setting sun looms large in the west in a subdued golden hue.

Looking down I see the twisting, stony path below engulfed in whiteness. I too am engulfed by memories of a whiteness that cries out for attention inside me.

As I feel the smoothness of these bamboo strips I realised how many years have passed since, as a child, I was introduced through stories told by my uncle of the critical importance of manoeuvres when waging war.

I grew up to become a general waging wars and these childhood stories remained deep inside me. With every war that was waged these thoughts matured. The essence of these principles found their expression in *The Art of War*.

1 ⚏ 2

If you sit and think about the wars being waged there is value in taking a *processual* perspective.

Among the populace war is marked as having begun when there is an official declaration to that effect: the king issues his commands to be undertaken by a named general appointed as chief commander.

Thereupon the soldiers are gathered and reinforced by people who are mobilised in the anticipation of a coming war – war in the popular sense of physical, armed conflict.

These conflicts often produce many what I call 'white'

deaths: bodies whose blood has been so drained through gaping wounds that they appear colourless.

Should a very large-scale effort be planned – as in a state that is bent on expansion or a tiny one confronting another many times its size – then imperial edicts are likely to be issued for the *compulsory* conscription of young men across the land.

But if the moral cause for waging a war is strongly felt within the hearts and minds of the people – as when they truly desire to be ruled by their present king – there is little need for compulsion.

The populist fervour may be such that volunteers are already streaming into the capital to serve the king and fight under the banner of the king's appointed commander-in-chief.

1 ⚎ 3

Since ancient times, there have been parables of how a small state is able successfully to resist the ambition of one much larger. Sometimes the entire population of the defending, smaller state is even less than the size of the larger, invading army.

The outcome of war is determined not by size alone, nor by an invading army's past victories; the will of a people to defend their lands is just as crucial a factor.

There is this deep, instinctive tendency of people to want to fend off invaders in to their lands. The astute strategist must be aware of this when he considers attempts at mobilising resources for the war effort.

A distinctive phase in war preparation is when the resources – people and materials – are marshalled, ready to be deployed in military action.

The general then skilfully blends the mix of soldier-people so as to shape them into a formidable fighting force – an army acting in harmony – before encamping them in readiness for battle.

He must decide how to group the men – volunteers and regular soldiers – now under his command and assign capable officers to lead the groups.

Weapons and uniforms have to be issued to those who have volunteered to fight the enemy. Training has to be planned, coordinated and effectively implemented. Proficiency in the handling of weaponry – spear, halberd, axe, sword or whatever implements – by the new recruits must be assessed, otherwise these men may be a danger to themselves if not to their fellow soldiers!

1 — 4

Even though the detailed sequence may vary from the official launching of one war to another, depending on the situation – whether acting in defence when an attack is imminent or launching an attack – there is a broad underlying pattern of activities from the imperial decree till the encampment of troops.

The commander-in-chief acts on behalf of the sovereign, gathering, training and welding together an army in readiness for war.

The commander-in-chief now weighs up the overall situation and devises stratagems. This is when his strategic skills come under severe test: how skilful is he in forming strategy under stress?

Will the commander-in-chief be able to turn what seems to be a misfortune befalling the city-state – such as being placed under the threat of annihilation by an overwhelming force – into a strategic advantage?

This is where his art of manoeuvring – a most difficult skill to master – becomes crucial.

For I can remember in vivid colours the cost of failures should a general appointed as commander-in-chief fail to appreciate the strategic role of manoeuvres in the art of war: fresh red splashed on icy white.

This story was told and retold so many times in my childhood that I became always conscious of the role of manoeuvring for determining success when waging wars.

The story follows.

1 — 5

Seemingly endless columns of soldiers were made to traverse lands in terrible wintry conditions – the worst for many years

Destruction

– when tracks (just like the stony path now below the mountain hut) were covered in knee-deep snow.

These soldiers, led by the commander-in-chief – a general inept in the art of manoeuvre – were utterly lost in the snowy wilderness deep inside enemy lands: many had tightened, empty stomachs and were battling against the bitter cold when the enemy struck on one moonless and starless night. So many were slaughtered like pigs that by daylight the scene is one of a sea of red splashed on white.

The enemy deliberately kept a contingent of utterly demoralised soldiers alive and led them across the borders back home so that the story of the debacle could be told first-hand.

When the catastrophic scale of the defeat – that a river of red flowed on a canvas of white – dawned on the people, it so shocked them that it sparked off an escalating dissension over the expansionist designs of the king.

The king finally had to abandon his wild ambition to be the King of Kings. The king's dream was shattered through sheer neglect on the part of the now dead general of the art of manoeuvring. The king's days of glory were now past, alive only in memory.

1 🦎 6

As far as nature is concerned, another round of blizzards and the morbid scene of red upon white becomes buried with the white snow falling again. Likewise the human mind is quick to bury ugly and painful memories.

With time this layer of memory becomes deeper and deeper, ever more difficult to fathom. The memories are stored many layers beneath the conscious mind.

I am reminded of the city walls where layer upon layer of stones are laid on top of one another. As also in the making of a straw hat, one line is woven after another.

With time this layer of memory lies buried deep inside the mind. Perhaps this is nature's way of relieving people from the agony of the past. So unless records of events are duly kept all these lessons on strategy will eventually be lost in the mists of time.

The dead bodies too undergo this process of layering:

249

more and more layers of snow pile on one another and deeper and deeper are the bodies buried.

1   7

I remember visiting this very site as a young general during one winter, and the place remains peaceful. Some isolated leafless trees stand in stark contrast to the overwhelming mass of white.

Nothing suggests this to be the very ground where many tens of thousands of soldiers were so brutally slain. The place as I remember was eerily quiet.

I wondered when I stood there in the cold whether in the distant past such massive loss of life had ever occurred. And if so, how many times had it happened?

Also I wondered if, in the future, these mistakes may be repeated. I have emphasised the critical importance of manoeuvre in *The Art of War* and hope future generals will take heed of my prescription and that such wasteful loss of life may be avoided.

I have written too on how to reach a destination before the enemy by marching on an indirect route. Alternatively the enemy may be lured off the beaten path by using a bait such as the promise of an easy victory.

When I acted as a general you would often find in my tent a large piece of cloth showing the battleground. Even better is it when the general becomes familiar with the detailed conditions of the terrain during each season – winter, spring, summer and autumn. He explores the terrain so much that there is present inside his mind a crystal-clear mental map of the ground.

2 ⚜ 1

Early morning towards the end of winter. I woke up to the spectacular return of the flying cranes. This time I am able to see more closely these migrating cranes.

High in the mountain the view of the cranes is even more inspiring. They move so effortlessly that they seem to float easily in the sky, and their movements are executed with such lovely grace.

The misty sky emanates a deep golden hue that adds a royal mystique to the entire spectacle. The long stilted legs trailing behind their elegant bodies that seem immobile. The wings in their rhythmic upward and downward thrusts, cutting through the thin air. No wonder that kings symbolise their throne with the crane too!

Oh, how these cranes fly with such imperial majesty! It looks as if Heaven bestows upon them imperial powers to rule the skies and so uplifts them effortlessly among the moving clouds.

As a parallel, in the water I can only think of the golden carp: how swiftly and effortlessly they swim without causing even a ripple! The movements of shoals of golden carp in ponds I consider to be very elegant, though they cannot compare with the flying cranes.

2 ⚜ 2

The only sight that I can recall in the army that even remotely resembles the grace and elegance of these cranes is the war dances by trained soldiers. The dance movements are executed through coordination of sight and sound. The flag waved by the officer standing in the front and the rhythm of the beating drums help the soldiers to coordinate their movements.

These dances performed under the moonlight amidst the fire torches had the effect of raising the martial spirit as well as instilling the discipline of coordinated movements when waging war.

Soldiers watching these dances are also inspired to move with coordinated and disciplined grace. Such movements contrast sharply with the desperate flight of soldiers

Cranes

who were left abandoned when their army had been routed by the enemy.

Nothing is worse for soldiers than to be left to flee in disgrace. So much so that, when confronted with an unexpected defeat, the general must organise an orderly retreat.

Soldiers in disorderly flight are so different from those that withdraw in a disciplined manner. One is like the flight of the migrating cranes and the other a scattering of birds in all directions when frightened.

As a general I too learned and mastered the art of dancing with a sword to the accompaniment of music and sometimes to the recitation of a poem as well. The music that was played to accompany the dance when the army was encamped flowed from the same instruments as used in the palace. But when the army was dispersed out in the field the dance was accompanied by the simple beating of drums or the clapping of hands.

2 ⚔ 3

I doubt if the army ever attained the disciplined grace of the cranes in their majestic flight to the marshlands of the north. Farmers welcome the sight of these cranes returning to their nesting grounds.

The return signalled the passing of winter and the coming of spring. One of the most critical factors for success in war is the morale of the soldiers. Orderly, disciplined movements help soldiers to maintain morale even when withdrawing.

The other mistake often committed by generals is the forced march – an entire army of soldiers being compelled to march across difficult terrain, presumably to secure some advantage or distant objective.

I have heard and seen many cases of troops being harassed by their generals who have issued orders to storm across thick undergrowth in forests or ride over barren mountain ranges or cross hot and dry deserts so as to seize some advantage – an advantage that was often so elusive.

Indeed, these forced marches happened so often that I was able in *The Art of War* to develop a scale of the costs incurred relative to the distance traversed.

Over a distance of just 30 *li* only two-thirds of the army would arrive; over 50 *li* only half would do so and over 100 *li* only a tenth. Not only would soldiers be lost but commanders too: after 50 *li* the commander of the van and at 100 *li* three or more commanders were likely to be captured.

Besides the soldiers and commanders, as I have recounted in *The Art of War*, there would also be the loss of stores when camps were hurriedly abandoned. In addition, heavy equipment, food supplies, fodder and stores may also be lost in the haste.

The weaker troops straggling behind quickly became demoralised and were easy prey to be slaughtered or taken as slaves. In such dire circumstances these soldiers may out of sheer desperation even choose to serve under the banner of the enemy's general!

2 4

I remember vividly the scene of embittered soldiers who told the tale of a forced march. The soldiers were remnants of a division in the army led by a general who wanted to make a hasty journey to the north, towards the marshes.

The general was given strict orders by the commander-in-chief to make a lightning dash across the border with the men. The order was to be there in time for the coming of the cranes. The forced march was made so as to satisfy the whim of this recently appointed commander-in-chief.

He wanted to capture some of these sacred birds of Heaven to appease the king – a pair of cranes as a special gift for the king's fiftieth birthday.

The order was specific: to capture the cranes at *any* cost.

The fact that the marshlands to which the cranes were believed to return for late wintering were located deep inside enemy territory made the prized catches even more attractive – if successful the venture would clearly be a snub to the enemy's defences.

In contrast to the beauty and elegance of the movements of the cranes towards the marshes, the forced march – like many of its kind – caused the division to disintegrate as it continued.

As speed was crucial for the success of the mission

heavy equipment, stores, and all but essential food supplies were to be abandoned.

Stragglers were simply left to trail behind and became easy prey for the enemy. The enemy general quickly learned of the motive for the border invasion from those soldiers who surrendered, having been abandoned in the rush: the division was headed far north for the cranes rather than towards the capital city.

Despite this the usual alert was sounded and city defences mobilised. But the division was far too small to be of any threat to the capital city!

The enemy general did not want to pursue the division as he knew how dangerous and difficult it was to ride through the marshlands during winter in search of cranes.

The marshlands cover such a wide expanse that even if an entire army of the state were despatched some ground would still remain uncovered. Detailed local knowledge was required to find the precise location where the cranes actually winter. This would be difficult to accomplish in a chase.

2 ≡▟≡ 5

The marshes were dangerous ground, as this division quickly found out to their utter dismay.

Now some 50 *li* inside the country, hardly a third of the division remained with the general leading the way forward. Those tottering behind became disgruntled as they suffered the bitingly cold winds of the north and pangs of acute hunger: food supplies had run so low that only pittances could be issued to the rank-and-file. What was left had simply to be conserved for the general and his senior officers. Knowing that they faced certain punishment and possibly even death if they were to return to camp many of those who broke off from the march chose to surrender.

Many withered away from sheer exhaustion. Many more died from unknown causes along the way – possibly sickness contracted from the wetness of the marshlands.

The march slowed its pace in the marshlands due to the simple necessity of removing leeches that stuck to the bodies of men and horses alike. From the loss of blood came debilitation.

After 100 *li* only a fistful of the toughest and most ardent of soldiers were able to keep up the pace for the ride north. Even senior officers fell out, unable to cope with the strain of the ride given their advanced age.

One fell from the ride and never recovered from the impact of the fall. Others rode into the marshes and were drowned when the horses stopped short of entering the icy depths of the waters of the marsh. Some officers were drowned along with their horses when they jumped into marshlands that were unusually deep.

2   6

Even the face of the general – the favourite of the commander-in-chief, one of the most silent but most resolute, respected and feared – told a tale of the march: shrunken, jaw bones showing, wind-beaten, sweat glimmering on the forehead yet eyes still with that steely, cold, determined glare.

The general was one of the rare breed of born commanders who would choose death rather than have an order ignored. With him were his most trusted officers and also the trained bird catcher who specialised in the use of nets and the laying of traps.

These officers had fought countless battles with the general and would follow him anywhere – even into the wilderness. Never did the general anticipate this would be his toughest assignment – the capture of cranes.

Although they were in the thick of the marshlands not a crane was in sight. The general pushed on with the search, surviving on raw roots of plants, fish caught by spearing, frogs – anything that would satisfy hunger.

After thirty or more days, for even the general had lost track of time, the cranes appeared from nowhere in a flock, looking as majestic as ever. Two cranes were caught and the journey back was equally hurried.

Only when the king learned of the loss of men in the division did he realise the folly of the whole episode.

Late evening with autumnal rain. I am taking a break from my studies after poring over different texts: bamboo, bone, tortoise-shell, cloth, wood. Perhaps these thoughts of mine may usefully be reflected here in these memoirs.

I have been pondering over this collection of a variety of classical texts concerning the elements of earth. This I have done many times over in my life.

I never tire of doing it again. As long as I live I shall always seek out any works on the topics that continue to interest me even in my old age:

- the cyclical nature of water;
- metals hidden beneath the ground;
- the eclipses of the moon and sun;
- the places where ice falls from a clear sky;
- the mountains where fire burns eternally;
- hot water springs on mountain tops;
- incidences of earthquakes;
- deep hidden valleys;
- unusually rich soils;
- places where there are seas of sand;
- sunken caves larger than palaces;
- powerful mysterious winds able to lift up homes, chariots, horses;
- lakes deep and wide where strange dragon-like animals live;
- strange plants in forests that trap animals for their food;
- sudden appearances and disappearances of stars;

and so on.

Such readings are necessarily a part of the life of a strategist – of one who, as I do, seeks to understand the Way of Heaven and Earth.

A master strategist is able to go beyond the immediate to perceive things that are afar and foresee events long before they happen.

Heaven and Earth

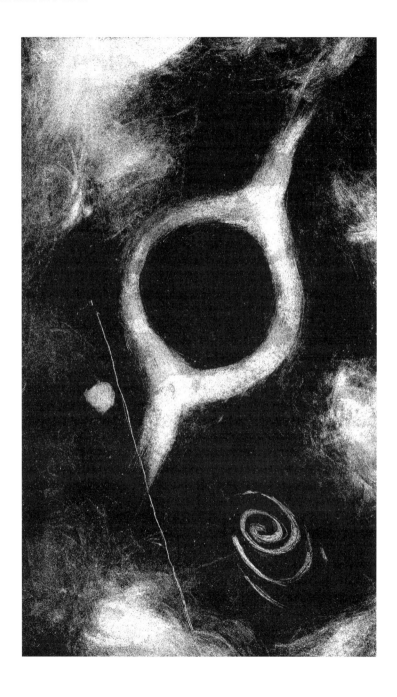

These records of military episodes, carved on tortoise-shells and shoulder-blades of sheep and bulls, contain for me the past follies of warriors; generals who failed when they were on the verge of success by putting too much reliance on the endurance and bravery of their soldiers.

Some failed because they did not adapt their strategy to conform with the conditions of the ground. One general drove his men on to invade a distant capital despite being warned of an impending calamity likely to befall the city. Indeed the general was duly informed of the possibility of earth tremors, but was not in the least deterred.

A local guide from the capital city had personally warned the general of destruction reaching catastrophic proportions. There were already tell-tale signs of the coming earthquake – the animals began to behave strangely.

And as I see from these etchings, many of his soldiers, warhorses, chariots, archers, banner-bearers and officers were crushed between blocks of land mass. Others are shown desperately trying to escape the closing (or widening?) cracks in the land.

If only the general had simply waited, he would have taken an entire city in ruins without any resistance!

3 ▰ 3

There was a record on another tortoise-shell which, despite its antiquity, had enthralled me when I was still active as a general.

I could make out that the author wanted to convey through his inscriptions and drawings a scene of warriors being hopelessly trapped in a mountainous impasse.

The army locked in the impasse became the target for an avalanche of rocks, stones, spears, arrows, fires and boiling water from the enemy situated high above.

The image of this crushing defeat on what seemed to be a rather formidable army affected me deeply. So I emphasised in *The Art of War* how such defiles are plainly hazardous.

Such a situation is made worse because the army is unable to reply: the enemy are stationed so high up and the sides of the mountains as pictured are simply too steep for the soldiers to climb.

I have used this ploy often enough to claim some mastery of it. I found from my extensive experience of waging war that the greater the numerical strength of the opposing army the more likely the general to be prepared to take the risk of pushing his men through these devious, 'short-cut' paths.

The general often realises only too late that the larger the army, the worse the consequences. In the pandemonium soldiers, chariots, officers, archers, banner-bearers simply squeeze each other breathless trying to beat a path out of the tortuously narrow pass, at some points of which no more than five soldiers could pass along at any one time.

For once trapped there is simply no possibility of quick escape. Indeed the casualties are just as likely to be due to the falling rubble as to the resulting stampede by fellow soldiers.

3 ▆ 4

There is another record that appealed to me as a strategist. The lines of the picture are blurred due to its great antiquity. They show military camps, warriors on warhorses, carts and footsoldiers engulfed by rushing waters. The inscriptions that remain visible suggest this to be the outcome of a secret stratagem.

I have yet to devise a stratagem using water as a weapon to effectively crush the enemy. It must, however, be a possible defensive ploy, especially when the enemy troops are completely unfamiliar with the terrain.

One idea may be to lure the enemy troops to entrench themselves by setting up camps on a vulnerable site towards the end of winter. With the breaking of spring and with water gushing forth from so many places, it should be possible to direct the flow to the enemy's camp-site.

If such a ploy worked, then the enemy would surely be caught in a dilemma not unlike that shown on these etchings.

Alternatively, depending on where the enemy encamp themselves, it may also be possible to redirect the flow of the river so as to inundate the enemy by surprise.

As water is a necessity for survival, when attacking the enemy's capital I would often, as a general, consider strategies to deny the enemy their regular supply of water by damming the flow to the city.

On humanitarian grounds I was reluctant to poison the water. Also such a strategy is short-sighted, for when the capital finally collapses the water may – depending on the type and extent of poisoning – remain undrinkable for years.

3 ▦ 5

What is most intriguing for me is this piece of carving, where an army is shown to be pelted by icy stones falling from an empty sky!

Is that possible?

The inscriptions clarify that these are lumpy ice cubes that came crashing from the sky – some the size of a human head! – at the very moment the army was being ordered to slay every member of the population that chose to defy the order to vacate the town.

The incident so shocked the soldiers that they took it seriously as Heaven's total displeasure with their officers and in particular the commander-in-chief. Many chose instead to rebel against the order to massacre the people. As a result there was a reversal in the tide of things, as the record intimated.

As a strategist I must seek to understand what causes such a rare phenomenon – something so out of the ordinary! I must guard against such an eventuality.

3 ▦ 6

The same is true for eclipses of the moon or even the sun: these occurrences tend to unsettle the soldier and often the king!

From this pile of records I am able to ascertain that these eclipses occur at rather regular intervals and may even be predictable.

The strategist should gain as much knowledge as possible concerning the movements of the earth and heavenly bodies, searching for answers to questions such as: When is there likely to be another earthquake? Or eclipse?

And as for weather conditions, he should search for charts and records that can inform these:

- the rain: heavy or light and how regular?
- the wind: direction, strength and timing of changes;
- the fog: a mist or haze and for how long?
- thunderstorms: intensity and how destructive?
- whirlwinds: where from and what capacity to damage?
- river tides: what level during the lows and highs?
- the moon cycles: full moon when?
- the sun: how scorching? Or just warm?

And thus the enquiring mind of the strategist must go on probing!

3 7

Here is another series of inscriptions on a faded tortoise-shell that I recall reading with intense interest many years ago.

The drawings show a group of soldiers utterly fatigued and shabbily dressed in their uniforms. They seem to be gasping for breath in the thick of foliage.

The text was surprisingly brief: 'An entire army trapped in the maze of a forest.' Perhaps due to my early reading of this record, as a general I had a predilection to use local guides whenever my army moved into unknown and uncharted territory: it is simply terrible to have an entire army trapped in a maze!

Also the local guide was able to tell me about the strange animals that lived in the land. And of foods that are edible – fruits, roots, animals, grains, vegetables – and what to avoid because it is poisonous.

Furthermore, certain specific illnesses are associated with particular places and the local guide should be able to tell us about measures to prevent and cure them.

I have yet to master the art of creating an inescapable maze through the use of growing trees in a specific pattern. But I am certain it is possible to entrap an army through such a stratagem. Thus I would always be alert to that danger when moving troops through a forest.

Not only must the strategist study the ground that is immediately visible; he must look at what lies beneath it.

Before me is yet another bone (a bull's shoulder-blade) with an inscription which shows clearly a lesson to be gained by strategists: a tribe being totally annihilated by another.

The victor had mastered the art of using metals from below the ground to forge new weapons. Though barely visible I could with some imagination 'see' what the engraver wanted to convey: the prevalence of metal weapons over wood and sharp-edged stones.

The most striking portrayal is of swords simply slicing through sticks. Other figures showed curved sharp-edged, metal-tipped spears penetrating through wooden shields and piercing the hearts of fallen men.

So I learn from these records some recent lessons, though most old and yet others very ancient – from time immemorial.

263

4 ▬🗡▬ 1

Dark clouds just outside the window!

I seemed to be hearing the murmurings of Heaven: now and then the distant howling of winds. The blinding light flashed out of black clouds. I held my breath: thunder, lightning. In quick succession. Again thunder, then lightning. And then a silence that was so pervasive.

The darkness brought by the clouds seemed to permeate the air. In the background winds were already bending the trees and yet I felt inside me a deep sense of stillness and quietness – despite the external tumult.

It has always been like this for me. I may have been in the thick of battle – blood spilling everywhere, arrows flying about, spears spinning through the air, cries of agony and death that seemed to reach out to Heaven – and still I could stand there watching and be undisturbed.

My mind remained entirely focused on the war as it evolved. Now the tension was released, with the rain pouring down in torrents. I sat there simply gazing.

For how long?

I knew not, for I must have fallen into a deep slumber. When I awoke the scene was so different.

The clouds left as mysteriously as they came. There was the welcome presence of the autumnal sun: mild, alluring, non-intrusive, calm and delightful. Peace resumed on the outside but evidence of recent uproar was written all over the floor of my study, strewn with memoirs engraved on bamboo strips.

Despite the falling rain there remained a faint scent of smoke. The lightning must have started a forest fire below. My thoughts began to stray into the past on matters of strategy.

For me smoke always had that effect: reminiscences of the past, especially lessons on strategy drawn from wars just fought, began their magical play on my mind. Perhaps this was habitual.

Immediately after the war I would always assemble my officers to review the aftermath of any fighting – in the midst of all the destruction, carnage, smoke, dead bodies, spoils.

Smoke had had for me an evocative role, stirring in me images of war, and this has seemed even more enhanced as I

264

have lived out the remaining years in this retreat up the mountains. As a general I was always in search of some eternal standards of performance for the soldiers to emulate. Men must imbibe the spirit of nature so as to be nourished and transformed by it.

But how?

4 ⚍ 2

By constantly meditating on the details of the qualities that I shall elaborate here. Masters of the various schools of martial arts have developed techniques of fighting based on long years of studying certain animals.

265

I know for instance a martial arts instructor who has evolved a sequence of bodily strokes resembling those of a tiger: its daring, fierceness, power, speed and sharpness – it is as if the spirit of the tiger has entered his person. A pugilist from afar who had spent his life studying the movements of cranes was able to evolve a style of fighting akin to that of the bird.

I was told by my men in the army that many more animals had been studied by other pugilists, including the monkey and even the snake. The movements of these animals helped the pugilists conceptualise the fighting strokes that may be imitable.

In a way, the animals served as benchmarks for these pugilists: the agility of the monkey, the ferocity of the tiger, the elegance of the crane and so on.

In the same manner the soldiers of an army also required models of performance by which to compare themselves and thus aspire to. So when I was posed the question by the king:

'What qualities distinguish an army as one that is legendary?'

I replied, as I had also written in *The Art of War* as follows:

- swift as the wind
- majestic like the forest
- firm or still as the mountain

- ferocious like the roaring fire
- powerful as the thunderbolt.

I could give examples for each of these qualities that may be said to some extent to have been attained in the past.

4 3

Wind. I once led a group of some one hundred men in the dead of a summer night across the grasslands. Only the stars shone brightly – surprisingly I did not feel the presence of the moon. The winds howled endlessly on these plains.

We were headed towards the capital city with the wind blowing strongly behind, pushing us on. As part of the route we had to pass through an isolated town that now stood right in front of us. And there was urgency in the matter at hand – to be in time to receive the royal command to lead a contingent.

I decided to just storm through the heart of the town rather than pause there for a rest. The winds were even stronger when we were nearer the town. The pounding of the hoofs of our horses thundered as we rode along the lanes. The paths that wound through the town were dry and sandy, yet stony. As we rode we stirred up so much dust that these dust clouds lingered on as traces of the path we took.

Next morning, as I was later told, the villagers all exclaimed that ghost soldiers must have swept through the town: for nobody saw any soldier despite the thundering sounds of horses and the columns of clouds that had been stirred up. To the villagers we rode like winds, winding through the lanes.

4 4

Forest. I was commanded by the king to lead an army to defend the border against further invasion by nomads from the north. No expenses were to be spared to ensure this expedition was to turn out to be a resounding success.

As I assembled the troops, I inspected them thoroughly, insisting on rectifying even the little details that constitute smart and proper military dress: uniforms that were discoloured, caps that did not quite fit, old banners, worn-out shoes and so on – these were all changed.

All the weaponry was inspected too: spears, halberds, arrows, swords, axes – tested, polished, varnished, oiled, cleaned or whatever to ensure that smartness of a well-disciplined army.

So when the army finally marched out of the capital city it was such a sight to behold: the people gasped for breath as they watched the display of an army in their march to the border.

The soldiers in their march – with banners flying, riding upright on horses, well-coordinated movements, and spears sparkling in the sunlight – were described as nothing less than majestic. The nomads too were smitten with fear by such a majestic display of force.

For the army was instructed to demonstrate their disciplined power before the eyes of these nomads: charging in coordinated formations, brandishing their polished swords and shouting in concert '*Sha, sha, sha!*' ('Kill, kill, kill!'), drilling with their spears sparkling under the sunlight and so on.

Many of the nomads chose to withdraw from the border for they had never seen an army that is nearly as majestic as the forest standing in the background. Their numbers dwindled; indeed, the chief of the nomads chose to pay me tributes as commander-in-chief and promised never to cause any harm to the villagers.

4 ⚌ 5

Mountain. Firmness or stillness is another desirable attribute for the army to acquire. Difficult as it is in defence to remain firm, yet this is the very quality that may convince an enemy to discontinue their onslaught or even to withdraw from their planned attack.

I remember the occasion when my own army headquarters, entrenched on the side of a mountain, came under threat of a direct attack. I was then away leading the main force in assaulting an enemy city. I immediately asked the messenger to return to the base camp with this written command to the officer – someone I had long known and trusted:

Stillness

"Do not be worried that ten times ten thousand are attacking our ten thousand. Fly high all my banners even though I may not be present. Deploy all the men in an all-night vigil: burn fires to make it seem as if the entire main force is inside the camp. Knowing the enemy's general well, I expect him to launch a surprise late-night assault on arrival – impress the enemy with your stillness."

As it was later told to me the scheme worked. The 100,000 troops, led by the general, made their way to the base camp. He was shocked to see the camp so brightly lit up with fires burning sky high so late into the night. Also, when the archers were moved within striking distance of the camp, the general was very surprised to see so many banners of General Sun Tzu flying in the strong winds – and the guards behind the wooden barriers looked ready but also remained passive and calm. The general held back the archers.

He stood there and stared with utter disbelief at what was before him – his anticipation was a poorly lit, desolate camp where a few armed soldiers might be found dozing off as they stood guard. Instead, before his eyes was a camp that appeared to be firmly rooted to the mountain, and more surprisingly, prepared not just for defence but a decisive battle.

The general became suspicious ('Was this all a trap?' he must have asked himself as he stood there). Then he decided to act cautiously and immediately withdrew his entire army during early dawn – and an army ten times bigger had been repelled!

4 ▆▆▆ 6

Fire. I had seen and heard how fires roar and devour the trees in the forest with such ferocity. What the barbaric tribes from the far north lack in strategy they often make up for by their ferociousness when destroying entire villages, towns and even cities. They could through their ferocious might flatten an entire city.

So it was often the case that a city that the southerners had taken centuries to build was destroyed by the northerners in a single day! They struck such deep fear in the hearts of those under attack that some were literally shocked to death.

Thunderbolt. As I ride through the stormy weather in the wide open plains I am always amazed at how lightning can flash so suddenly out of ominously dark clouds that hang in the sky. I would ask my officers and soldiers to emulate the thunderbolt when striking at enemy troops.

The bolt of lightning that flashes out is so blinding to the eyes! The thunder that follows is so terrifying to the ears! If only an army could strike likewise! So when laying an ambush for enemy troops I try to lure the enemy to a place where my soldiers can strike them down at lightning speed and, through charging downhill, gain such momentum as to resemble the thunderbolt.

5 ⚏ 1

A sleepless night. In the shadowy room the tiny light flickered. I got out of bed to do something that had long been overdue: change the wick. On putting out the light a pitch darkness settled on the room: I was awakened to how crucial fire is to man.

Through the device of fire man overcame the limitations that darkness would have imposed. I ought to resume my writings to discuss more extensively the theme of how a strategist should overcome human limitations through exercising his ingenuity, as he overcame the constraint of not being able to see in the dark through the use of a small fire.

There are so many uses of fire in wars besides illumination: destruction, signals, warnings. Indeed, in some situations the use of fire is fundamental to winning – in destroying the enemy's provisions, weaponry or defences.

Many examples may be cited of how other constraints imposed by the human condition may be resolved through the innovative use of what is available to us.

5 ⚏ 2

Thus without our ancients who mastered the art of taming horses we would still be unable to be *swift as the wind* in moving soldiers across the grasslands.

No general of repute would disagree about the significant role of warhorses – horses selected because of their build, strength and toughness to be trained for the conditions of the battle-ground – in successful war efforts.

But not everybody can ride a warhorse. These skills must be acquired through training. Besides initial training, many years of riding are required to master the art of handling a good warhorse. Imagine the majesty of being able to ride these horses, *swift as the wind* and firing piercing arrows from them.

5 ⚏ 3

To enhance the *range* of killing effectiveness warriors of the

Wind and fire

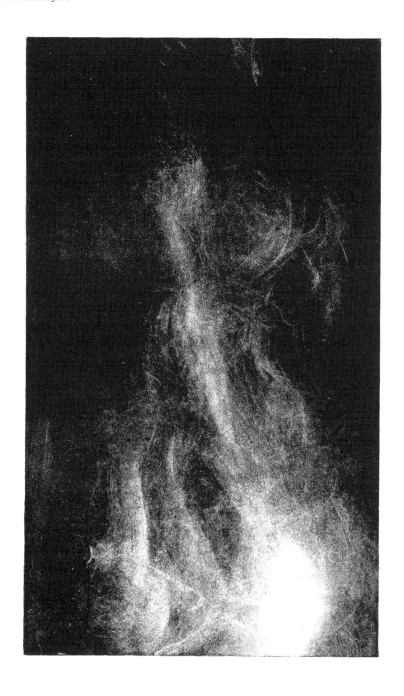

past invented bows and arrows. These, I was told, were first derived from the early crude tools used in the hunting of wild boars.

The bow and arrows that now hang in my study are very dear to me. Over the years I have come to believe in the spirit of the bow and arrow. To fire an arrow with deadly accuracy a man's spirit must be at one with that of the bow and arrow. I engrave on my personal bow and arrows my own mark of *Sun Tzu*.

Every shot of an arrow from my bow has my spirit in it. In that way the arrow is an extension of myself and therefore reaches out to where I intend it to go. I find little difficulty despite my age in hitting whatever target I set my heart on. Archery skills do not seem to diminish with age; indeed, getting old may even enhance them.

In some neighbouring states there is now a tendency towards the professionalisation of archers within the army: soldiers who have mastered the art of archery.

5 ▰ 4

When archery is used in conjunction with fire, by wrapping small oiled cloths at the arrow tips and lighting them before firing, the destructive power is immense. This is especially so in a strong prevailing wind.

I have seen how a city is quickly razed to the ground when soldiers are deployed as archers and rain these fire-arrows in the midst of howling winds.

Another effective combination is that of wheels, horses and a wooden carriage – to provide the chariot. That happened because somebody – probably a strategist – first conceptualised a chariot, etched its outline on shells, built a prototype, and tested and refined its features.

The prevalence of chariots in some armies has led to the formation of a special cavalry division: selected soldiers trained in the art of fighting using chariots. A chariot often has an archer, horse-handler and an officer. The officer is often highly skilled and armed with his personal weapon, such as a special spear, double axe, an unusually heavy halberd, a double broad-edged sword – something unique and rather formidable to wield.

Due to its visible might on the battlefield the cavalry has long been regarded by many as an elite wing of an army.

Besides these instruments of latent destructive power there are devices which, though lacking destructiveness themselves, often contribute in the equally if not more important role of coordinating the different wings or divisions of an army.

For nothing is more disastrous on the battlefield than a discordant movement of troops. It is equally detrimental when each soldier does only what compels him: the brave charge blindly forward and the intimidated and cowardly run away.

So to heighten the fighting spirit of men and yet to control their enthusiasm for action drums are used. Since the voice of the commander-in-chief will be drowned by the din of battle, soldiers skilled in the art of drumming – *bong! bong! bong! bong! bong! bong!* – are deployed to relay specific orders so as to regulate the movement of troops.

Soldiers trained as trumpeters – *tooo! tooo! tooo! tooo! tooo! tooo!* – may also participate. Trumpets are often used to focus or call to attention tens of thousands of soldiers so as to signal the arrival of the commander-in-chief during an inspection of the army.

The waving of a banner of a specific colour – white or red or blue – is often used to relay a signal such as the right time to launch the assault. Or the signal may be given by the use of smoke or fire.

To alert soldiers to return quickly to their army garrison – such as when the enemy forces are amassed outside the city – huge bells on top of walls are sounded: no human voice can reach every niche and corner of a city as they can.

Also the beating of the gong – *tung! tung! tung! tung! tung! tung!* – is used to coordinate the actions of troops. Soldiers already deployed out on the grasslands and involved in the thick of battle may still be controlled through enhanced sounds and/or sights.

Despite (and often because of) its simple design, the hand-held gong (as distinct from its larger version) has many uses in the fluid situation of war. On occasion a certain sector in a long line of an evolving battle may require immediate reinforcement through redeploying surplus soldiers from other sectors – the gong will then be able very quickly to signal to soldiers where to gather themselves to reinforce the weaker positions.

5 🔖 6

In some armies the general may prefer to use differently coloured banners – red, white, blue, green and so on – for the mustering of troops to be put under different commands; there is also the morale aspect to consider in the use of banners or flags.

There is nothing quite so *de*moralising as to see the main banner under which a soldier is commanded being torn down by the enemy, for example, from the main city tower. For many soldiers this signals the likely collapse of the command and imminent defeat.

As the commander-in-chief I was always alert to that possibility. When I was defending a city, the best soldiers would be deployed to keep the command banner flying high.

The Sun Tzu command banner, one of which is now hanging in my study, has never been subject to any indignities by the enemy. On abandoning a major position, my Sun Tzu command banner would be taken down in time before I set out with the army.

Conversely, on attacking a city my best men would be assigned the task of seizing the enemy's command banner, often flying high on the city tower, and replacing it with my own. These soldiers were given very special rewards once the task was done.

I still keep the different command banners that now form my collection of war memorabilia. Each is a reminder that the removal of the symbol of authority in an army – that of the enemy general's command banner – at an early stage of battle often *hastens* the collapse of a city's defence: soldiers take it as a clear signal of an impending defeat.

Some soldiers may take flight; others lose the will to battle on; still others may surrender. In night fighting I would coordinate the mass movement of troops through the use of torches and drums.

Since it takes time for messengers on horseback to relay messages, I developed a system so that I would be alerted of any possible surprise attack by enemies from afar.

I relied on a system of military outposts strategically located on hill-tops or high places. Through the use of black smoke in the day and fire in the night my soldiers were able to forewarn of any impending attack by enemy troops.

5 ⚏ 7

There are many other ways to overcome the limitations that the human condition imposes in waging war.

In order to ram through the heavy city gates a huge tree is felled and a log is obtained. Iron chains are strapped to the log and tens of soldiers then ram the city gates with such momentum that they are forced open.

Devices for war are limited only by the strategist's imagination: the power of an attack may be enhanced in many varied ways.

The latest I heard of is the terrifying use of bulls that between them pull a huge wooden plank set with sharply pointed knives directed outwards. The oiled cloths tied to the tails of the bulls are then ignited. Needless to say the bulls charge with a fury unseen in my days as a warrior. All this is part of a continuing evolution in the art of war.

6 🕮 1

I am experiencing one of the most pleasant summers so far. The conditions are conducive to the bustle of activity in a forest. As usual I am tempted to go for a hunt in the woods.

Had I not seen what I saw happening among the bushes, I would not have turned back so soon to these writings.

An event occurred that made a deep impression on me even though I would agree in the broader scheme of things that such a happening in the jungle – a wolf hunting a rabbit – would pass as rather mundane.

What struck me about the happening most was its direct relevance to strategists. Despite my official retirement from the service of the king I still continue to draw fresh lessons on strategy from my daily encounters.

The scene triggered in my mind an almost immediate recall of what I had written in *The Art of War*.

Now, flashing back, I often use contrasting images to bring out the significance of some of the conditions critical to success in waging war.

6 🕮 2

Thus there is the idea of pitting *rested* troops against an army that is *exhausted*. Of keeping one's own troops in *good order* to fight another in *utter disorder*.

Appearances may, however, be deceptive. The enemy had once thought that my army was too dispersed and disorganised to pose a major threat. But true order or disorder is a state of mind.

It depends ultimately on how tightly organised an army is. So although my troops may be widely scattered over a thousand or more places, if they are still in tight control I should have little difficulty in mustering them for a major offensive. The enemy never thought this possible.

Another example: ensuring *warmly-clothed and well-fed* troops are countering an enemy that is *cold and hungry*. Stratagems and counter-stratagems must be creatively coined to bring this about. The master strategist must be equally alert to the possible stratagems employed by the enemy to bring about the same sharply contrasting conditions – but to his advantage.

Another contrasting condition: to have one's own troops *wait in the field* for an enemy that has been made to *rush from afar*.

The master strategist can quickly see through an enemy's ruse designed to cause unnecessary movements of your own troops. The enemy too prefers to have his soldiers rested.

So the temperament of the general is critical here. For if he is by nature hot-tempered and impetuous, then there is greater likelihood that such ploys will work successfully against him.

Another advantage of a contrast: soldiers in *quiet discipline* lying in readiness for an enemy whose troops are always in *noisy clamour*.

6 3

I see this principle of *contrast* among the animals in their constant struggle for survival: the *rabbit* versus the *wolf*.

The rabbit, which feeds on grasses, is often described as tender, lovely and timid. The wolf, by contrast, is wily, tenacious, and armed with powerful front teeth and sharp claws.

At first appearance, one may consider the rabbit as an easy prey for the wolf: in a pitched battle, there is no question who will emerge the victor.

Despite such differences, the rabbit is not entirely at the mercy of the wolf. The rabbit does seem to have a defensive ploy against the predator.

During these summer days, while camping inside the forest, I often observe the wolf in its hunt for the rabbit. For defence against its predator the rabbit seems to rely on the strategy of digging many deep and narrow burrows.

The network of burrows is the result of the collective burrowing by a family of rabbits. Whenever the wolf (or, when hunting in a pack, wolves) appears, these rabbits hop quickly into narrow openings dug in the ground.

6 ▰ 4

On this occasion I saw a lone, strangely long-bodied (almost the length of my spear), very thin wolf with snow-white fur. The wolf had its long tongue sticking out and was salivating profusely in the heat.

This may have been the Great Northern White Wolf that our ancestors have spoken of with deep veneration – the one that has been said to be able to survive the bitterly cold winds in the icy lands of the far north.

If so this wolf must have strayed too far south for its comfort and have been cut off from its pack: this may perhaps explain why it appeared far too lean, given its body length.

There was a forlorn look on the face of the wolf. Its stalking seemed tired and disorderly. On seeing the well-fed, brown rabbit with snow-white fur underneath and the bright sparkle in its eyes standing neatly on the mound the wolf rushed up to the hilly ground.

The wolf simply found it impossible to keep pace with the rabbit as it hopped about. The rabbit then quickly disappeared into one of the many openings to the underground burrows.

Perhaps due to severe hunger pangs – the rib bones could be seen jutting out of its lean frame – the wolf furiously clawed itself into the hole. But somehow it got stuck!

Desperate but muted whines could be heard as the wolf struggled to wriggle out of earthly bondage. In its haste to satisfy its gnawing hunger it got itself entangled in the burrows of sunken roots of a nearby, enormous tree. Even I had difficulty later in extricating the dead wolf.

So despite the edge the wolf seemed to have over the rabbit – much bigger in size, sharper teeth and claws – still the rabbit prevailed over the wolf.

The rabbit may be said to employ a strategy of avoidance of fighting (hopping about) and luring the enemy (the wolf) into its own familiar terrain (the burrows).

6 ▰ 5

I dug into the burrows to study the interconnections. I was amazed at the intricate pattern of inter-linkages.

Burrows

Could it be that these burrows are the very structures that inspired ancient kings to build such extensive networks of underground tunnels?

It is said that any person who got himself lost in these underground tunnels beneath palaces would simply die of exhaustion; he might die a slow painful death from sheer hunger and thirst.

Skeletons are said to be found in every hidden corner of these tunnels. These are mainly the remains of thieves who believed that priceless treasures could be found in these tunnels.

Are not such dead like the Great Northern White Wolf trapped by the hunger within them – the wolf for food, the thieves for riches?

So should the strategist, when countering a superior fighting force, not do likewise? – lure the enemy into unfamiliar terrain.

Thus if the barbarians in the far north – who are as ruthless and brutal as the wolves – are to be contended with, those living further south should employ an avoidance strategy. Never should they be confronted directly on open ground. Instead, the southerners should lure these northerners to fight deep inside the forests.

Another possibility is for those states familiar with the waterways to use a river as a major divide. The strategy is to entice the northern barbarians to cross the turbulent waters and to confront them there.

Or, as the northerners are unaccustomed to the bumpy rides on the waters, to engage them the moment they have crossed the river. Most of them are likely to suffer from riverborne sicknesses such as vomiting and dizziness.

The stratagem here is to lure the enemy to fight on ground where they are unable to capitalise on their strengths such as their excellent skills of fighting whilst riding on warhorses – *swift as the wind.*

The forest is preferable to open ground for one simple reason: in the thick undergrowth it will be easier to lay booby traps.

6 ⚊⚏⚊ 6

Alternatively, like the rabbit benefiting from the wolf's entrapment in a very narrow burrow, a strategist should exploit the disunity and petty rivalry that is rife among the northern barbarians.

One stratagem will be to alert the neighbouring tribes to capitalise on the opportunity to seize the territory of that tribe which has set out to invade yours.

The invaders will then be forced to withdraw their army once news has arrived that their homeland is now under direct threat of seizure.

You may then follow up with a counter-attack. As the invaders now have to fight on two or more fronts simultaneously, their odds of winning are slim. You may later share the spoils with the neighbouring tribes and thus prevail over them.

That will require, as part of the art of war, mastery of diplomacy. The strategist must configure circumstances that alter the balance of forces in war.

6 ⚊⚏⚊ 7

As I have emphasised, when leading the army in waging war – watch for that opportune moment to strike. So too it is written in my *Art of War*: during the course of a war, depending on what happens, the fighting spirit of the army may be lost and even the courage of the commander-in-chief be diminished.

But success also hinges on knowing when *not* to strike. For example, never take on an enemy that is entrenched on high ground with hills behind them.

Nor fight head-on with an army that remains in an orderly and impressive display – banners flying majestically and contingents of troops in their proper places.

Use stratagems instead to cause disorder and discontent inside the army: lure, divide and frustrate them with hit-and-run tactics – attack their granaries, cut their supply lines, disrupt their communications, use spies to cause dissension and so on.

Attack enemy troops that are feeling *forlorn* and *homesick* with troops in the *keenest fighting spirits* – especially when dawn is breaking.

Again, remember the principle of contrast.

Today time itself seems to have stood still – so still that I begin to wonder if there may indeed be places on earth *where time does not pass.*

For if things could remain unchanged one ought not to age – aging is itself a process of change. There must be some intricate relationship between the flow of time as seen in the *external* changes such as the seasonal cycle and our *internal* aging process. Since all, according to the *Tao,* are aspects of the indivisible One, our body must form an integral part of the cosmos.

So whilst I have made prescriptions for the art of war as a facet of human affairs, war itself must be viewed as a manifestation within the much wider scheme of things, an integral part of an ever-evolving and changing universe.

283

I have just completed reading and reflecting on a *Taoist* text describing the secret dwellings of immortals. Strangely, I found during this period that the sky outside had remained very much the same as before. I remembered the sky as a wide stretch of dull grey with the sun hidden behind some cloudy formations. The sky seemed to have stayed that way – unchanged for the time it took for me to complete reading the *Secret Dwellings of the Immortals.*

Or had another day simply passed by without me even realising? The text was so old that the writings on the bamboo strips were hardly visible even during the daytime, unless one read it close to the fire.

I was so immersed in it – not just reading and reflecting but also meditating, enquiring almost to the point of imploring the author (or authors whom I know not) to reveal the subtler meanings behind the words in the text.

I must have been through the book so many, many times already. Yet every time I unfold these worn bamboo strips I gain new insights.

Since my days as a scholar-general I have found guidance on the art of war through conversing with *Taoist* priests who live up in the hills.

By reflecting deeply on the rare classical texts on *Taoism* that I could lay my hands on I discovered useful insights relevant to the art in waging war.

I see the relevance of emphasising not only the positive aspects – that is the 'do's' – but the negative as well – the 'don'ts' – in waging war. The *yin–yang* thinking is very much engrained in the system of beliefs of the *Taoist* priests that I had come to know personally.

The art of waging war is often perceived as involving the *yang* aspect – the *doing* of things. There also seems more of the *yang* in *The Art of War*. The don'ts, or the *yin* dimension, is however equally important in determining success when waging war.

I have therefore tried to give the *yin* perspective some attention in my writings. Are the 'don'ts' sufficiently emphasised for me to say that the book reflects a balanced 'do's and 'don'ts' approach to the art of war?

I often ask myself this question.

7 ⚏ 3

Some of the 'do' prescriptions contain within them an essentially 'don't' message. For instance, I advocate that when fighting the enemy they should be left an escape route. In other words, *don't* attempt to do battle to the extent of pursuing and completely wiping out the enemy.

But why?

Part of the reason lies in the potential for things to change into their very opposite – this is a characteristic inherent in the system or nature of things.

Fleeing enemies that have been denied of any possibility of escape may resolve to fight to their death. Once that happens enemy soldiers may become stubbornly fearless and vicious.

In the context in which the enemy soldiers are left with no alternative but to fight to the bitter end, there is every possibility that the tide may turn in the enemy's favour.

Indeed, there have been war stories since ancient times of how men, when they have overcome their fears of death, can against all the odds triumph – even in the most adverse circumstances.

So I prescribe: let the enemy keep the escape route, so as to secure victory. To push things to the limit is risky as it may result in much heavier losses than thought likely or even result in defeat. In the fluid situation of war there is always the potential for unexpected reversals. Again: *don't* advance on an enemy who is cornered.

What are some of the don'ts that have found expressions in *The Art of War*? I said in the book – on the art of employing troops – that when the enemy is merely pretending to flee, *don't* give chase. Seeing through a pretence is the hallmark of a master strategist: ask, probe, enquire, test, observe, query – never simply believe. Look for signs that may possibly betray the true intent of an enemy.

Another prescription: *don't* attack the enemy's elite troops. Why battle with the best and demoralise your troops in the process – especially at an early stage of battle?

Avoid it.

7 ▆▆▆ 4

Also: *don't* blindly swallow baits set by the enemy. Here the accumulated skills of a master strategist are truly tested. A deep probing mind is essential.

Here too I see the relevance – though indirectly – of an aspect of *Taoist* philosophy that may be paraphrased simply as 'what *is*, *is not* and what *is not*, *is*'.

What *is* spoken (or written, displayed, shown) *is not* (as may often be the case when a bait is intended) the true purpose and what *is not* spoken (unspoken, hidden) *is*.

Thus when conferring with the enemy, study his facial expressions too. When reading a message from an enemy, enquire about what is left unwritten (unsaid). Act only when a more complete perspective is gained on the issue.

In a painting, the empty unpainted spaces are of equal significance with the painted. Indeed, in some paintings, the empty spaces are of much greater significance than the painted!

So the master artist–strategist studies the painting and tries to reach for the inner conception present in the artist's mind at the time of executing the work.

Similarly the master strategist searches and tries to

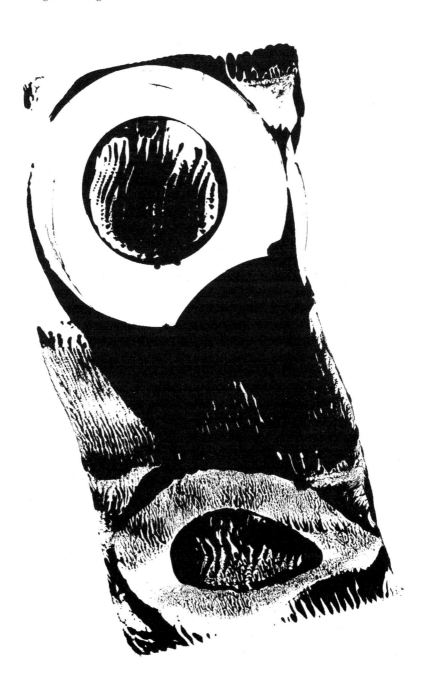

read the strategic intent behind the initiatives (some proffered as baits) of the enemy.

Lastly: *don't* frustrate enemy troops that are homeward bound. Nothing angers and infuses the individual enemy soldier with raw, relentless fighting spirit more than any attempt to thwart his journey home!

Engaging such an enemy is like trying to breach the sea at a time when the tidal waves are surging skywards.

7 ⚌ 5

The *don't* dimension connotes conscious efforts of *non*-doing on the part of the strategist. In the context of war such *non*-doing must be distinguished from merely letting the troops idle away. It implies a capacity on the part of a strategist to hold back from rash or compulsive actions.

There is implicit the justification that more can be gained through *non*-doing than doing. Embedded in *non*-doing is the principle of conservation: avoiding the wasteful dissipation of an army's energy.

Thus if the elite forces of an enemy are engaged rather than avoided the losses sustained are likely to be so substantial as to negate any possible gains.

Some of my own officers mistakenly took such avoidance as indications of cowardice on my part as commander-in-chief.

Such an avoidance strategy had other payoffs that are less immediately obvious. The enemy grew in haughtiness, became less circumspect and were therefore more easily trapped.

It is through quiet contemplation and meditation of *Taoist* works that I grasp the significance of the concept of stillness as a strategy in waging war. Stillness may be interpreted as the *non-doing* in *doing*.

7 ⚌ 6

The alternation of *doing* with *non-doing* is least understood by the warrior-general types who are more doers than thinkers. The process of quietening or 'stilling' thoughts (*non*-thinking) is necessarily an integral part of strategic thinking.

When formulating strategy I often found it useful to allow thoughts generated by strategic thinking to sink into my mind. As an analogy: in cooking things that are hard – nuts gathered from the forest this morning – my wife closes the lid of the pot and lets a small fire burn quietly so that they simmer.

Likewise the hard, knotty problems of strategy in war, that are manifest in me as thoughts, are left in the mind – like the putting of the lid on the pot. Even though my wife may forget about the pot the simmering still goes on.

So deep inside my mind, even though I may not be consciously working and reworking on them, the strategic problems remain. As often happens – after an afternoon nap or a night's sleep – solutions emerge from the mind, reappearing again as thoughts.

All of a sudden, while I may be about to doze off or doing something as unrelated as painting, these ideas spring to my mind. But these processes of the mind which remain hidden or metaphorically beneath the lid are as mysterious as the workings of the cosmos – why is the sky today a dull grey?

There are many *why, how, where, when* and *what* questions for which I am still in search of an answer. Just as mysterious is how time flows or, more precisely, *does time ever stop flowing*? But I do know I ought to stop here.

8

1  1

VERY EARLY DAWN on a day in the middle of summer. I reach out from my bed with sweaty hands for something – bamboo strips, tortoise-shells, pieces of cloth – anything to etch down my dreams before they escape me.

I want to capture in words the power that underlies the images of war as they unfolded in my dream. I must do so before the sun rises.

For like the mist that disperses when the first rays of the sun penetrate through the thick undergrowth of this virgin forest, so do the dreamscapes and dream sequences recede, to be buried deeper and deeper in the recesses of my mind.

The dream scenes are varied and shifting. They are often reminiscent of the past, with the shocking interwoven with the pleasant. Dream sequences are full of surprising twists and turns.

1  2

In this particular dream I recalled the mighty roars of my soldiers shouting '*Sha! ... sha! ... sha!*' ('Kill! ... kill! ... kill!') as they dashed across the bridge crashing into the city whose defences had just fallen, but suddenly the water beneath the bridge mysteriously surged up – something I would never have imagined – tearing up the bridge and drowning my soldiers.

The waters shocked me even more by transforming themselves into giant hands groping for soldiers and pulling them down into the deep. I stood there in the distance as the

Dream

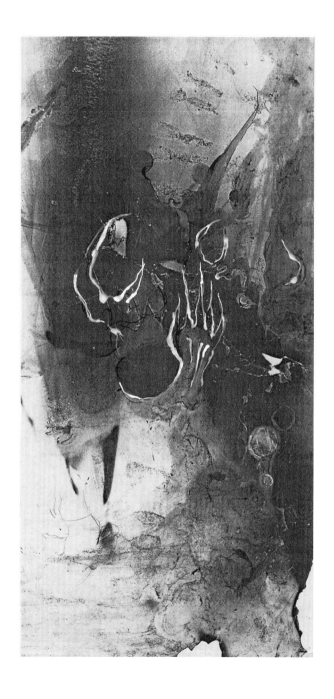

glorious commander-in-chief – helpless, speechless, dumb-founded – and after a period of silence I myself charged forward yelling '*Sha!… sha!… sha!*'

Pearls of sweat streamed down my hot face before the monstrous watery hands withdrew into the waters beneath the bridge. Bodies of dead, bloated soldiers were thrown up into the air and on seeing the swollen faces of my beloved men I was stunned.

And so the dream continued vividly in my mind before I was finally awakened. I wanted to record these dreams so that I could study the frequency of their occurrences and their content.

1 ⚔ 3

I know I have said little about dreams in *The Art of War*: dreaming is by far the most complex process of the mind.

Since wars are such tumultuous events, inevitably those affected by wars – kings, commanders-in-chief, generals, soldiers, prisoners-of-war, common people, city dwellers, the wounded, the lost, the handicapped – often dream during wars.

I have only talked in *The Art of War* about aspects that are more concrete: that the general must utilise what is favourable when formulating plans; or that the general must consider the unfavourable so as to resolve difficulties.

This does not mean, however, that I am denying the role of dreams as a facet of war. Indeed wars may so traumatise a general that there is no escape from the dream processes.

Why do such unexpected transformations emerge in my dreams – water becoming monstrous hands – in a war that I fought and won so dramatically?

Perhaps in part it may be because in dreams my latent fears, that have been consciously suppressed, find their expression when my mind is unconstrained during sleep.

As the commander-in-chief I had nobody with whom I could freely discuss some of the underlying fears and doubts when waging war, so that they appear with ever more vividness and vigour in my dreams.

Thus despite my calm exterior when formulating

strategy, the human instinct, the fear of the unknown, remained very much a part of me.

As I grew older and freer from the direct pressures of the battlefield I became more interested in things that seemed too ethereal to be dealt with in a prescriptive work on the art of war.

But to leave out dreams entirely is to produce a work on war that is only partially complete. Or it may be that I had wracked my brains for far too long and hard on strategic issues such as anticipating the contingencies, and the many 'what ifs', as a result of which these may have been etched deeply into my brain.

So now after all these years these images can still well up in my dreams. Perhaps from niches hidden somewhere inside my brain. Even so, the creativity manifest in the many possible transformations of a war scene that I experienced directly simply astounds me.

The mind of a strategist has to be a creative one. But I had difficulty when young in entrusting the creative side of strategy formulation to the process of dreaming alone. Even now I am still unable to will myself to dream.

There have, however, been several occasions when I did gain from dream inspiration. In creative dreaming, strategic problems that remained insoluble – despite my thinking over them for a considerable period of time (sometimes an entire season) – were solved through flashes of creative insight as a consequence of dreaming.

One such insoluble problem I still remember clearly is how best to reconfigure my small army so as to counter success-fully an invading force – anticipated to be ten times larger than originally thought likely.

That was when I had a dream that seemed unrelated to the problem. In my dream I floated in the clouds and saw below a beautiful landscape. What is most interesting is that in a dreamscape objects often contort themselves.

Thus I found that through mere wishing I could manipulate the landscape in my dream. So by will the valley below bulged skywards to be a hill. I could also divert at will the flow of the river. In my dream I could fly and cut through mountain ranges and even tunnel underground and emerge at the other side of the world.

This dream of landscape continued to be with me for some time. On reflection I must have felt, as commander-in-chief, so constrained by the circumstances in working out stratagems to counter the threat of an enemy attack that the dream came for me as a relief.

In my dreams I was entirely unconstrained. I could mould mountains, rivers, valleys, hills, streams and more. Then one evening as I contorted the landscape of my dream I saw soldiers on the ground. My contortions of the landscape affected the soldiers too.

So when valleys were raised into mountains the soldiers seemed to be thrown completely off balance. When I transformed a little, bluish stream into a mighty, yellowish river I saw soldiers being drowned in the process.

I awoke that morning with the sudden realisation of the need for a detailed survey of the ground. For although I might be outnumbered, the ground, which I remembered as being hilly and heavily forested, favoured those in defence.

So whilst I am unable to contort the ground as I could in my dream, it is possible for me to employ 'unmovable, invisible soldiers' in the landscape.

For nature, too, provides 'soldiers' – the ravine, forests, valley, mountains, narrow passes, hills, waterfalls, wind, rain, thunder, mist, haze, boulders, fires and so on.

Had it not been for the dream, I would not have realised this. As it turned out, by a detailed study of the configuration of the ground, I was able to deploy my soldiers so that the enemy, despite their superior numbers, found it impossible to penetrate.

1 ⚔ 6

I had always been against blind dependence on unfounded superstitions. I preferred to rely on concrete factual information gained through spies when waging war but dreams, despite their mystery and imagery, can still in some rare circumstances be useful.

I recall the time when I was forewarned of an impending, massive attack being instigated by the strategy adviser of an ambitious king from the north-eastern state.

Secret dialogues had already been initiated between kings from two other states – which had then concluded peace treaties with us – as to the day, season, year and detailed contributions by each in launching the attack.

My childhood friend and a citizen of our state happened to discover these documents relating to the secret alliances. He was employed in the administrative service of the general now appointed as commander-in-chief for this secret mission.

His plan to hand me a copied version of the documents failed when his colleague reported his suspicious behaviour to the general. Before he was arrested he committed the details of the plan to memory.

His punishment was death through beheading – to be carried out in the wild, windy plains. On his way to execution he met a priest who sympathised with his cause – wanting to inform me of the secret alliance that had been forged – and the priest instructed him in the secret of how to appear in my dream after his execution.

1 7

This he did.

His head, with blood still dripping, loomed large in my dream. He revealed the details of the military arrangements: on the tenth moon of the new year, the armies of the states were to assemble at the estuary of the two rivers.

The contributions of the two other states were: foot-soldiers each a hundred thousand, soldiers on warhorses ten thousand, and chariots a thousand.

The dream was so realistic that I had no doubt whatsoever that the information was authentic and reliable despite the mode of its communication.

When I woke up I bit my finger and wrote with blood the details on the sheets. I then immediately set about destroying the coalition of these states.

In such dire circumstances dreams may be the only means for the recent dead to communicate with the living. For an enormous distance separates us.

Dreams too have a useful function in the context of war – something which I duly recognise in these writings.

Late evening in the middle of early spring. I have spent my day trying to decipher these inscriptions – many faded – on the underside of this unusually large, heavy, whitish-yellow ancient tortoise-shell.

Inscribed symbols – some obvious and others less so – on the shell reveal interesting patterns. There seems evident a network of winding paths that interlinks a cluster of villages. Or are these towns, or even small cities?

Very intriguing contrasts in the relief are suggested in the landscape. Especially towards the lower edges on what appeared to be the tail-end of the tortoise-shell, the land as depicted appears to be densely criss-crossed by rivers. Or streams?

The confluence of the rivers points to an estuary. When seen from a distance, the villages seemed to fan outward from the estuary as its centre.

This seems to make good intuitive sense. The fertile soil around the estuary means that those who populate these villages would benefit from the easy availability of food – grain, fruit, fish, poultry and animals.

Over time a growing population is likely to lead to a mushrooming of new villages. These villages are likely to fan outwards from the estuary.

What puzzles me especially is the presence of what seems like a mountain immediately north of this central cluster of villages – the symbol is unmistakable: a well-etched cone-shaped mark. Or is it a hill?

Even more intriguing and towards the north-west and north-east of this mountain appear what seem like oval-shaped lakes. The lakes appear to be equidistant from the mountain. Or are they ponds?

Immediately to the north of these two lakes appear to be mountain ranges densely covered by trees. Or are these hilly ranges?

At the upper edges of the shell (on the head side), beyond these mountain ranges lie higher but flatter mountainous plains. Or are these flat lands?

The sketches too reveal that thickly vegetated forest dominates the land beyond this stretch of highland.

2 ⟫⟪ 2

I am struck by the resemblance that this relief map etched on a tortoise-shell bears to the human face!

How?

The estuary – wet – is akin to the mouth.

The mountain near it the nose.

The lakes, one to the north-east and the other the north-west, the eyes.

The mountainous ranges of trees the eyebrows.

The highlands resemble the forehead.

The forest to the 'north' the hair.

I remember the physiognomist who once practised on the side alley near a food stall towards the south of the old capital city. He studied my face very carefully before making his predictions on my future.

In the art of physiognomy as it is practised a person's fortune may be told by studying the contours of his face! Even how oily a specific part of the face is has relevance!

It is like a master strategist able to tell the outcome of wars by studying the deployment of forces on a map as large as this tortoise-shell.

Is it always possible? I often wonder.

2 ⟫⟪ 3

For the strategist a map showing features of the terrain – rivers, passes, mountains, cities and so on – and deployment of the major opposing forces is invaluable for strategic analysis.

Thus I would instruct my officers to draw up these maps before any major engagement with the enemy. Information on the enemy's deployment must be gained through the use of spies.

A commander-in-chief must once have used this tortoise-shell map in waging his wars. For on closer scrutiny there seem to be some secondary etches on the shell. The etchings seem to suggest that the shell map was used for planning major military manoeuvres.

Streams of arrow-like symbols (some only hinted at) are seen on the shell. I have, since possessing this shell, been deeply fascinated by such intricacies. Tracing these arrows and hypothesising the presence of others I am able to decipher the various alternative routes of advance being planned. All these converge on the estuary.

With such a map I should be able to judge the mind of the commander-in-chief. Even though I did not known him personally, from the details on the shell map I can assess his qualities as a strategist.

Clearly this commander-in-chief is a highly cautious, calculating sort of a man – so different from the typical warriors of his day. Indeed, it is only for critical military operations that such a map would be drawn up.

Warriors of the past typically tended to march off to engage the enemy with little forethought as to strategy. Evidently the shell had received far more etches than are now visible on its surface. These may indicate that the commander-in-chief must have used it in his deliberations on strategy with his officers.

Given such detailed inscriptions it may also be possible that he was using the shell map for the purpose of defence rather than attack. The arrows show all the possible routes of advance by the enemy. The commander-in-chief must have surveyed the ground over and over again.

2 ⚔ 4

In waging war I used also to be particular about gaining a superior knowledge of the contours of the land. I would gather impressions of the land that I surveyed. I let these conceptions of the different types of land settle in my mind. Then, having mulled over the strategic implications of the terrain – the spatial relations of one *vis-à-vis* another – I would then use any writing material available to produce an initial sketch.

I would then confirm the relative positions either by taking another trip, or by discussion with people who were more familiar with the area. Then, taking a sheepskin or something as durable, I would map these positions using symbols annotated by words.

By reflecting deeply on the principles of how best to utilise the ground as a weapon against the enemy, I derived some basic rules.

After classifying the ground according to its various categories, I then set about prescribing the appropriate actions to be taken.

Thus in *The Art of War* I laid down the rule for the army never to encamp on low ground nor linger around desolate ground.

Certain grounds, by virtue of their particular configurations, allow no means of escape. These are what I would recognise immediately as 'death grounds' – in such circumstances prepare the soldiers to fight to the bitter end.

On ground that may be said to be 'enclosing', the resourcefulness of the army, officers and commander-in-chief will be severely tested.

Given a map drawn up by an ally, I would scrutinise it to identify grounds that are 'communicating': these are grounds where my army may join forces with allied troops.

2 ⟫📖⟪ 5

My interest in collecting maps – on shells, skins and bones of animals, cloth, wood, bamboo, paper – sprang mainly from my role as a strategist.

These are my treasures which I store with great care. I often rely on an *invisible* map – a map encompassing so wide and large an area that it is simply impossible to sketch on any available material.

Such a map can only be viewed with the mind's eye. The vision of such a map is gained through piecing together – mentally – many different yet interrelated maps.

Despite my extensive collection, there are still stretches of land that remain unmapped. To complete the mental map I need to extrapolate on the basis of what little I learned through simple enquiries.

So over time I have become quite knowledgeable in the geography of places. Indeed, clearly marked out on my mind-map are things that my army should avoid, so that there are, besides grounds never to be contested, roads never to be followed, troops never to be struck, cities never to be attacked.

Besides these maps, I used also to gather as much information as available to draw my own maps of the night skies. For what better guides are there for the movement of troops

Northern Dipper

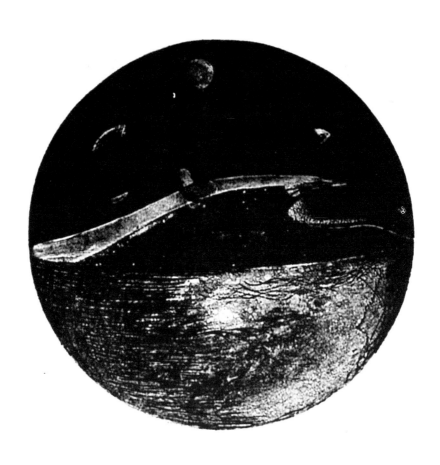

in the sometimes pitch darkness of the night skies than the star constellations?

Once I had to lead the army in a surprise night journey through the plains. We kept our direction northwards because a soldier was able to recognise the Northern Dipper. Since then I have become deeply interested in the study of the stars.

In a clear night sky I can observe the presence of many, many stars. But they may easily be distinguished. The stars vary in degree of brightness and in the frequency of their pulsations.

There are however exceptions, with some displaying constancy in brightness like tiny 'moons'. In studying the night sky it is important to recognise the possible configurations of stars – their spatial interrelationships.

Maps of the ground are significant too because of the spatial relations that these reveal between types of ground: army camp sites, cities, rivers, passes, forests and so on.

Star configurations are given names for their resemblances to earthly creatures – animals like the Great Bear or the Lion and insects such as the Scorpion.

Soothsayers often looked up to the stars when predicting the impending fall of a king, indicated by the dimming and even disappearance of the once bright star associated with him.

The rise of a new king is suggested by the emergence of a new star whose brightness is growing. This is based on the principle of Oneness in *Taoism*: that major earthly events are mirrored in the cosmos.

So those who are skilled in the art of cosmology should accordingly be equally adept at predicting earthly occurrences. Thus wars may be preordained by Heaven, as seen in disturbances manifest in the skies.

Moon and Sun

Today I am glad that I have taken a quick, early morning walk to the very edge of the mountain-side. Peering from the rocky edge through the ever-elusive clouds I saw a sky greatly different from what I had seen for a very, very long time.

It was as if Heaven wanted to entertain me with a visual delight. I was fascinated by the heavenly scene – that of the rounded, fading moon that reminds of past grandeur, appearing alongside the rising, gloriously yellow sun destined to rule the morning sky.

This was totally unexpected as I had long been told and believed that only the sun rules the sky in the day.

My spirits are simply lifted on seeing the majestic beauty of the moon and sun. I feel as if I am transposed into a dream-like world where the impossible suddenly becomes possible.

So many thoughts flashed through my mind and my only regret is that I did not capture these rushes of ideas, images, feelings, emotions, illusions and insights permanently, whether on paper, cloth, bamboo strips or even tortoise-shells, wood or a grass-woven mat.

Now I understand why so many poets and artists find delight in retreating from the city to dwell in isolated mountainous retreats. I could almost sense the gushing of creative energy in my veins.

Inexplicably the scene stirs in me what I thought were long, long buried memories of war – beneath layer upon layer of new impressions, perceptions, reflections, introspections, recollections and so on.

Yet when I sat beside the light – ready to write – before going out for an early walk, such a flow was simply denied to me.

3 ▨ 2

It is almost like in a dream, in which one is simply left to be surprised by what unfolds. In the flood of memories I recall the day many years ago when I was given the imperial order immediately to replace a fellow general.

The general had been shot dead by a stray arrow in a

skirmish fought after several incursions by enemy troops into what was believed to be our territory.

Our base camp in the south-eastern corner of the state was set up along the border. The border was often disputed as it was marked only vaguely by mountainous ranges. The enemy, now reinforced, eyed the base camp as the prize.

I was transferred from a northern frontier city which had earlier been in imminent danger of coming under siege by the barbaric hordes from the distant northern plains.

Now after several crushing defeats – I had led the expeditions against the enemy with the Sun Tzu banners flying high in the winds – we had captured some of their best and mightiest warrior-officers, mostly sons of the several tribal chiefs of the north.

I had personal audience with each of the warrior-officers so captured and treated them with the decorum due to army officers. My philosophy was one of countering barbarism with culture.

I wanted them to see the folly of their attacks when much might still be gained through peaceful negotiations and dialogue.

The warrior-chief who led the barbaric hordes had urgently sought an audience and asked for the quick release of those captured. Many of my own officers and I too suspected that one of those captured must have been his own son.

3 —✝— 3

It was at that very moment that the imperial order came. Its terms made plain how critical the situation was at the south-eastern base camp: no time to be wasted, I was to set off on hearing these orders.

The imperial order also proclaimed the crown prince – a man also highly skilled in the military arts – to be installed immediately as the new commander-in-chief.

The king believed the city to be no longer in any danger as the barbaric hordes had so recently suffered such embarrassing defeats. I was therefore given the more challenging role of the newly appointed commander-in-chief of that key south-eastern military base. I half suspected that the king might secretly have desired that the honour for securing peace be bestowed on the crown prince.

My mission was stoutly to defend this base camp – a major military installation – sited on the forested mountain-side of the south-eastern frontier land.

The king knew of the grave dangers of waging wars on both fronts simultaneously. The crown prince was therefore asked by the king to exact peace from the warrior-chief in exchange for the release of those warrior-officers captured.

I knew too that until peace was secured in the north it was perilous for us to declare war with the south-eastern state. The base camp was on the high but thinly shaded part of this odd-shaped mountain.

3 ▬▬▬ 4

Seen from the distance the mountain has a flat peak but the sides rise sharply up. One of the most trusted officers whom I selected to accompany me for this mission had commanded that the Sun Tzu banner be hung up as high as possible near the entrance to the base camp.

Two freshly-cut, very tall, upright bamboo poles were cut for this purpose. The words 'Sun Tzu' were written in very large, bold characters. By then I was in my forties and had acquired a wide-spread reputation for invincibility.

I was told that even the generals from the neighbouring states held me in awe. My trusted officer intended to exploit that reputation by a display of my presence as commander-in-chief.

Under the blazingly hot summer sun a strong shadow was cast down on the ground at the entrance to the camp. Soldiers lined both sides, standing on guard.

Many days passed and all was quiet during that time. The soldiers however trained and practised their skills inside the camp.

The enemy's presence was strongly felt as they were nearby: columns of dark smoke from their cooking fires rose regularly into the sky. These were clearly visible from my commander-in-chief's camp.

Besides playing the strategy game of Go, which I enjoyed as strategic massaging of my brains, I continued with reading my collection of ancient texts.

Taking a break from these readings, I ventured out of my camp. As I walked I pondered on the true reason why the enemy troops were holding off their assaults on the base camp.

The enemy general had since my arrival held back the troops. I had also noticed the columns of smoke from cooking inside the enemy's camp begin to diminish.

Spies sent by me claimed that some enemy troops had withdrawn. I also learned that the enemy general was simply too shocked on learning of my presence. It seemed, if the accounts of the spies were reliable, that he was under instructions from his king never to engage with me directly in any battle!

3 ▬▬ 5

I then noticed the sharpness of the shadows cast from my banner. I was suddenly struck with an insight – I had just passed the section on how even the sun may be eclipsed in broad daylight.

I searched for these descriptive passages again. This time I read them thoroughly and reflectively:

"The process is gradual but may be frightening to the overly superstitious. Many claimed the Sun was being swallowed by a mighty Invisible Dragon. Gongs were sounded.

The sky still darkened. Slowly day became night. Stars sprang from nowhere out of the sky. Screams and cries were heard from the farmers across the land: farming would be impossible without the Sun.

Even the King knelt to pray.

Generals called forth troops to battle with the Invisible Dragon. Archers shot fire-arrows skyward. Panic seemed to have struck the state. By now drumming, clanging, screaming, shouting, beating, clapping, banging – all to scare away the Invisible Dragon.

What a sight to behold if one had been standing on the city walls!"

I followed closely the passages in the ancient book which describe how to predict an eclipse of the sun. To my surprise such an eclipse might be expected in about ten days' time!

The ancients had warned of the dire consequences of such an event – how even seasoned soldiers would look upon the eclipse of the sun as something shocking and frightening.

I could imagine what would happen if the enemy seized such an opportunity – pitch darkness during the day – to strike the base camp. My soldiers would be thrown into massive disarray.

Alternatively, I could make preparations for a surprise strike deep into the heart of the enemy now encamped in the forest. I was however disinclined to widen the scale of conflict.

I was still worried about whether any lasting settlement would finally be reached in the northern frontier city. Perhaps I ought to have disregarded the imperial order of the king and stayed to seal a peace settlement!

3 🕮 6

It was precisely at that moment that an urgent messenger arrived from the capital city with a fresh imperial order:

"The northern city is in danger of collapse, the northern barbarians have resumed their attacks … the crown prince's life is at stake! General Sun Tzu is to immediately lead an army to save him …"

Although I was shocked by the turn of events I could not possibly leave now. It would be disastrous – both would be lost, the base camp and the city.

The enemy would so easily learn of my immediate departure: they would witness the eclipse of the sun and the missing Sun Tzu banner. The timing could not be worse. The enemy was only beginning their withdrawal!

That is why I prescribed in *The Art of War* that the imperial order may be ignored if the situation in war so demands!

In war the commander-in-chief must decide, depending on the urgency of the situation. Otherwise it would be like what I see now, which is most unusual: the moon and sun both ruling the sky!

4 ⚏ 1

Late in the afternoon on a day a long time after the sighting of the moon and sun in the sky together.

I just felt I ought to continue with capturing my inner thoughts. For this very morning I returned to the same spot, cherishing the hope of delighting myself once again in the visual display: the heavenly vista of both the moon and sun appearing in the sky.

But disappointingly, this was not to be the case. The weather was so changeable that by the time I got there the fog had thickened so that even the sun – often glorious in the early morning – was only weakly and faintly visible.

Dismayed, I returned in a hurry lest the fog should become so thick that it would simply be impossible for me to find the short path back to my little mountain hut.

The sky, despite the earlier morning promise of a clear, bright though windy day, darkened as I hurried through the woods. I did not fear the rain but did not want to be caught wandering amidst these tall trees in the company of roaring thunder and blinding lightning.

Oddly, it was in these circumstances that my mind kept flashing back to the themes that had consumed me so many days before: the eclipsing of the sun and my defiance of the imperial order.

4 ⚏ 2

The imperial order was for me to set out immediately to counter the renewed siege by the northern barbarians on the border city up in the far north so as to rescue the crown prince.

Not that I lacked sympathy for the prince, the favourite son of the king sent north to finalise the arrangements for peace. Having lost so many battles against me – and his son also had been captured – the warrior-chief of the northern barbarians sued for peace.

But I anticipated that if I did go north, this base camp, lying on the south-eastern corner of our state of which I was newly appointed the commander-in-chief by the king, could yet again be the target of vigorous enemy onslaughts.

With the son of the warrior-chief among those of the warrior-officers taken prisoner of war by me as a basis for negotiation and settlement for peace I was surprised by such a sudden adverse turn of events.

The crown prince was sent to relieve me of my northern command so that I could turn my attention to the danger in the south – possible loss of the base camp in disputed ground to the enemy.

As I was told, the enemy intensified their encroachment after the shocking death of the general of our base camp: a stray arrow in a skirmish.

4 ▰ 3

That was the stage in my life as a general when my reputation for military genius was already known far and wide.

It seemed that my arrival had unsettled the enemy very much. They least expected my presence, knowing how involved I was with the war in the north.

The enemy general was someone whom I had defeated in so many encounters that I had simply lost count.

On learning of my presence the general began to rein in his troops ever more tightly. He must have been seeking fresh orders from his king, probably thinking that the strategy should be reassessed in the light of this new twist in development.

Possibly my presence had signalled to him that his northern neighbour (that is, us) had finally prevailed over the barbarians.

It was as if the storm had quietened down: no more skirmishes, night raids, disturbances – not even a whimper.

Before I proceeded north I had to strike fear so deep into the hearts of the enemy here in the south that their withdrawal of forces, now initiated, would be hastened. Yet I must not cause such offence as to enlarge the scale of the conflict. Only then could I turn my attention to the alarming situation in the north.

The enemy troops encamped in the forest had, according to my spies, been preparing to withdraw their main force. Some of the enemy units such as the scouts had already been sent back.

The imperial order from the king of the enemy general, I later learned, was to wait for another opportune moment for seizing the base camp.

4 ⚔ 4

Five days before the anticipated eclipse of the sun I discussed my strategy with my inner circle of most trusted officers.

All agreed that it would be highly dangerous for me to set out on a journey north without first driving deep fear into the hearts and souls of the enemy soldiers.

Since the enemy soldiers were once farmers, they often harboured fears – some bordering on the irrational – of any person vested with divine power over the earth and sky.

For the ex-farmers the sun and the earth had always provided them with a livelihood. Once this engagement was over these soldiers would return to farming again.

I therefore had to take the lead to break this impasse and at the same time intimidate the general and his officers by using the eclipse of the sun.

So I sent a messenger with an invitation to the general that entreated him to a conference to resolve any *future* problems that might arise concerning the border on an amicable basis rather than through pitched battles: the day and time were chosen to coincide with the eclipse of the sun.

I made it plain that we knew of their good intentions to withdraw and thus the conference was planned for those high in command of the armies to meet.

4 ⚔ 5

As I had anticipated, the invitation was accepted almost instantaneously. The general and his entourage arrived at the appointed time.

The enemy general, to the surprise of my own officers, brought along gifts as gestures of goodwill. Apologies were profusely proffered for having caused any misunderstanding. The gifts were in part to atone for the misdeeds of his men that led to the unfortunate killing of our general.

After having being welcomed by my deputy commander-in-chief and magnificently feasted with wine in abundance and entertained with sword dances by women soldiers, the enemy general showed apparent displeasure at my absence; this despite my banner being hung high in the base camp. He thought it could be yet another ruse. Indignant, he questioned my deputy commander-in-chief and insisted on an audience with me personally.

It was only then that the general and his entourage were told that I had been summoned only this morning in a dream to prepare to lead a heavenly war against the mighty, Invisible Dragon.

The general and all his officers gasped in utter disbelief. When told they might witness this for themselves some became visibly awestruck. They were led to the stepped, massive wooden structure upon which the altar rested – with prayer flags, fires, incense, offerings, and so on – that was unveiled at the centre, on the high ground of the base camp.

4 ⚞ 6

All were amazed to find me dressed in priestly robes and wielding the Heavenly Sword. The other soldiers who were dressed in gowns befitting those of my assistants took their positions along the stairs up to the altar.

At that very moment the sky began to darken as the Invisible Dragon appeared to be at work swallowing the sun. I started to chant loudly, reinforced by the echoes of my assistants. The cymbals, drums and gongs were sounded and all present were immersed by eerie feelings of a darkening sky.

In the area surrounding the altar and even as far as the enemy's camps cries of soldiers could be heard – pandemonium seemed inevitable.

I whisked about near the altar and performed a sacred sword dance as my assistants chanted ever more loudly. The whole scene spoke of a massive holy undertaking that tried to evoke the latent powers of heavenly spirits. My sword dance movements became ever more vigorous and it appeared as if I was engaged in a duel with the Invisible Dragon.

The sky darkened even more as only half the sun remained visible. Now, as the ancient text had described, cries, shouts, screams, clangs, gongs, drums, bangs and so on could be heard in an otherwise silent forest.

Stratagem

As the others watched I seemed ever more deeply engrossed in my dance movements. From the corners of my eyes I could see admiration written on the faces of the general and his entourage.

Obviously our dispute now seemed to dissolve into the background and of immediate and common concern was the eclipsing of the sun. The moment then came when the day turned into night and stars sprang up in the sky and even my assistants turned hysterical in their chanting.

These assistants, though dressed in prayer gowns, were actually carefully selected soldiers. They were selected partly for their melodic voices and superb skills in the handling of weapons within enclosed space, but mainly because of their loyalty.

These were precautionary steps taken in case things turned against us. But clearly the looming danger of a sun being swallowed by the Invisible Dragon that confronted us all at that very moment had made the two sides comrades-in-arms.

My voice became high-pitched and I appeared to be as if in a frenzy, invoking heavenly powers to cause the Invisible Dragon to release the sun.

Then in a short moment the sun began to emerge from what seemed like the Invisible Dragon's mouth. The sky then slowly brightened and behold – the sun ruled once again in the blue sky.

The chant and prayers were now over.

The general and his entourage performed a deep kow-tow to me in deep reverence.

4 ⚊▙⚊ 7

As I wandered about in this forest with the winds against my face I could so vividly recall the spellbound faces of the general and his entourage – they looked utterly intimidated by the divine powers that I seemed to be capable of wielding.

I had written in *The Art of War* that one must often intimidate the enemy by causing harm: in this case, no harm was even required. I did it through deep knowledge of the Way of the Heavens.

5 ⚋ 1

Again a day a long time after the sighting of the moon and the sun in the morning sky. On many early dawns now I have been hurrying up this mountain slope.

The desire to recapture those fleeting moments of ecstasy still burned in me: the visual spectacle of moon and sun.

Each time I went up to this vantage point and saw only the sun but not the moon as well I became very disillusioned.

Yet at that instant of experiencing disappointment and a hint of remorse I would be overwhelmed by what rolled before me.

I would become absorbed, drunk and transformed by the unfolding panoramic vision: overflowing mountain ranges below; brushes of distant green in their varying shades; cloudy contortions of every shape imaginable.

I stood in the early morning amidst the all-encompassing quietness on this side of the mountain peak. Yet it dawned on me that this was not merely absolute silence.

For there seemed to be a music-like quality about this mountain quietness permeating the air. In these moments of quiet solitude I became conscious of the rhythm of my breathing – *in, inner, in, out, outer, out, in* and so on. This was but one rhythm.

I was awakened to many unseen rhythms of life teeming below me. In unveiling the unconscious rhythm of my breathing I too became more attuned to the wider rhythms in nature – pouring rain, flowing streams, rustling leaves.

I realised that rhythms must exist in things. One only had to slow down, and unlearn so as to *re*-sense the rhythmic patterns underlying life.

Even for an aging strategist like me there was joy in *re*-uncovering the rhythms of wars past – some so many years back and buried deep in memory. There must, too, be a rhythm peculiar to this mountain that remains for me to uncover.

5 ⚋ 2

The immensity of nature suddenly dawns on me – I am but a tiny speck in the universal scale of things.

A gush of caressing wind as I gazed at the sun and I felt myself gently transposed by its momentum to the ethereal reaches of the sky.

Imagining myself in that ethereality: I, the sun and the moon. I – ever-learning, reflecting, strategic. The sun – ever-ruling, warm, majestic. The moon – ever-elusive, cool, mysterious.

Will I be wearied by the climb only to miss the vista of moon – sun?

I had in *The Art of War* written about the strategy of wearying the enemy by offering them ostensible advantages.

Does nature too weary through promises of the lure of glimpses into peerless ethereal beauty?

I consoled myself that I was still partaking of the delightful atmosphere: fresh air that reinvigorates; coolness of the early dawn – often windy but at times windless; whisperings of the forest.

5 ⬛ 3

Such delights could not by themselves justify the strenuously steep climb up these last eight hundred paces.

Strangely, without being conscious of it, I had been counting and recounting the steps from my hut to the mountain top many times.

The paces and their places I remembered only too well. At the two thousand and first step, if the direct path had been duly followed, one should encounter an old, tall but slight tree.

This tree appeared serene despite the fact that the days of its grandeur were obviously past. On some misty mornings the old tree had a look of stoicism. On others it exuded a quiet charm.

I was drawn to this tree. In my mind's eye I saw images of the old tree across the four seasons. Like portraits of faces captured on paintings: in early spring the sprouting of the young green leaves; in mid-summer the thick foliage of matured leaves; late autumn the scene of falling and fallen leaves; and winter its stark brown nakedness against a spread of white.

This morning I woke up with vivid impressions of my dreamy encounters with the tree. In my dream I floated in the air and tunnelled into the ground.

Afloat I remembered drifting with the air current to rest on top of the tree's canopy of leaves. In a moment I sank through its trunk to the roots. The roots of the tree I remembered were wriggling very slowly in the search for water beneath the ground.

Oh how deep the roots had sunk! I rose again through its roots up the trunk to the top of the tree. Instantaneous glimpses of the tree across the seasons raced before my mind's eye.

5 ▤ 4

The changing seasons are but nature's silent reminders to each of us of our own mortality – the inevitability in the cycle of birth, growth, maturity and decline in old age.

As a strategist I have always been acutely sensitive to the cyclicality inherent in the nature of things. Yet in these very mountains I was told lived some immortals who had freed themselves from cyclicality.

Could there be secrets that remain to be unlocked in this mountain?

Perhaps one endures longer when life has been less burdened by wearisome worries. Weariness saps one of vitality.

Could anything ever be more wearisome than the waging of wars?

I was becoming weary of the daily ritual of embarking on the climb. I had counted so many times that I knew by heart the distance as measured by the paces taken: at least eight thousand give or take a thousand if shorter, more obscure paths were taken.

Sitting here I could even articulate the contour of the path leading to the mountain spot: *out, turn, down, up, up, up, down, turn, up, up, up, more ups* . . . and so on.

The labyrinthine feelings were recaptured inside me again and again as I sought to *complexify* (rather than merely complicate) the journey up and down.

The narrower the paths, the sharper the bends, the more angular the twists and more puzzling the turns, the greater the challenge for my strategic mind to configure the quickest route.

For, though long retired I often regress back to my old self as commander-in-chief. As such I often had to act according to the flow of changing circumstances – configuring ways of evolving lines of battles that had turned difficult.

Or when the defences were in danger of collapse under the weight of the onslaught of enemy troops, I had to find the shortest route of escape into the wilderness.

Such dire situations were fertile ground for giving birth to terse maxims of war – *rout out or be routed*.

5 ▰ 5

These deepening lines on my face capture my growing fondness as I grow older for more and more intricacy, complexity, intrigue.

Depending on the day I could be seen trying out the various routes up the mountain top. I was often tempted to structure a labyrinth out of these forest paths.

From my battle experiences nothing so wearies an army as to be lost in a labyrinth of paths through the forests. I never allowed my army to venture into a labyrinth.

I remember once visiting, as a young commander-in-chief, a labyrinth near the edge of a distant mountain to the far west.

The famed labyrinth was constructed by an ancient master strategist using plants and bushes that bore poisonous fruits. This labyrinth was used to entrap enemy forces.

His home was impossible to find unless one was led there by him personally. It was at the very centre of his labyrinth. The secret key for journeying through the labyrinth I promised never to reveal.

Labyrinth

The code through the labyrinth was far more complex. It had the elements: '*out, turn, down, up, up, up, down, turn, up, up, up, more ups*'. But being a true labyrinth there had to be more intricacy.

Elements added included *how many* of the *lefts*, *straights* and *rights* as qualified by the *befores* and *afters*.

5   6

Those entering without such initiations into the code were doomed to meet their end – slowly yet inevitably.

At the beginning they were certain to become weary, driven more by their own haughtiness, anger, impatience, frustration and desperation.

Next, the food and water supply would become depleted. Their bodies became exhausted as much from rushing about as from stress. Some met instant death through taking bites of fruits and berries.

Then, as acute pangs of hunger and burning thirst became impossible to bear, warhorses would be slaughtered for their meat and blood.

As the days wore on weapons were simply abandoned. With gnawing hunger and burning thirst setting in even the war veteran may find his uniform too burdensome a load for his body.

Many more would die from eating tree-barks and roots. For care was taken by the master strategist when constructing the labyrinth to cultivate as many poisonous plants and shrubs as possible.

Worse things could happen as depravity set in. The hunger-stricken souls salivated at the dead bodies of the poisoned soldiers. Some even took bites of the meatier soldiers in the dead of the night.

Wandering in the labyrinth and having been lost for so many, many days, the once sturdy, disciplined soldiers now appeared almost skeletal and mentally distorted.

The final phase. These soldiers – many the brave, honoured and admired fighting heroes of the kingdom – became mere skeletal rubbish littering the hidden corners of the labyrinth.

5 ⟨⟩ 7

Why am I now back this morning on these memoirs instead of going *out, turn, down, up and up*?

Perhaps through the physical act of writing I can free myself from the haunting spectre of the moon–sun. For in my mind's eye I see the pair so vividly.

And perhaps even more because I was driven by a desire to explore, on these bamboo strips and grass mats, intricate, labyrinthine designs.

6 ▤ 1

An unusually cold winter night. I had decided against taking a stroll. The snow down the path was almost knee-deep. Snowflakes from a jewelled night sky drifted lazily down to the earth.

The moon in her dazzling beauty adorned the star-studded sky. Inexplicably I felt a gentle warmth emanating from the moon. But such warmth if any was quickly dispersed by the iciness of the still cold night air. The breezes if any at all were so gentle that my skin hardly felt their presence.

As I passed through the gate I was reminded again of its disrepair. Stamping my feet and shaking the snowflakes off my grass winter coat I quickly bolted the doors so as not to lose whatever warmth there would be in the room.

To warm myself up I was drawn to repeat the usual ritual. I would stretch out my hands and put them just above the small fire that kept the room alight.

Then I would let the warmth of each hand penetrate into the other by rubbing them vigorously together.

I then blew short, intense bursts of warm, internal bodily air into the small enclave formed by palms clasped together: *hoo! hooo! hoo! hoo! hoo!*

The warmth so generated would then warm my face which had been exposed to the cold. I would press both palms on my face. Following that I would squeeze the fingers of each hand in turn.

As always I would be disinclined to fire the hearth beneath my bed to cope with the chill of a winter's night. That would make the hut too warm for comfort.

6 ▤ 2

I would rather turn my mind to writing my memoirs and recapture my further thoughts and reflections on strategy.

Once I became immersed in these reminiscences on things strategic I seemed almost to forget the cold altogether, even the cold that seemed able to seep into the marrow of my bones.

However I am ready, should the weather, unpredictable as always, take a turn for the worse.

I had a sufficient stock of the best firewood to outlast the entire winter, if not longer. For having long been a strategist I believed in being prepared for the worst scenario.

I had written in *The Art of War* about not assuming that the enemy would not attack, but rather depending on being invincible in battle. So instead of making this assumption, I preferred to be prepared for any possible assault.

When would be the best time to prepare against an enemy?

6 3

The answer may be surprising: the best time would be during peace, indeed when relations between the states are at their most friendly.

Why?

Just like the best time for gathering firewood for use in winter is during the hottest days of summer – then the firewood burns long and deep into the night with the muted crackling sounds: *klizz! clizzz! glizz!*

Thus the facts and figures about a neighbouring state, relevant when engaged in war, are most easily garnered and ascertained when relations are at their warmest.

Here an analogy may be drawn.

Good quality firewood would be most warmly appreciated during the very depths of the winter. Likewise, intelligence about a neighbouring state gathered during times of peace would prove most valuable when relations with that neighbouring state turned cold – so icy cold that war seemed inevitable.

Relations between states are as changeable as the weather. So rather than hope for continued good relations, I would prefer to be ready for the worst eventuality: war.

Thus despite the prevailing peace, with harvests aplenty, the strategist should counsel the king on the need for preparations for war. Granaries should be constructed, underground tunnels dug, secret armouries built, martial skills sharpened, the spy network intensified, strategic thinking cultivated, new weapons invented and so on.

Since time immemorial only one thing has been constant in relations between states – change. So even if one generation did not benefit immediately from such efforts in preparing for war, the subsequent one may.

6 ⟨⟨⟨ 4

But the king must be counselled never to act too rashly. Flames of war should never be ignited lightly, even when relations between states have turned cold.

Like the ritual that I had performed to warm myself, so the king should continue efforts in diplomacy to keep relations between states friendly.

Another analogy may be appropriate.

I had used only the little fire that burned on a tiny wick to warm myself before igniting the crackling fires of the hearth.

The best firewood should be used to heat the hearth only when the night has turned severely cold – such as when the bitter winds of the north howl ceaselessly in the ears.

6 ⟨⟨⟨ 5

Similarly, the king must be cautioned against the very destructiveness inherent in raising the flames of war.

Those flames, once roaring fiercely – the fighting, killing and destroying – would be difficult to quell. Such burning flames of war must be contained – much like the fires in the hearth. If uncontrolled the fires, instead of warming the house, may even destroy it.

An analogy again.

Even if those flames in the hearth were to peter out, the soul of the fire could remain undiminished – smouldering on, quietly emitting heat. Likewise in the aftermath of a war, the ill-feelings aroused would probably linger on for some time.

The room has suddenly become severely cold. Shadows dance in the room as the northern winds are again penetrating the crevices of the door and windows. I hear the beating of my wooden gates gathering momentum: *pah! pah! pahh! pah! pah!* almost in the same rhythm as the chattering of my teeth *cher! cher! cherr! cherrr! cher!*

My body shivers. My hands quiver as I hold the brush.

Ravine roll

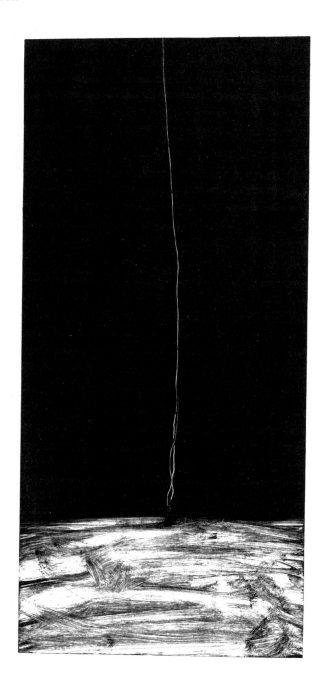

My mind's eye seems to be sharpened. The vision is so clear, as if I were gazing into a pristine pond up in the mountain where every detail of the weed, fish, stone, fly, moss and rock are seen.

6 ▧ 6

In these circumstances memories of the past flood back with incomparable vividness. I recollect the chatter of this same set of teeth as I shivered deep inside the ravines, overgrown with bamboo trees.

This, despite the commander-in-chief's uniform with its fine silk undergarments beneath the armour I wore. I was then young and supposedly full of vigour and vitality.

But this particular ravine, with its stench of rotting, dead wood, was simply too overwhelming for me. Although the two men – one an officer, the other an old soldier, seasoned jungle pathfinders – before me were retching, neither reacted as weakly as I did.

In that moment of bodily fatigue and weakness I even dropped the treasured gift from the king: an imperial sword – the symbol of authority. The imperial sword, that took the blacksmiths many years of toil and sweat, simply slipped out of my right hand that had suddenly turned limp. This alarmed every member of the advance party moving up behind me. Immediately my personal physician rushed to the fore.

The imperial sword plummeted down the steep, moist incline and there was a splash – *plonge!* – which resounded upwards. There must have been a stream meandering way down below. Perhaps due to the hot midsummer the air, despite the height, was uncomfortably humid.

My uniform was all wet on the inside with cold rather than hot sweat. Inside my head things were in an impossible spin. Despite that I tried to hold myself up. My legs too began to tremble.

In ordering the advance party of the imperial army to tear through that mysterious ravine I had acted against the advice of those who had made these peaks their dwellings for many, many generations.

They warned that since time immemorial very few of those who attempted to cut through the thick black bamboo undergrowth in the deep, dark ravines to the other southern side ever came out alive.

And because of their forebodings I decided to lead the vanguard personally. As a precautionary move I had asked the army in the rear to be on a look-out for signs of smoke that might emerge.

That would be a signal that we were in danger. Immediately on seeing me in such a drastically weakened condition the officer raised the fires and generated columns of smoke.

Although the fires were some distance away I felt terribly irritated by the faint smell of smoke. I had consciously to fight the onset of delirium in my mind to recognise my physician. My eyes had to do the pleading: 'Please do what you can and I will be most grateful!'

I remember my pulse being taken. Next I was made to drink an antidote – a bitter liquid – in a small porcelain bottle.

6 ≡▮≡ 7

I still feel indebted to my physician who took the initiative in insisting on following me in this journey. And also to the brave and loyal soldier who risked his life to retrieve for me the imperial sword, which now hangs proudly in this room.

Till this day I can recollect, if not vividly relive, this traumatic episode. How strange that now, with shivering hands, I am recording it in my memoirs!

A day in late summer.

But today the weather is bewildering and it is simply inaccurate to describe the day as being one in summer.

Although it is obviously still summer – autumn is some moons away – yet I experienced a freak snowfall all morning, afternoon and still continuing even now.

This is something altogether unexpected. If it persists, by late evening the snow will accumulate to be at least thumb-deep in the front yard. Yet here in my memoirs – *A day in late summer* – is how I describe the day.

I checked the ancient *Book of Weather* which, interestingly, warned towards the end of the third roll of bamboo strips of such possibilities. It describes such a happening as a wintry day during the summer period. This, according to the *Book of Weather*, is likely to occur when, due to heavenly changes, the bitterly cold winds of the north blow south even during summer.

I am suddenly awakened to how dependent human beings are in their communications, whether written or verbal, on their tendency to classify or group similar things.

Thus a year is divided into seasons – spring, summer, autumn and winter. A day, besides its twelve divisions of time, into morning, afternoon and night.

And in our daily life we describe and so in the process classify things around us: people – male or female; old or young; tall or short.

Indeed in our conversations we implicitly assume the classifiability of things. In respect of food we may classify a dish simply as tasty or not, but there are categories within taste: salt, sweet, bitter, sour, and hot.

Of the entities we classify, the most interesting must be people.

Had it not been for this sudden snowfall I would have journeyed down the mountain. For what remained of the day I had resolved to reflect on the art of war.

Within these bound bamboo strips I would explore the

Book of Weather

deeper and wider aspects of things – especially of personalities as these relate to strategy.

In waging war I also needed astutely to observe and classify things, for example, the nature of land, types of spies and so on.

Today I shall, however, turn to personal characteristics of generals – aspects of personality that may be exploited when waging war. I would map out as comprehensively as possible the personal characteristics and attributes of the opposing general. To draw reliable inferences I would gather as much information as possible about the general from as many diverse sources as were available.

Particularly important were the impressions I gathered from my direct interactions with that particular general.

If that were impossible before battle, I would enquire of reliable people about him: his bosom friends, former officers who had served under him, his close servants, relatives, even his enemies – anybody who had insights into his personality.

I would often try to procure a painting of the general that captured in detail his facial features. Though I am not a physiognomist I still find that a detailed painting of a person at a known age yields useful insights.

Thus, having seen such a painting, I am able to tell from meeting the man if his health has improved or declined drastically. Also if he has aged during that time.

Where possible I would study the writings of the general: the way a person writes may tell me something about him too. His lineage should be enquired into in detail. Such background information is useful in many ways. For example, if the general came from an unknown, poor family then I might be able to tempt him with a life of luxury – something which he may never have enjoyed before. Or if he came from a line of painters and was one himself, I might offer as a gift a priceless painting which he could appreciate. And if he was known to be a womaniser and a lover of wines to offer him beautiful women and jars of wines. In this way he would merrily while away his time and dissipate his energy rather than focus on state or military affairs.

Whatever details are useful should be collected and maintained in a special roll of bamboo strips.

Also, if I could gain details of the year, day and the hour of his birth, that would equally be helpful even though I am not a soothsayer. For from these details those skilled in the art may be able to give a useful reading about him.

7 ░ 3

I recognise that an individual's character and personality may be multi-faceted; therefore such a diversity of sources would help me better frame a picture of the opposing general in my mind.

I do not, however, unless circumstances otherwise dictate, act on mere hypotheses, no matter how probable or reasonable.

For I often want to test these out for myself through experiments in given social or battlefield settings of my own design.

Therefore, if a specific tendency is critical in formulating my strategy, I would set about to reliably confirm that belief. For that I might devise trials so as to allow such a latent tendency in the personality of the general to manifest itself.

Thus I might order a feigned attack just to observe how the general responded with troops under his command. From his responses to my manoeuvres I would try to comprehend more of the person behind the military moves taken.

Many still believe that wars are simply outcomes determined by how big or well-equipped and armed an army is. I do not go along with that notion. I believe that the personal qualities, skills and character of the general in command of these resources also matter.

7 ░ 4

The mind of the general may be said to be the very centre of the army, determining the *whys, whats, hows, wheres and whens* behind the deployment of forces.

I am more likely to triumph if I am able to influence or even control the nerve centre of the army. So I formulate strategies that attack the very roots or heart of the army of my enemy.

I had long observed that in a game of Go, besides skills, personalities have a role in determining the final outcome.

When two opponents are equally matched in technical skills the game of Go is often won by the player able to exploit the weaknesses inherent in the personality of the opposite player.

Thus a player who is technically weaker in Go may counterbalance this through goading his opponent into acting carelessly or rashly.

7 ▦ 5

So I have written in *The Art of War* specifically about the dangerous qualities for a general to have: recklessness, cowardice, quickness of temper, too much sensitivity to honour or too much compassion.

Each of these qualities in the general can be dealt with, as I have mentioned in *The Art of War*.

For the reckless, the stratagem is to anger the general so that he acts on the spur of the moment and thus commits serious strategic errors in deploying his forces. He allows his army to be lured into a prepared killing ground.

For the cowardly general, to chastise, demean and mock him in the presence of his men so that his esteem among them is drastically reduced. For the quick-tempered, to annoy him so as to cause him to act, heedless of the dangers that are before him.

For the honour-bound, to create and propagate slanders about him so that he takes impulsive steps – and in so doing falls into our traps – to act and quash them. To take advantage of his compassionate nature boldly to harass him.

7 ▦ 6

I have implied by such characterisations some polarities in personality: carefulness versus recklessness; bravery versus cowardice; even versus quick of temper in disposition; the thick-skinned versus the honour-bound; and the cruel, hard-hearted versus the compassionate.

But are there ideal qualities in a general? Is it better for a general to be at the other extremes: careful, brave, even-tempered, thick-skinned and hard-hearted? Or is it better to be in the middle?

The ideal characteristic of a general is intelligent and sharp adaptivity (or adaptability) to the changing circumstances. So if the situation demands bravery, the ideal general is brave. Where the situation demands quick decisive responses, the general so reacts. If a strategic advantage is to be gained by dramatically venting the temper, the general is able to do so without any hesitation. Should it be advantageous strategically to defend one's honour, the general does so without question. And the general shows true compassion if there are strategic gains from showering kindness.

This capability of a general to appear as a person that is able to defy classification is truly a strategic asset: lack of constancy, unpredictability, unforeseeability, inscrutability and uncertainty.

Like the chameleon in the jungle whose skin changes colour depending on the tree on which it rests, the true character of the ideal general is beyond simple classification.

Like today's entry in my memoirs, *A day in late summer*, the ideal general is full of surprises and impossible to predict.

9

1  1

A night in late winter.
Quietness.
Thin crescent moon afloat in the sky.
Stillness.
Stars sparkling.
Windless.

I was inspired to climb to the thatched roof of my hut simply to relax on top of it. Lying with my back on the roof I gaze with ecstasy at the jewelled night sky – as I had always delighted in doing since the early days of my youth.

One of the exquisite gifts or treats of nature for mortal souls is to have a special wintry night like this to enjoy.

As in the past my mind seems intoxicated by the all-encompassing, boundless, mysterious beauty – the enveloping darkness, the *hissing, twitting* and *teeting* in the forest that enhances the deeper mysteries of nature.

In the days when I was so much younger I would fantasise about the future. The immense sweep of the terrain in its varying formations would roll before my eyes: sometimes green, other times snow-clad, often silvery riverlands, occasional mudlands, marshlands, mountains and so on.

Army upon army sweeping across the vast terrain. Sometimes the army moved with terrifying speed, flags fluttering – green, blue, brown and various hues. At other times, it was a majestic flow of troops that flashed across my young mind.

Zizz!

Now in my declining old age the past keeps on flashing back to me, again and again in a seemingly endless stream of consciousness. Sunk deep within me – where precisely I cannot fathom; I only know that they exist – are memories that keep flooding back.

Strangely, however, it is not the bloody, forlorn scenes of wars that dominate my recollections tonight, but simple characters etched in the ancient, classic style that loom large in my mind. It is these that have again ignited my interest in recording today in the memoirs.

I relived those rare exclusive moments of sheer ecstasy that I had experienced as a young man on first reading these ancient scholarly classics on war.

I was fortunate to be born into a family which sought for and kept such priceless works of the long distant past. And where the originals could not be had copies would be made, where possible etched on tortoise-shells and shoulder-bones – at whatever price it took to acquire a masterpiece.

These are truly treasures – timeless works on the art of strategy which I was fortunate, at least for some time, to be able to study quietly.

For in those works the secrets of how to use *invisible* (some may say *heavenly*) *soldiers – that is whatever nature provides* – are so well encoded that deep insights are only realised after long reflection on the contents.

I felt remorseful that these works, which inspired my own thoughts as reflected in *The Art of War*, etched on shoulder-bones of goats (or sheep and cows) and tortoise- (possibly also turtle-) shells, were consumed in the roaring flames.

Fires of war, started by the enemy, raged quickly through the city during an attack in the deep of the night when I was away.

Fires are fires.

So despite my absence, the sound of fire, that took away my collection of the *Works of the Yellow Emperor* on the 'art of strategy', remained recorded in my memory – zIZz! zIZz! zZiZzzz! zIZz! zIZz! zZiZzzz! zZiZzzz! zIZz! – as I imagined it to be.

For the mighty yellow flames – as told by those who had lived through the painful agony of witnessing the destruction – seemed like an emperor in terrible anger.

Nothing could stop the tall flames.

The annihilation was total. Nothing of use or value remained in the aftermath. Despite long strenuous efforts by my soldiers in combing the ruins of the city the divine *Works of the Yellow Emperor* were never found.

No trace.

I knew it would simply be impossible for the *Works*, when burnt to ashes, ever to be restored.

Staring at my own fire, that dances on this tiny wick as I record the flow of thoughts, I wonder if the burning of these very *Works* – consumed so totally and quickly in the flames of war – might not have been predestined.

Had the Yellow Emperor, dwelling in ethereality, foreseen the changing times?

For certainly these are times marked by unprecedented outbreaks of war.

1   4

It was this that set me on to writing *The Art of War*. What I truly regret is the loss of the deep insights of the Yellow Emperor in the art of war, sharpened possibly through countless battles and the loss of many, many human lives.

I was moved to write *The Art of War*, *not* so that more lives would be lost in the flames of war, but for the very opposite reason: so wars may be waged without needless loss of human life.

Some of my friends consoled me on the loss by remarking that perhaps the Yellow Emperor himself, now abiding on the other ethereal shore, had wanted to retrieve his *Works* for his own study! And fires are the only means by which what belongs to the living may be conveyed to those on the other side.

The Yellow Emperor drew useful distinctions on types

of landscape, and gave specific instructions on how, given each terrain-type, to position one's forces in readiness for battle.

These prescriptions unveiled for me the extent of his mastery of the art of war so long ago – so many, many, many years ago.

Yet his guiding principles are as relevant to us today in waging war, despite the evolution of warring techniques, as they were all that time ago.

1 🔖 5

So I cited the Yellow Emperor when I wrote *The Art of War* on what to do when battling on the different types of ground: flat, marshy, mountainous and riverside.

But I completed the writings only after I had been successful in applying his principles in many pitched battles. Thus I took seriously his counsel to position the army on flat terrain where military deployment is easy.

I took to heart too his other advice: ensure that from where the army stands with the battleground in the front the ground to the back and sides should be at a much higher level, preferably very high.

For I found through battle experience that such a con-figuration allowed the army total flexibility in the transition between attack and defence.

How many human lives were saved by my adherence to the Yellow Emperor's warning to cross marshy land quickly!

For these circumstances spelt hidden danger. A division of enemy troops from the far south who, unknowing, hid in the rotting marshlands, were later all found to be dead.

These bodies, floating in the marshes, were killed not by weapons but by the evil air, so it was said. For not a single wound was to be found; only faces turned pale.

Another general I knew had his men encamped near these marshlands, only to find them very sickly after a few nights of sojourn there.

Like fighting on flat land, the strategic positioning of an army is critical when wars are to be waged in the marshlands: be near the grass and water with the trees behind.

1 ⚎ 6

From flat land to marshland and then to river land the Yellow Emperor had given clear and specific instructions. These I recalled from what I had committed to memory as recorded in the *Works of the Yellow Emperor*.

As he had instructed, whenever I crossed a river I would hurry the army to move to some distance away from it.

So too when attacking an enemy that is in the middle of making its way across the river: according to the Yellow Emperor strike only when one half of the enemy forces has crossed to the other side.

Also he cautioned: never counter the enemy head on at places that are simply too close to the water.

For the mountainous areas the Yellow Emperor also had his prescriptions for encamping and fighting: camp on sites facing the sunny side and attack downhill. And never ascend while attacking.

1 ⚎ 7

What I had hoped to do in *The Art of War* was to present the essential principles in waging war. What the Yellow Emperor had learned through the wars he fought I too emphasised.

The fire before me is glittering happily away. In its glitter little does it realise that many years before it took away from me one of my treasures: *Works of the Yellow Emperor*.

If not for the quiet time up on the roof I might have just let all these thoughts of the past be buried beneath layer upon layer of memories. But then, had it not been for the fire, I might not have been driven to write *The Art of War*!

A day in the anticipation of the transition from summer to autumn.

Again I am moved to get off the bed and return to my memoirs on a theme that engulfs me. I feel the compulsion to write these thoughts down more completely than many years ago.

This may perhaps be due to my living almost in isolation. The rush of inner thoughts is the more acutely felt. Consequently the greater the inner pressure to express them.

Or it may be that as I grow older I become more and more concerned with reaching out to posterity.

Transition.

I have always been sensitive to critical moments of transition as experienced in life: dark to bright, low to high, wet to dry, weak to strong, slow to fast, light to heavy, peace to war, loss to victory.

As a strategist I would try to be alert to these turning points in transitions. The day would rise and fall (as I shall explain later) and I remained ever sensitive to the flow of time in that change.

I often try to sharpen my sensitivity to the *turn* of things in the process of change. The idea is to hold on to that very moment as the transition occurs.

Even in watching the sunrise and sunset my mind is attuned to that very moment in time when *day* is *night* and *night* is *day*.

Or another way of describing that instant: *what is,* is not *and simultaneously* what is not, *is.* Besides transition I am alert also to the *increasing–decreasing* tendency in the nature of things.

Thus even as I sit here reflecting and writing from early dawn the *day* tendencies are growing stronger (*increasing*) as time passes. Correspondingly the *night* influences are becoming weaker and weaker (*decreasing*).

So after the morning has broken the *day* tendency *increases* and becomes ever stronger. The pinnacle is reached at the very instant when the sun rests vertically in the sky right above the roof.

Then the *day* tendency begins to *decrease*, slowly and

Transition

almost imperceptibly. Thus even though the sun remains bright the decline has already begun.

In the night this *increase–decrease* tendency is being repeated too. After midnight, despite the surrounding pitch darkness, things are beginning to turn towards day.

2 ⚏ 2

I observe the things around me. The more I reflect the more I find this *day–night* cycle of change inherent in many other things of everyday life.

Mastery of everyday skills seems to depend on one's innate talent or more likely innate capabilities to catch that moment of change.

Thus the adept farmer is one who studies changes in the sky and causes the *Book of Weather* to be compiled. For farmers must determine the ideal moment for sowing the seeds.

The fishermen who venture out in to the seas, I was told, also study the night sky and compile their own *Book of Tides*. The fishermen are interested in the ideal time for setting their boats to sea.

Among those who cook, those who have mastered the skills may be distinguished by their ability to *seize* that very moment from those incapable of doing so. For example, in steaming, the master cook is able to tell – having seen the raw fish and the fires under the stove – the exact moment a steamed fish is ideal for dinner.

2 ⚏ 3

So it must also be for the strategist who has mastered the deeper secrets of the art of war. However, the skills of the strategist are far more intricate and complex in that the onus on him is extremely heavy.

For the lives of an entire state may hinge on a major strategic manoeuvre by him. Also he must be sensitive not only to just one aspect but a *multi*plicity of changes.

Some changes, like the ground, are visible – although what lies beneath the ground is often not – other changes, such as the morale of the men, are invisible.

I alluded when writing *The Art of War* to aspects of transition in the ground: low to high and shady to sunlit – for very good reasons.

A strategist must be alert to possible dangers at that moment of *necessary* transition of ground. Thus when there are urgent mass movements of people – troops accompanied by young children, women and old men – the strategist must be especially alert to possible changes of ground.

I have in mind those grounds where enemy troops are likely to take advantage to launch attacks. Where the army alone is involved I would avoid short cuts that are between heights.

Enemy troops prefer to attack from a height downwards rather than from below. So a path that cuts through two hills provides ideal ground for an ambush.

Also there are dangers when an army dwells too long in shady areas. For without the curative and nourishing rays of the sun many soldiers in the army might become prone to a multitude of diseases.

So as I moved along with the troops my mind was always alert to transitions apparent on the ground. I would say to myself when planning ahead as I moved with the army:

"The ground we have been traversing is changing now from the largely sunlit to being mainly in the shade; I must ensure that the men have sufficient sun to remain healthy."

Or from the top of a hill I would study the ground ahead and my mind would work thus:

"To cross quickly over to the other side I ought to take that direct path. The path is clearly visible from here. But somewhere in the distance it seems to plunge down (low ground!) and rather steeply even though it rises again (high ground).

'I must send my élite troops forward to ferret out any enemy soldiers who may lie in wait on both high sides of the path – particularly where it sinks so deeply down."

So I would be alert when on the move to the changes on the ground. I would try to anticipate these changes, and remember the view I had while on a hill.

I truly envy the eagle, which has such a sweeping view

of the land from being so high in the air. But the transition of ground is not the only factor I must be sensitive to as a strategist.

2 ▰ 4

I would also monitor the enthusiasm of men to do battle. Before leaving the city gates, their enthusiasm to fight, spurred by the cheers of the crowd, would reach exalted heights but after long, weary marches over dull terrain – the rolling, seemingly perpetual grasslands – the martial spirit would begin to wane.

So as a strategist I would ensure that the will to fight with gritted teeth stayed with the men. Throughout the journey I therefore scheduled activities to enliven them.

Also I had talks with the men so as to remind them of the lofty ideals that they were fighting for: to rid the homeland of dangers.

The morale of men is also linked to other things such as adequacy of such basics as rest, food and water.

The weaponry skills of the soldiers must remain honed. Boredom that seeps into the minds of soldiers, whether through passivity or inaction, is a factor to be countered.

So even during a long march or with men guarding a distant outpost I would often hold simple contests in archery, riding or any essential military skills (scaling wooden ladders) among the men. Such contests sustain the competitive as well as collaborative spirits, if held between divisions of the army. Although I would have liked to maintain the momentum of the march these factors must never be neglected.

More important to the strategist is to grasp intuitively that *decisive* moment in a battle as it unfolds, when an uncertain outcome turns towards victory.

As I write this passage I recollect vividly the moving images of war. I remember wars which were won when the army was able to seize that decisive moment in forcing a victory against all the odds.

I also recall those wars lost when the decisive moment passed into the hands of the enemy.

Just as the inspiration and hope of winning in men engaged in the fighting may rise and grow in brightness, there is too every possibility that they may fall and sink into darkness.

Before every battle the *will* of each and every man in the army to fight and win must be stirred up.

The commander-in-chief who excels in battle is the one who, when overseeing the battlefield, is always alert to changes in these feelings – no matter how subtle – as the battle evolves.

I would always avoid, whenever possible, a long indecisive battle, in which the spirits of men may be utterly worn out.

When men become wearied and tired of war – in their eyes you see a longing for a return to peace – even the best of generals may not be able to reignite the old flames and enthusiasm.

Timing.

Through redeployment or by deploying standby forces the commander-in-chief may seize that decisive moment to prevail irretrievably over the enemy.

Thus if a crack is made in the seemingly impenetrable lines of the enemy forces then the commander-in-chief ought to seize that opportunity – pile on fresh forces – to turn the tide of battle.

Conversely when a crack appears in our lines immediate action must be taken to shore it up. Otherwise, if the opposing commander-in-chief is able to drive a thin wedge through it, this may in turn become a decisive moment for the enemy!

For that is the moment when the morale of the enemy forces and their will to win would *increase* whilst yours – though imperceptibly at the beginning – would *decrease*.

Oh the fate of a war – its ebbs and flows! Perhaps I should have called what I have just completed '*A day in transition*'.

Otherwise an ordinary autumn day. Lightning. Flashes! More flashes! Ever more flashes of the blinding heavenly light across the darkened sky!

I have taken a journey down from my hut. Some days have passed since I left my mountain abode. I have already gathered what I needed from the town.

I have been longing for the quietness up in the mountains. So I have decided to cut the journey short. It is only midday, but I have chosen to reside in this inn – desolate on the outskirts on a wind-swept grassy plain.

I smell danger.

This is no ordinary thunderstorm. The clouds are so strangely convoluted. From above they look ready to engulf all below.

Lightning.

The lightning fans out like the roots of a thousand-year-old ginseng plant – those that grow in the northern wilderness.

The lightning seems to stretch out from the top of the sky, reaching down to the earth. The speed so much faster than if I had unfurled a roll of bamboo strips vertically.

Split seconds from first making its appearance the lightning then streams downwards, darting towards the sides as well.

At the edges the lightning resembles tiny ginseng roots that search for water. But what a display of power!

As a strategist I recall the sudden thrust of a thousand sharp-edged glittering spears. A pause. Then,

ROars.

How frighteningly deafening these cosmic roars! Louder than a thousand large war drums struck in unison. How the land itself seems to have thundered! It shakes more than if ten thousand hoofs of warhorses had rumbled through the grass plain outside.

Lightning.
Thundering roars.
Lightning.

345

Lightning

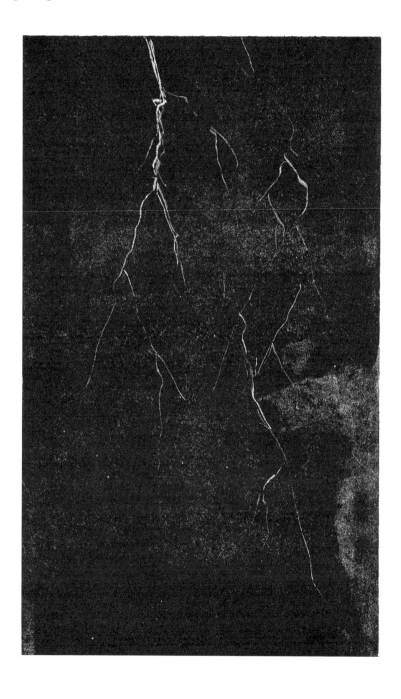

Thundering roars.
Lightning.
Thundering roars.
And on it goes.
Then silence reigns.

3 ≡📖≡ 2

Now all is so mysteriously quiet. Stillness emerges – suddenly even the winds seem to have lost their vigour. The room had become darker.

I had to ask the lady inn-keeper who, incidentally, was endowed with great beauty, for some more oil, wick and fire.

The lady had a peach-shaped face with a moon-like glow and elegant manners. Seeing me startled, an old man with flowing silvery white hair, she said simply,

"No danger, you are inside now. This inn, though it may look ramshackle, is sturdy. It has stood here for more years than anybody could ever remember. Do continue with your writing."

Her face so calm and unperturbed as she spoke in a smooth, pleasant, melodic voice.

I was stunned less by the flashes and roars than by the omnipotence of the Divine. I did not want to tell her of my dream whose verification I was then awaiting – the pouring rain. She left me alone to resume my work.

3 ≡📖≡ 3

I had had the dream while in the town. I had eaten a very full and heavy meal of my favourite foods before the strange encounter in the dream.

A figure, with a deep echoing voice, which said that he was the heavenly rain general of the locality then appeared before me. I cannot now recollect his face exactly but I re-member vividly the luminous yet darkened aura of blue that surrounded him.

Ah yes!

The appearance of the figure in my dream was of a cottony form – much like the clouds now above these skies –

though the outline of his shape was akin to human. His voice had a booming resonance. He said these echoing words:

"*Sun Tzu*" – surprisingly he knew my name – "*As you set out on the journey back to the mountain, beware of unusually stormy weather. There is an inn along the route in which you could stay to wait for the storm to subside. I will do what I can so that your journey is not unduly delayed.*"

Yet the weather so far had been quite fine! The heavenly rain general even knew of my work, saying thus:

"*Perhaps you may want to reflect on your* Art of War *whilst waiting for the storm to subside.*"

I did not then think much more of it. I attributed the dream partly to my earlier visits to a temple for the worship of the Rain and Thunder God. I had enjoyed my conversations with the old priests there – men of my age.

I had made my offerings of fruits and flowers to the heavenly altar. Perhaps the paintings of the heavenly patrons left a deep impression on me. I then thought that to be the cause of the dream.

But today my feelings are entirely different. I had been foretold of the storm and it is unfolding right before my very eyes. That visit by the heavenly rain general must have been real!

3 ▦ 4

I sensed danger and suspense in the atmosphere outside. Despite the quiet I felt as if a battle is about to be waged by those cosmic forces!

The calm was agonising.

Suddenly the pelting rains came – *da! da! da! da! da! da! da!* in such rapid succession – like ten thousand arrows striking the inn's doors, windows, roofs and so on.

Immediately I knew the dream had come true. And now I am ever more inclined to reflect on the heavenly aspects of my *Art of War*. Yes, I did indeed refer to those heavenly matters.

I hold in awe what I see as heavenly entrapments –
impossible for men to overcome – in earthly situations: the
heavenly wells, heavenly prisons, heavenly nets, heavenly
traps and heavenly cracks. These are dangers to be avoided.
The wise strategist is always on constant lookout so that these
may be avoided by his own army.

I remember warning in *The Art of War* of dangers inherent in other situations: when the enemy is deliberately
lying low, or is clamouring for battle yet does not appear.
There is every likelihood that the enemy wants to take advantage of the ground against you.

In waging war, however, the strategist will utilise these
heavenly contexts or dangerous situations to his best advantage in battling against the enemy.

349

The idea, as already prescribed in *The Art of War* is to
suck the enemy forces irresistibly into any of these heavenly
wells, heavenly prisons, heavenly nets, heavenly traps and
heavenly cracks and other dangerous places.

These places are such that, once the enemy was trapped
inside, would spell its untimely end. Like mountains strewn
with unwieldy undergrowth and narrow passes across steep,
uncompromising cliffs, they mean only danger to the uninitiated.

In these places spies and ambushes are often found, as
they are too in places such as deep valleys or ponds or lakes,
often thick with underwater plants.

3 ☰☰☰ 5

The torrents of rain fell ceaselessly. Sitting where I was I
could hear the rushing of rainwater from the thatched roof of
the inn. I threw open the windows and stretched my hands to
touch the downpouring rains. These rains were unusually
thick, so I saw an almost sheet-like image.

In my mind's eye was the image of tens of thousands
upon tens of thousands of swords raining down from the sky. I
pinched myself to make sure that I was not dreaming.

I was worried that with these rains the grass plain
would be flooded. And as if she read my thoughts the lady
appeared with some cooked food, saying:

"Sun Tzu, there is no need for you to worry. The rain will not pour for long enough to create floods. Have some buns and noodles."

Though I must have eaten such food many thousands of times I found the hot buns and noodles unusually delicious. I almost exclaimed to the lady that these must be heavenly foods when she disappeared.

3 ⬛ 6

The rain had made me think more about dreams.

Are dreams another facet of reality that we live through while we sleep?

In other words, are they a kind of double life which we do not remember?

Whilst I am inclined not to rely on the supernatural when waging war as a commander-in-chief – just too much is at stake – I cannot help as I grow older becoming less and less sceptical. The transition between reality and dream is interesting.

Are dreams just wilful imaginings? Is there a division between the concrete realities I am indeed experiencing when awake and the elusive fleeting nature of dreams? Do I dream every night? If so, why am I unable to recollect these dreams?

And even if I do remember the specific contents of a dream, the memory is often partial. Such remembrances fade so quickly as the day dawns. These questions continue to plague me in old age.

The rain did stop by late afternoon, as the lady predicted. Strangely, the path seemed clear of rainwater.

How did she know all that beforehand?

Thanking her profusely for the food, I offered to pay for the half-day stay at the inn. But yet another pleasant surprise – she refused payment, saying that the inn only charges if the guest stays overnight.

We bade each other goodbye and I assured her that I would long remember her very warm hospitality. Recording this in my memoirs is my way of keeping it for eternity.

3 ▰ 7

Epilogue.

Some years later when my friend – a fervent scholar but an unbeliever in the supernatural – read these pages he said something that truly shocked me. For he said,

"You must have written this out of sheer imagination. For there has never been any such inn along the route that you took. I grew up in the town. Nobody has ever seen any inn!"

I knew better than to argue. It is not surprising to me now why the lady was such a wondrous beauty – she must have been divine.

Or was it indeed my imagination?

4 ▨ 1

A day of yellow luminous clouds arising from the horizon. What a sight to behold! I am still on my way back to my mountain hut, having left the inn.

I have sidetracked to this wayside stall near a little village. Nobody else is here except me and the stall-keeper.

Since the time when the heavenly rain general appeared in my dream I have not had any more of these dreams.

So whether dreaming is truly a transition to another reality, I have no means of ascertaining. But the idea still intrigues me now as it did then. Perhaps I was then too tired to recall any dream even if I did have one.

It is the distant clouds that stir me to draw out my writing implements. I am reminded of the cloud-like appearance of the heavenly rain general.

Out of the bundles I take a smooth roll of bamboo strips nicely bound together. They are pleasing to the touch.

Seeing the clouds mushrooming in the sky has caused me to recollect past memories in waging war.

Not a few generals I knew tended to rely on the soothsayers for predicting what would be the next phase or move of the enemy in the war.

I would rather sharpen my skills in the reading of signs that often indicate the intentions or impending actions of the enemy.

This morning's clouds have reminded me of my habit of studying the patterns of dust clouds. Not for predictions, but as signs of what may possibly come.

4 ▨ 2

Dust....Dust.....Dust.

I am intrigued by dust thrown up into the air as soldiers on horseback journey across different lands.

For from what is dust – the tiny hardly visible bits of things that rise to the air – constituted?

I had read as many records of past wars as are known to be available. As I traversed these old battlefields I often wondered to myself:

"Could some of these particles of dust in the clouds be the very last traces of the many soldiers killed in past wars, perhaps some thousands and thousands of years ago?

For instead of leaving the dead lying about with the stench of their rotting bodies filling the air, the commander-in-chief often ordered that these bodies be burnt, a practice that must be as old as war itself.

Such measures are implemented to avoid the spread of diseases from often maggoty bodies. Open wounds attract flies. Also animals are prone to feed on these bodies.

The sights of these discarded and dismembered bodies – the bits and pieces (fingers, eyeballs, ears, legs, hands, tongues and so on) – strewn about on the battlefields is equally demoralising for the soldiers.

Can you imagine the feelings of soldiers on seeing the eyes of their once comrade-in-arms being pecked by a bird of prey?

Others, more perceptive, may be so disturbed by these sights that they begin to question the very meaninglessness and futility of such large-scale murder.

Some sane, loyal and disciplined but inexperienced soldiers, on seeing the panorama of human carcasses, may suffer severe emotional breakdown. Some may become mad and remain irretrievably so.

4 ▬▬ 3

On one occasion I remember the dead bodies – our own soldiers and the enemy's too – piled up many times the height of a city wall.

As I stood by the mountain of human carnage and debris I was overcome by very deep feelings of remorse – this huge mountain of dead soldiers. Tears filled my eyes as I stood there simply staring into this monument of war. And these feelings of mine found their expression in *The Art of War*.

Indeed, a reader who had studied and grasped the deeper significance of *The Art of War* would have understood my purpose in writing the book: I wrote it so that generals may, through strategy, avoid having to burn mass after mass of human remains.

353

Violence past

The fires burned for days on this mountain of carnage –
of cut, bruised, battered, pierced, shot, sliced, disembodied,
bitten, pecked, torn human bodies and the pieces of this and
that.

The columns of smoke from that carnage were seen to
rise high into the sky. Strangely, shortly after the burning,
dark clouds began to hover over the place.

As if Heaven also wept, very light rain began to fall.
Soldiers who stood on guard claimed that the rain that
dripped on to their lips tasted much like human tears.

I recollect how my men first reported seeing 'dust' over these
very grounds, 'in patches'. I knew, therefore, that according
to *The Art of War*, the enemy had encamped.

I had sent many warnings to the enemy to evacuate
these lands. But to my utter dismay I never heard what I had
hoped: 'of birds about the camp site' which would have
signalled that the enemy had abandoned camp.

The enemy stood their ground till I was given the
imperial order to march against them. That was all before the
long pitched battle that was finally waged for the supremacy
of these grounds – long considered grounds that belonged to
our ancestors.

Patterns in the dust clouds are a means through which I
gain information about the enemy. Now, with these dark
columns rising so high in the sky, I am certain that the enemy
on their side of the border would also have guessed that a
major tragedy had happened – one involving many many
lives.

Is any ground anywhere on earth worth that many lives?

4 ≡📖 5

I had written too in *The Art of War* in detail about using this
technique of dust observation. Some of my scouts who oper-
ated at the very edge of battle acted as my eyes and ears. Over
time many had themselves become experts in the reading of
signs.

Thus whenever I saw my scout dashing to headquarters I would anticipate that he, though panting, would burst out in staccato,

"*Commander-in-Chief Sun Tzu* ... (pause to catch his breath) ... *dust seen spurting* ... *in straight columns* ... *high in the air* ...*"

And if he was a seasoned scout, he would add, after having calmed down,

"*I put my ears* ... *to the ground* ... *The sounds were unmistakable. It had to be the enemy's chariots* ..."

Or another scout would be up there confirming this by reporting that '*even the trees were seen as if to be moving too* ...".

That meant, as was explained in *The Art of War*, that the enemy was advancing strongly. I would then have to respond quickly – with *lightning* speed – as success depended on how fast we could mobilise our forces.

I would call for an immediate conference of all relevant personnel: the commanders, generals, officers of special forces and more if necessary.

Indeed, the very reason for mastery in reading signs is to reap the advantages of being able to take early action.

Thus no matter how involved I might be in entertaining guests or whatever, the scouts had *priority* status to report to me personally. Indeed I had even delayed a conference with the king when a scout sought immediate audience.

Had the sighting been that of 'dust that hung low but widespread' then the scout would have inferred the approach of infantry troops.

But if the dust were seen to be 'rising but scattered' then a different conclusion would be likely – probably the enemy bringing in their firewood.

4 ▰ 6

The ability to read signs is of paramount importance to the strategist: a hallmark of one who is a true master. For through these signs, the master strategist may act early to avert any impending calamity that may befall the army.

Thus when I was leading an army through a forest, I was able to discern a pattern in the *obstacles* that dotted the increasingly thick undergrowth we encountered along a specific route.

Consequently I ordered the army to take another route of advance. Had I ignored these early signs the army may well have been entrapped by even more difficult obstacles set up by the enemy. I had trained myself to be alert to the movement of things – no matter how innocuous these may appear – especially the *sudden* and *unexpected*.

So surprise movements up in the sky and on and about the land would often arouse my suspicions. When I was on the road with the army I was always on the lookout.

Thus when I saw the rising of birds in the distance I would signal to my scouts quickly to check that out. For there was every possibility that the enemy was ahead, secretly waiting in ambush. When wild animals were startled and darted about I immediately became wary and asked myself:

"Could the enemy be on the verge of launching a surprise attack on us?"

4 ▬▬ 7

I have written about many things in *The Art of War*. The aspects of war I have discussed here – dust clouds – may seem trivial but the technique is fundamental in waging any war.

The art of anticipating from visible signs is so basic that I doubt any commander-in-chief could ever ignore these matters.

The yellowish hue has now given way to something darker. I should resume my journey back.

5 ▰ 1

Very early morning – possibly still starlit outside – deep in the wintry season. I remember that only last night the moon was thinly visible, like the sharp edge of a curved knife.

I was awakened by the cries of the wind. These cries, some of which sounded human, seemed to be embedded in the howling of the wind: winds that blew in from a northerly direction. Winds that could make their icy presence strongly felt even when I was sleeping inside the hut.

The room seemed as if it was transformed into an invisible whirlpool of currents. I could feel the icy currents in the air as they whirled round and round the room.

With my hand outstretched, I felt as if the winds were curving round my fingers, as if my hands were being dipped into a stream of icy water.

I rubbed my eyes and stared around me. All the windows were tightly shut. Such winds as these were truly remarkable – like invisible soldiers penetrating through little crevices of city walls.

Awake, I lay on the bed and listened quietly to the cries of the winds. These voices reverberated in my ears as I stilled myself to concentrate.

5 ▰ 2

As I concentrated in the dark, unlit room I could hear not simply a litany of noisy cries but also voices in the dark.

Though my body and mind ached for a return to some restorative sleep these voices seemed to want to be heard.

In the tussle inside my mind I was left dangling and afloat in this divide; my mind was somewhere between widely awake and sunk in deep sleep.

Militarily it was akin to being under strict orders to contain an undeclared war between ill-defined borders – in the meantime solutions to these border problems were being sought through diplomacy.

But this divide, which ought to be familiar enough – I must have passed over it every night as I crossed from wide wakefulness to deep sleep – seemed less familiar the longer I lingered.

It was as though I stood on a plank of wood that linked two great mountain plains, and the plank was slowly beginning to sink into the chasm.

The pull on each side to go back suddenly stopped. I floated down into an abyss that seemed to be situated at times inside and at other times outside my mind.

I was able to decipher in the continued howls of the winds, among the various voices, sharp cries reminiscent of soldiers I had known.

Some shot by arrows: *'Ahhh!'*, some leading the charge forward, *'Shaaa!'*, some scream to frighten, *'Yahhh!'*, some agonizing in pain, *'Awww!'*, some panting badly, *'Hooo!'* Some reminded me of the fluttering of banners, *'Pah! pahhh! pahhhhh!'*

As I continued to float down into the abyss human voices instead of just *'Ahhh!'*, *'Shaaa!'*, *'Yahhh!'*, *'Awww!'*, *'Hooo!'* became more and more distinct.

5 ▰ 3

I could even hear distinct voices that spoke. In a moment indistinct faces emerged out of the darkness of the abyss as I floated downwards.

In my mind's eye, as far as I could recall, I saw – *is it a dream or is it not?* – blank and featureless faces: no eyes, eyebrows, hair, noses, ears.

Only lips that seemed to be moving but making no sound. Their spoken words were drowned in the litany of oceanic noises. Slowly I could feel myself descend more and more deeply into the abyss.

As that happened the oceanic noises too seemed to recede into the background. Then the featureless faces became more distinct in my mind's eye: I began to be able to put a name to a face and later to more faces.

It was strange that as I became more able to recognise the faint features of one specific person his face too became more distinct.

Besides that, his voice, instead of uttering incoherent sounds, came to be heard ever more clearly and distinctly.

Through observing the movements of his lips I could make out what he was uttering. Even though I tried to focus

Mystery

my attention solely on him, there surrounded me not just one but several faces.

All these faces cried out for attention. Yet if I continued in my efforts to concentrate on him and him alone the others became less and less distinct, and finally melted into the background.

In an instant these other faces and their voices merged with the mass of an indistinct whirr of noises.

5 4

Yes!

I could recognise this person. He once sought an audience with the king and me ostensibly to negotiate for peace. He must have been dead for many years now.

As he spoke I realised he had an added metallic quality to his voice as he intoned:

"Sun Tzu, how could you see through our secret scheme to deceive your King? Tell me, as I have always been puzzled. Did my own men betray me? For my commander-in-chief put me to death after my return. Now that is all in the past, please enlighten me. For years I have been waiting for this moment to reach you."

I do not remember speaking out loud but it seemed he could hear my thoughts. All that had happened in the years before instantaneously flashed back into my mind.

The story, simply told, was that I became suspicious of his true intentions after he made a verbal slip. He came to our capital city as a representative from a neighbouring state seeking an audience with our king and me.

His visit, he professed in his own words, which I clearly remember, was to negotiate 'for a long and ever-lasting peace'. I could sense that he already had deception in his mind.

I could sense a total lack of sincerity in what he was trying to put forward. He seemed surprised by our gesture to see him immediately.

I had long expected those who hungered for peace to come with a certain demeanour and composure. I found words could not express what I could intuitively perceive.

Nevertheless, he could not hide his lie. His behaviour spoke a lie. Perhaps our readiness to confront him with our very own peace terms took him by surprise.

He had expected days of deliberation on his proposals before being received. I had convinced the king that a peace proposal coming at this stage of the war was rather odd.

So we decided on an immediate meeting so as to put him to the test. Instead of showing true joy, he seemed a little confused by so quick a response.

I had arranged for him to leave the capital city immediately so that he could convey the good news of our substantive acceptance of the peace proposals.

He erred, however, in repeatedly requesting permission to extend his stay in the capital city: he wanted to visit a distant relative.

We then suspected that what he truly wanted was time. The peace terms advanced were nothing but a ploy to slow down the pace of the fighting that was still raging.

We saw through his ruse and did nothing to lessen the fighting. His own commander-in-chief needed time to reinforce his army after having suffered unanticipated and severe losses.

So we quickly set him on his homeward journey. I only learned later that he was murdered by the trusted aides of the commander-in-chief: death by strangling.

His commander-in-chief suspected from his early return that he might have colluded with us.

5 ⚓ 5

Confronted by him, in this dream-like state, I found I had absolutely nothing to fear or hide. It was his own folly to have coined a stratagem that failed to work.

Every strategist has to take that sort of risk. His face slowly faded into obscurity as my thoughts on these matters emerged. Then I felt myself floating gently upwards in the dark abyss of the mind.

And when I opened my eyes I saw light in between the crevices. The winds had died down just as the sun had arisen. I came off the bed and quickly wrote what I had experienced:

was it a dream? Or was I in a particular meditative state?

Certainly I recalled that in *The Art of War* I had written some lines on how the strategist must remain alert to a deceptive speech made by the enemy.

5 ≡🕮≡ 6

Thus an enemy's humility in speech, despite the continuing efforts made in preparation for war, may suggest that extensive plans are being finalised for advancing the forces.

Also, when the enemy uses deceptive words, but pretends to be moving forces forward, his true motive may be to withdraw.

Plots are often indicated by a surprise request made by the enemy for a truce.

When the enemy speaks in apologetic terms what they truly hope for is some reprieve from war.

These skills in reading accurately the minds of an enemy from mere conversation – what was said, how it was said, when it was said, where it was said or, more importantly, what remained unsaid – must be acquired by the strategist who seeks mastery in the art.

These talents may simply be innate in the strategist. In my own case, I had practised for a long time to perfect these finer aspects in the mastery of the art of war.

6 ▰ 1

A day on the verge of spring. The signs are there of a coming change in the season: more activity about the forest, the icy river breaking up and tiny buds wriggling out of the branches of still barren trees.

The aspiring strategist should acquire skills in reading signs that are often embedded in emerging situations. Just like the master physician who is able to tell from little things the state of a person's health.

The person who has truly mastered any art can deduce a lot, given a little. The pulse in a person's wrist is all that a physician requires to diagnose illness.

I remember a particular physician whom everybody called the heavenly physician. I was told he could accurately read the health of a young lady of a wealthy family lying on a bed by merely feeling her pulse through a thread tied to her wrist.

She did not want to be seen by the physician while lying on her bed. Arrangements were then made for a thread to be led from her left wrist to outside the bedroom where the physician stood waiting.

How remarkably sensitive and attuned to tiny pulsations he must have been to do that! Despite these constraints the heavenly physician was able to describe vividly what her ailments were. After taking the prescribed medicine for several moons, the lady was healthy again.

The physician was also known for his wide knowledge of plants and herbs – where these grew, at what heights, whether in the shade and how best to prepare them to extract their medicinal properties.

Although an expert on medicinal herbs, the heavenly physician did not recommend their consumption for sustaining good health. Indeed he often prescribed food, bodily exercise, rest and even meditative practices as cures before turning to herbal medicine.

6 ▰ 2

The master fisherman, through merely observing the pattern in the flow of a stream, would know what types of fish could be found in it. He would know what traps would be best for the kind of fish to be caught, or in which spots a particular type of fish may be found.

Given a block of wood, the master woodcutter would be able after a few cuts of his knife to produce a carved object of exquisite beauty. From his skilled hands would emerge an artifact resembling a still rock or a preying eagle or a leaping tiger.

So a master calligrapher could seize the inspiration of the moment and, through poems composed of only a few words, evoke deep human feelings. A few more brushstrokes and the essence of a scene unfolds before the eyes: the mountainous ranges, moving clouds, tall pine trees, morning mist, birds and streams would be captured as well.

365

6 3

I recall a story told of how a village head warded off a man-eating beast that came in the evening, killing horses, sheep, pigs and sometimes even human beings. Nobody wanted to guard the gates on hearing of the deviousness of the beast.

The village head asked a mountain recluse reputed to be a fairy calligrapher to draw pictures of tigers so that these could be hung outside the village gates. He did this with his magical hands and painted tigers, one on each side of the gates. Both looked so real that from then on the beast never entered the village again.

There is also a story about a man who had mastered the art of farming. This master farmer had the skill to tell the different varieties of rice plants from the feel of the seeds in his palm. Also from the eggs of poultry he could tell their different breeds. Needless to say a master farmer is most sensitive to likely changes in the weather.

One legendary farmer from the past I remember being told about was even able to predict accurately the weather conditions – rain, wind, heat and so on – days, months and even years ahead. His warning of impending drought or flood had always been taken seriously and acted upon. As a result the people never suffered despite the vagaries of the weather.

Omniscience

6 ≣▓≣ 4

Seeing the coming of spring I thought it timely to re-read some of my earlier works on strategy.

What essential skills must a master strategist possess?

Omniscience?
For one thing, the master strategist should be able to discern accurately the hidden potential in things. Unrolling my own copy of *The Art of War* – a work whose prescriptions I had spent my entire military career verifying – I pondered again if I had succeeded in these chapters in capturing the true spirit and mind of a master strategist.

Future times would mean more sophistication in the art of war. The fundamental principles on strategy as embodied in *The Art of War* would however remain relevant for ever.

The master strategist would definitely not depend on mere strength in numbers to prevail. Numbers for him would just be another factor in the reckoning.

As I have written in *The Art of War,* the principle is for the strategist to contrive situations that enable him to pit his strengths against the weaknesses of the enemy.

6 ≣▓≣ 5

In *The Art of War* I also drew on my extensive experience to suggest what certain signs mean – at least during the prevailing conditions of war.

Changing war situations mean that some of these signs may be less suggestive of a certain phenomenon. Also new, more significant signs may emerge in changed contexts. In addition, for the same phenomenon there may be different or even more significant and directly relevant signs.

The strategist must realise that here, as everywhere else, change is inevitable. Time passes as things evolve.

Thus whether those signs as described in *The Art of War* remain valid – of enemy forces forming up or reinforcing or merely luring – would turn on the context in which future wars are fought.

Predetermined moves by the enemy may be anticipated

if certain signs, as suggested in *The Art of War*, are seen. Thus forming up is indicated by *flanking of chariots* and reinforcements by the *parading of chariots along with quickly marching soldiers.*

When the enemy is merely luring the other side on, then *half the enemy forces may be seen to advance and the other half withdraw*. These signs may become less and less relevant as time passes but the basic idea remains valid: inferring the enemy's true intentions from reading external signs.

Some of the advice inherent in the reading of signs will be relevant for a long time to come. One is the call for in-depth investigation when the enemy appears high-spirited and yet delays in doing battle.

External signs, if well read, may tell of the enemy's internal situation. This principle too will continue to be of relevance in the wars to come.

Many examples were given in *The Art of War* of knowing the inside, given the outside. Knowing such conditions of the enemy is critical – like the reading of the pulse by a physician – if successful strategies are to be implemented.

Thus plans to coerce an enemy to surrender may work if the enemy is in an utterly desperate situation.

In *The Art of War* many examples are given of reading the 'pulse' of the enemy when hunger, thirst, exhaustion, tiredness, despair and disorder are indicated:

- troops seen leaning on arms – *enemy suffering from acute hunger*;
- soldiers assigned to ferry water seen jostling to drink – *enemy suffering prolonged thirst*;
- enemy failed to take an obvious advantage – *enemy must be exhausted*;
- enemy's camp full of clamour – *fear has seized the enemy*;
- tempers flared easily among the officers – *enemy must be tired*;
- enemy seen feeding on meat and their horses' grain; utensils no longer being washed and hung – *enemy in utter despair*;
- officers are aggressive to their own men but later afraid of them – *limits of military order reached.*

The foregoing relates to the general state of the enemy forces. But of equal if not greater significance is the condition of the enemy's commander-in-chief.

The condition of his command may be known by reading the signs that indicate declining status or a confused or troubled commander-in-chief.

Sometimes even the loss of confidence of troops in the commander-in-chief may be indicated. There are again many examples of these in *The Art of War*:

- disorderliness of troops (declining status of the commander-in-chief);
- random flying of flags and banners (the commander-in-chief is confused);
- soldiers seen often to gather in groups, whispering (loss of confidence of the troops in the commander-in-chief);
- rewards repeatedly being made (the commander-in-chief is at his wits' end);
- punishments meted out once too often (the commander-in-chief is deeply troubled).

369

The work of a strategist is however far more difficult than merely interpreting these signs. For unlike the physician, farmer or fisherman, the strategist must be alert to possible false signs being made intentionally to deceive.

And as my work, *The Art of War*, gained greater circulation among the military officers then even I, if ever asked to wage another war, had to be more wary. For wars must never be fought relying entirely on the prescriptions contained in a book. For if any person applies any of these prescriptions without deep thought, then a cardinal principle of *The Art of War* has been violated – that of being *flexible* when waging war.

Also, stratagems used in war must never be applied rigidly. For stratagems to work they must be continually adapted to the changing circumstances of war.

With this comment I intend to put away the memoirs for the day.

Aging

10

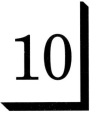

1 1

A SUMMER DAY. With the sun shining bright I decided to wash my hair. Whilst I was letting my shoulder-length hair down to dry I noticed the remaining strands of black hair had all turned white.

Alas, I had become an even older man. My beard too had turned all white.

But am I any the wiser?

This must have happened during this last season. One of the little delights I still now enjoy is in seeing how these long, silky white hairs glisten under the summer sunlight – rays of light that dazzle in the sky.

In this remote mountain retreat where I lived in almost total isolation there is the freedom just to be oneself and to be at one with nature. In such moments I am inevitably drawn to unroll the bamboo strips that record my memoirs.

For I am moved to write. Maybe I should also leave my hair unbound and bathe its length under the moonlight too.

Ah yes, tonight is the fifteenth day of the month: the moon at her most round and bright. What a rare delight it is to study her complexion in the quietness up here in the mountain.

I feel a growing sense of intimacy with her. These feelings are not the same as I experience for the sun, even though I find its light beautiful in early morning or late evening.

The sun, perhaps because of its often overpowering presence, inspires in a different sort of way: more functional than emotional.

Thus I have used the shadows cast by the sun to estimate heights that had to be scaled. In the morning I often take in a deep breath of air and gaze at the sun and the sky. I do this with a purpose.

I often had to judge what the weather would be like for the rest of the day, whether sunny, rainy, snowy, windy, cloudy and so on.

The path that the sun took across the sky would warn me of the beginning or ending or the passing of a season, be it winter, spring, summer or autumn.

1 ⚎ 2

As I stand here I recall vividly how once upon a time, when my hair and beard were as black as soot, the unclouded face of the moon had triggered me to reflect on the undulating ground over which the army had just traversed.

To be precise it was not her face as such but its reflection on the surface waters of a lake near the mountain ranges to the west of the capital city.

The rippled image caused by the strong winds blowing over these waters had aroused strategic thoughts within me: the nature of the ground as a major consideration in waging war.

Since that initial flash of intuition I have thought long and hard about ground as one of the major elements besides the wind, thunder, rivers, ravines, and so on of what I would call the 'invisible' soldiers provided by nature.

Indeed, as commander-in-chief I would call upon all my generals to reflect deeply on the nature of the ground as a factor determining success or failure when waging war.

1 ⚎ 3

Now I remember how ground had in fact been classified by me in *The Art of War* into various types, which I may describe as follows: easy to approach or enter; easy to be trapped into; neither favouring the enemy nor yourself; restricted access; sudden sharp rising or falling; and remote.

For each of these types of ground I prescribed, especially for the general, what had to be done or avoided. One strategy is to be the first to occupy favourable spots: the high ground bathed in sunlight.

Another element of strategy is to entice the enemy out of these favourable spots if they are already encamped there.

When on ground difficult to return to, the general must only leave it to strike an enemy that is totally unprepared. Otherwise, if the general is unexpectedly defeated by the enemy, the entire army in hurried retreat may be trapped in this difficult ground.

Thus always watch for the condition the enemy is in: are they prepared and ready for a surprise attack?

Besides these general principles I made more specific suggestions in relation to some types of ground. Thus in ground found to be neutral – favouring neither side – care must be taken not to take any bait proffered by the enemy. Instead the general should strike the enemy when *half* of their forces had been lured out.

1 4

The undulating image of the moon in the rippled waters of the lake had once sparked new ideas in me about ground as an invisible, destructive power of nature.

Knowing that the enemy would be advancing on the city I ordered the army to dig deep trenches on the flat ground that surrounded the outskirts of the city. These trenches were then to be camouflaged with topsoil so that it would be impossible for a soldier falling in to climb out.

Into the trenches dried grasses and twigs were thrown. Archers at the city walls were trained to shoot their arrows into these trenches.

At critical places I designed devices to enable pellets of rolled grasses to be thrown from behind the city walls into the trenches.

Thus that evening, when the enemy's army roared on under the bright moonlight towards the city, stirring up thick columns of dust that rose skywards, my men were all ready to rain fire on them.

Many enemy soldiers were roasted alive when lighted arrows or fireballs rained on them as they fell into the trenches. That evening there happened to be a full moon.

The fires danced inside the trenches amidst the screams of those being scorched to death. Some enemy soldiers in their desperation even scrambled out of those pits of fire.

I remembered again how the inspiration for that stratagem came from a chance observation of the moon reflected in undulating waters.

1   5

In *The Art of War* I also recommended a strategy for a general to cope effectively with ground that rises or falls precipitously – one must await the enemy after having been the first to encamp on the high, bright and sunny side.

If, however, the enemy already occupies these choice locations, the general must contrive to lure the enemy and lead the army out of this very ground himself. In this way the enemy will be denied the use of the 'invisible soldiers'.

Now, standing here and letting the summer winds lift these white hairs, I remember a particularly scenic view of the full moon, looming large on the horizon.

I was then riding up a high windy mountain pass strewn with wild grasses and bushes. Instead of the bronze mirror-smooth bright surface usually seen when the moon is hung in the night sky, what I saw was different.

I saw clearly that her face was cratered: etches of dark carved upon a surface of glowing white. As I rode the thought struck me that the face of the moon may not be what it seems.

When seen so close up the moon seems to be rough and uneven on the surface, rather than smooth. I was deeply struck by such a revealing sight of a cratered moon.

It was then that I, as commander-in-chief, ordered an officer with some scouts to make a closer and more detailed observation of the true conditions of an enemy before we launched a massive attack.

We were then residing on ground best classified as difficult. The secret foray into enemy territory enabled us to formulate a far more incisive attack.

As I had recorded in *The Art of War*, what ought to be done in those circumstances would depend on how accurately the true condition of the enemy had been read.

For unless the enemy could be overwhelmed through

wave upon wave of surprise attacks, it would be unwise to engage them. But if the enemy countered us effectively we might be trapped in this difficult ground if withdrawal became necessary.

1   6

Oh, how I had always to vary my strategy in accordance with the ground conditions in the many battles that I have fought!

My ground strategy may be portrayed as water, which always adapts itself to changing ground as it flows from the mountains down to the sea.

Perhaps that is why I prevailed over the enemy in so many battles. My enemy chose however to try to prevail through sheer force of weaponry, numbers or raw courage.

As for ground conditions, many a general chose simply to ignore them. In contrast I was very keenly observant of the changing conditions.

I tried always to anticipate these changes as I moved the army around. Even for ground deemed easily reached by either side there is a precept I observed: the general must hurry the army so as to be able to occupy the high, sunny ground and so critically control the routes of supply.

To control the routes of supply is much like putting a stranglehold on a person's throat. By tightening our hold on such routes we would be able to deny our enemy food, water and other essential supplies – like choking a person through gripping his air passage.

By contrast, ground that is restrictive in terms of routes of access, the strategy must first be to secure such passes as there are. But if the enemy has already reached these points, the strategy must be to stay outside the restrictive ground.

I run my hands through my long hair to relax myself. Perhaps enough has been written for the day. It is time to roll these strips up and just sit idly to watch the passing of time.

2 📖 1

A cloudy, cold and rainy day. Incessant rain for many days past. The skies for these last days have presented just one monotonous face – one that evokes nothing but gloom.

I sit here and listen to the monotonous sound of falling rain ... *cher* ... *cher* ... *cher* ... Outside in the windless atmosphere rain falls invariably straight down. Even the raindrops on my outstretched palm seem alike in shape and size, like tiny peas made transparent.

It must have been a long long time since I had been overwhelmed by such boredom. Had not there been days and nights when I had thought that time stood still? For everything outside seemed to be one continuum: rain, rain, rain, rain and ever more rain.

To exercise my body I walked about inside my little hut. Walking does not kill boredom even though it does provide some relief.

So I began counting the steps:

"one, two, three ... a hundred and one ... two hundred and three ... four hundred and eight ..."

On and on I went around the room till I reached eight hundred. Then I sat down again.

What a contrast between those tumultuous times of war and a boredom that invariably seeps into everything you do!

To escape from such boredom I turned again to my favourite copy of *The Art of War*, one that I keep in this mountain hut to remind me of what I had once written.

2 📖 2

As usual I would turn to my memoirs to capture in writing whatever further thoughts on strategy sprang to mind.

Interestingly, as I unrolled *The Art of War* my eyes quickly came to rest on the pictograph or word 'defeat': that section of the bamboo strips directly below my eyes.

Could this be a mere coincidence?

*Or does my unconscious mind search for a theme to corre-
spond to the gloom that prevails outside?*
Or is it an omen of times ahead?

As a strategist I never encouraged my generals to rely on omens in formulating strategies. Yet in my old age I am confronted with this issue again.

Perhaps I ought to record here that as I grew older I became more interested in the art of interpreting the heavenly signs.

I remembered a principle that may help to explain why such signs may be indicative of the scheme of things.

The principle is best (though not exactly) described as that of 'synchronicity' – according to one illustrious general.

There were often times when I could not help but agree that *good* or *bad* things tend to occur together, though not exactly synchronously. Once I had a problem or difficulty, the tendency was that a spate of problems or difficulties occurred.

What remains puzzling to me even now is that these may arise from different and unrelated sources. Thus if I had encountered difficulties in my office as a commander-in-chief I would also begin to encounter problems emerging from other quarters of my life, such as from my family.

If that is the case then for a person who has commenced a course of action synchronous with the emergence of certain ominous signs, the secret must be to break off from this underlying trend or pattern of things.

But is that at all possible?

I am still wondering.

2 ▨ 3

So, as stated above, a keen reader of these signs must learn to depart from the course of action altogether. This may require drastic measures, such as withdrawing the army from a mission or calling off an impending attack.

Thus that general whom I respected deeply and who happened to be exceptionally receptive to such heavenly signs would always act and change his plan.

Signs

As I was told, this general once interpreted an unexpected breaking of his banner by a very light wind as a sign that his planned attack was doomed to fail. He immediately recalled his army from the front. Later he found out that the enemy had made elaborate preparations to attack him, including a call for huge reinforcements from the interior.

On another occasion his horse, which had served him loyally since his early youth, suddenly leapt up high, throwing him off balance to the ground. He read this as a warning that a calamity lay ahead. Could this possibly be due to the horse's intuition of the danger? He was supposed to lead a division of his men through the pass. He feigned to suffer a back injury from the fall.

The officer who was ordered to replace him on the mission did not survive the rains of arrows that fell on him. A secret arrow fired from the high cliffs hit him. He died instantly when it pierced his neck, through the gap between his helmet and armoured uniform.

Not surprisingly, therefore, the general always took such signs into consideration when implementing strategy.

2 ⬛ 4

There appeared to the general another plausible reason why such signs may portend of what is yet to come.

These signs may be seen as indicative of the power of change inherent in nature.

So in flipping through *The Art of War*, with my eyes falling on the section dealing with 'defeats', my mind could unconsciously be uncovering my pessimistic outlook as underlying the changes that take place around me.

Things of nature are so complex that even now I find them difficult to comprehend and even more so to express in writing.

Heavenly signs often take on a meaning that is only symbolic at a personal and intuitive level. Instructions using written words alone may be grossly inadequate. Also there is a danger in over-generalising about the significance of heavenly signs.

So rather than counsel my generals to be on the lookout for heavenly signs, due to the difficulty in interpretation, I

wrote about how to see equally ominous signs of danger that
may befall the army.

2 ▰ 5

Thus in *The Art of War* I wrote of the danger to an army that
attacked another ten times its size: the consequences may be
disastrous – troops under your command may flee from the
scene.

In such a situation the blame rests squarely on the
general for having taken such high risks. There are other
imminent signs of danger that the wise general should look
out for.

Where feeble officers are put in command of troops that
are headstrong and determined – that is another sign of
danger.

In such a situation military orders are likely to be dis-
obeyed by the rank-and-file. Resolute action must therefore be
taken to alter such a state of affairs.

Where the officers are tough and daring but the troops
weak, then the army is truly in trouble. Again the perceptive
general must take immediate action to remedy the situation.

Other signs of danger often involve the general personally. This can only be rectified by the commander-in-chief or
the king himself.

If the general is both dissolute and irresolute – he makes
decisions capriciously – the officers lack a framework within
which to lead the soldiers. Such an army may be said to be
lacking in orderliness. These are signs to watch out for in an
army.

So whilst I might inspect the rehearsed displays of the
power of a general's troops under my command I never failed
secretly to enquire into their true condition.

The worst signs are seen in an army that is close to
collapse. Such an army is often characterised by unruly
behaviour among the senior officers, who may not bother to
investigate a situation thoroughly before engaging an enemy
nor wait for orders to be issued from the commander-in-chief
before advancing.

Other signs are seen in the commander-in-chief himself.
For example, he may be unskilled in estimating the size of an

enemy force or unable to select and deploy troops.

Only a king who is sufficiently perceptive can prevent a calamity. If he attacks an enemy when manifestly outnumbered then the consequence will surely be a rout.

Therefore there is danger when a king depends too much on a commander-in-chief or a commander-in-chief places too much reliance on his general.

The defeat does not spring from the small size of the army, but from the fact that a small force is directly engaging one many times its size.

Only through strategy can an inferior force eventually prevail over one that is superior – in terms of numbers or weaponry or both.

381

2 📖 6

Yet on second thoughts, these signs may also be interpreted as indicating a broader pattern of change in the nature of things – that of the inevitable collapse of a dynasty when the heavenly mandate to rule had been withdrawn.

How else does one explain why good generals arise in one state and bad ones in another?

There is one thing I do know. And that is that writing has truly helped me cope with the all-encompassing boredom!

A day that passes by fast. How time eludes me today! I remember the morning wind caressing my face as I set off along the short path.

Now it is already all darkness.

The narrow path has become all the more difficult to traverse. With rain falling for that many days past the sogginess of the ground simply wears you out.

Or is it that an older man, such as I am, is far less nimble of foot?

Whatever the case, I still managed to replenish my essential supplies of soybeans, oil, rice and salt from the little village shop.

Once in a while a man ought to take the advice he has proffered to others! I should have taken heed of my own advice recorded in *The Art of War:* the general should always estimate accurately the time taken to cover the ground.

Had I been later I could have become lost in the darkness down the path. I remember as a commander-in-chief I would often be conscious of how much time different activities of an army would require.

Thus when time was critical for any particular mission I would assign men whom I knew to be fast riders on horses capable of covering very long distances without rest.

I lit the wick and sat down on the floor to undo the knot that held pieces of cloth in a bundle.

I also untied the memoirs.

On these pieces of cloth – some tattered and torn – are kept records of all the more difficult journeys made by the army: details such as the nature of the journey made, the distance and the time taken for movement are recorded.

More important, are the lessons learned? These records now help me better estimate the time needed to travel between any two localities.

I often instructed my men to keep count of the steps

taken for any specific journey. Also recorded are details of the terrain over which the army had traversed.

If there had been any delay I would note specific causes: factors such as special crossings to be made over rivers or narrow bridges.

On one of these pieces of cloth I recorded how my entire army was slowed down for days. We were then crossing the mountain ranges. My men had to cross a very narrow and sharp-edged ridge.

It was so narrow that horses had to be left abandoned while each soldier clawed one after another as they crawled across in turn.

I did not hurry the men.

Had a stronger wind been blowing even an able-bodied soldier would have been blown off the ridge.

If he had fallen that would have been the end of him. For he would tumble steeply down. He would be gone for ever and it would simply have been impossible, even if he were, miraculously, alive, for him to rejoin us. He would have been too far down in the pit. So far down that a man would first appear as a tiny dot on a painting before disappearing into nothingness.

Not a thud would be heard either.

The rest of the journey was later completed on foot. This was one of my more memorable journeys made in my earlier days as a commander-in-chief.

3 ▰ 3

I had a habit of keeping with me a grass map of the terrain that I battled on in the day. I would call this a battle map.

Marked on the map would be where the forces – enemy and mine – were already known to be deployed, together with their estimated sizes.

I would despatch an advance party to study the battle-ground ahead. In the evening, when we had encamped, the men would return to report to me on what they had observed. In the process of hearing them out I would note any recent changes in the configuration of enemy forces.

Also of interest were changes in their key sites and more detailed aspects of the terrain. So on a grass map already marked with a river I would add where a crossing might best be made.

Also my men would have enquired into the availability of boats – types, number and sizes – along the river.

In addition I often marked out land that was descending, flat or ascending and whether it rose or fell sharply.

Even in the day I would mentally work on it. If I sat in a carriage the grass map would be kept unfolded as I planned.

I have contemplated many army movements using grass maps. Using them helped to sharpen my strategic thinking. More accurately, these are the *mental* mappings of my strategic thinking processes as my mind unfolded and formulated strategies.

On them I had drawn possible directions for attack, retreat, counter-attack, flanking, barriers to be constructed, traps and so on.

As a result over many campaigns I had amassed a vast collection of these grass maps. Some had withered over the years but still a substantial number remained on the shelf in my house in the city.

A few of my favourite grass maps are kept right here with me. So what I have written in *The Art of War* represents the essence of what I had gained as a commander-in-chief.

3 4

My wife had told me years ago:

"Those who read The Art of War *would absorb the essence of your long years of battle experience.... It is not unlike how you would now benefit from drinking this cup of ginseng soup ... I have extracted the very essence of ginseng roots through simmering them with chicken over a fire for a long time..."*

In *The Art of War* I stressed the importance of the use of terrain in waging war. A superior general is one who is best able to wage a war in a manner that conforms with the ground conditions.

In other words, his strategy *fits* the terrain on which it is implemented. Such a general should also be able to work out the distances between places and anticipate the difficulties likely to be confronted.

Detailed calculations and prior knowledge are then used by the general to control the outcomes of war.

I even wrote in *The Art of War* that successes may be predicted based on how skilful a general is in utilising the ground as an instrument, if not as a weapon of war.

This is not unlike the warrior skilled in wielding the halberd – a little twist of the wrist and the weapon emanates a divine power.

The general who knows his ground well will be able, when hotly pursued by the enemy, to waylay them inescapably into dangerous ravines and yet emerge unhurt himself.

3 ⬛ 5

I took out one of my most memorable grass maps and hung it across the wall of the hut. I ran my palm across the surface as I recalled those moments: some triumphant, others agonising, yet many more of lessons learned as part of the process of waging war.

The very unevenness of the surface stirred in me an undercurrent of tumultuous feelings. I felt almost as if I were at that moment riding across undulating lands.

Though inside this hut, I could feel the expanse of the terrain unfolding and the wind beating on my face.

Oh how this grass map can conjure up these feelings within me! For drawn, crossed, marked, written, scribbled or whatever on this grass map were the many lessons drawn from those experiences of war fought along the borderlands.

The very best times of my military life were spent hurtling over and over this ground. I ought to have known every crook, corner and crevice of this stretch of battle zone after battling on it so often.

Born into an era besieged by war after war I often yearned for a time of peace but that was not to be.

The grass map again – although I did not colour them as such, I vividly recall those places which I would paint red, a deep blood-red.

Throwing this map on to the floor I see pools of warm, fresh blood in those places – how stupid of men to have killed so brutally for so little.

I would never have sacrificed that many young lives simply to secure ground, but in my absence my general did. For these are the very places where so many – countless – lives were lost in clashes. Oh, how memories of the past – some ugly, some thought to be forgotten – simply bubble up into my consciousness!

If I had to paint a picture of what my mind's eye now sees, it would appear distorted. Flashes of different images seen during these wars would appear and disappear here there and everywhere. It is as though this grass map is a window through which I can view my past, not sequentially, but sporadically.

3   6

Interestingly, past time, once unlocked, seems twisted, bent and malleable. Some scenes flow past so slowly, like a river on its last bend before merging with the sea.

Oh, how I liked being attacked or pursued on the ground that I knew best! For it is like trapping fish in a pond by casting of a net, except that I was the bait and these forested, thickly wooded, sharply falling terrains the net. Like all traps they must be well-laid.

And like the pulling in of the net, timing is critical in yielding the best catch. So at the right moment I must make the critical turn to safety while my men unloose the traps.

Sometimes it was just the momentum maintained by the enemy that led them to their end – over the edge and deep down a hidden cliff.

Looking at the grass map again I wonder how high in the sky a pile of skeletons now buried beneath the grass would have reached if all those killed in action were unearthed!

For since time immemorial the place had been a favourite battleground of kings and princes. No wonder my hands tremble as I write these lines! But not from fear; rather from the sheer idea of the carnage that I now imagine to have accumulated over time on this ground.

And the carnage continues even now!

4 🔖 1

Unusually bright and warm for a winter's day. The low-lying sun seems to dominate an empty, cloudless, clear sky.

This scene of the sun dominating a winter sky made me ponder on the role of a king within a state that is at war. These thoughts I should record in my memoirs.

The root of the peasants' original desire to have one king to rule in a given state must be very old.

According to a tale about the origin of the earth – on account of its great antiquity I would regard this tale as legendary – this sun is one that Pan Ku had allowed to remain after having shot down eight others. Since then only one sun has ruled the sky.

For with nine suns in the sky, the land, as recorded by the ancients – it must have been thousands upon thousands of years ago – was so scorched hot and dry by the suns' heat that no farming was possible.

Drought led to famine, whereupon millions and millions died of thirst and starvation. People suffered terribly under the rays of the nine suns till Pan Ku came with his magical bow and arrows.

Could such a story, told so many times by so many farmers over so many years, have led them unconsciously to desire rule by one strong leader?

I often wonder if there is any truth in the belief that the sufferings sustained by so many people during this war-torn period are simply due to the presence of too many kings.

These kings vie ruthlessly for absolute domination of the kingdom which, according to the ancients, lies at the centre of the earth.

The ruler of this 'middle kingdom' would be Ruler of All Below Heaven. Such a king would be different from all other kings. For he might claim to receive the mandate to rule directly from Heaven.

Adorned in yellow, he is like the sun which rules as the Son of Heaven. Perhaps it is the deep desire of all farmers to see such a benevolent one as ruler.

No wonder that each king is so determined to prevail over all the others! With his magical bow and arrows Pan Ku could more easily shoot down the eight suns than all the kings in the different states!

When young I was often told by my father the ancient saying, 'One mountain, one tiger' – on a mountain only one tiger may rule.

Again such a belief may underlie a deep unconscious desire for the emergence of the Worthy One to rule over the entire kingdom.

4 ⬛ 2

Today, as I walked along under the sun, I spent some time reflecting on the role of the king in the conduct of war. The fine and intricate art of kingship is different from that of a strategist, even though a king would gain by learning to think strategically.

For the ideal king of the middle kingdom – if ever this is realised – should benefit many, many, many others through his virtues as manifested in the wisdom by which he rules.

But sadly, such an august one I was not destined to meet in this life. For those kings whom I have encountered and served during my life pale in comparison with my notion of the ideal king. Such a king, destined by Heaven to rule, resides only in my mind.

Although appointed as commander-in-chief I often felt dismayed at the lack of a true and mighty king to serve: one with broad, all-encompassing vision, a mighty king who could build a great wall out of mere stones, and pave wide roads and carve mighty canals across the middle kingdom.

The kings I have served were far lesser men than the one whom I had envisioned. As I recollected in the earlier roll of bamboo strips a king whom I once served almost caused the collapse of a border city.

4 ⬛ 3

This king had ordered me before the peace agreement was formally signed to head south whilst the crown prince – his favourite son – was assigned to take over my role as the commander-in-chief of northern defences.

But the crown prince had hardly taken over when the city once again capitulated into the hands of the barbarians.

It was unfortunate that court politics prevailed: the crown prince would have appeared better fitted for succession as the next king if he had been seen to have a role in securing peace in the far north.

On another occasion I had to rely on a *Taoist* soothsayer to save the very life of the crown prince – skilled as he may be in the military arts – of whom the king was too fond ever to see his inadequacy in direct war experience.

The crown prince once led a number of my elite – the very best of my men – in hot pursuit of the barbarians. Their leading warrior was wounded in the arm by an arrow shot by the crown prince. A fine horseman, the crown prince rode up north together with my men.

Needless to say, he would simply be overwhelmed by a much larger force which the leading warrior and his men were heading to rejoin. Every one of my men – the best of my personal guards – were under orders to protect the life of the crown prince.

Earlier he had accompanied the king and queen to visit our military headquarters in the north-west. But none of the men had the courage to confront the impetuous crown prince and persuade him to call off the chase.

Sensing the danger – with a mother's intuition – the queen pleaded with (rather than ordered) me to investigate the whereabouts of the crown prince. He had failed to turn up for the imperial feast which had been arranged for them at the headquarters.

4 ▆▆ 4

As I stood on the city wall my officer indicated to me the direction in which the crown prince and the men had headed. I knew instinctively through experience that they were riding into real danger. For they were headed towards the most barbaric tribal people known in this northern region: men from these tribes would still roast the dead for a feast. To make matters worse, a storm seemed on the verge of being unleashed and the wind was blowing strongly against us.

Nevertheless, I ordered an entire division of horsemen

be be assembled, including our best archers. The force was to be put together by one of my most able generals so as to rescue the crown prince.

I planned to be part of this force too.

4 ▆ 5

It was then that my men informed us – me as the commander-in-chief, the king and queen – of a famous soothsayer asking for an audience.

To my utter amazement he knew our predicament: how could we ride against stormy winds in time to rescue a crown prince heading towards grave danger of being captured?

I had to give some credence to what he said. The sooth-sayer explained that as he was about to leave the city for the wilderness he had felt the pull of the intense yearnings of a mother (the queen) for her lost son (the crown prince).

He was thus moved to help. Taking me aside he suggested that I should let the general lead the division and stay behind myself to do as he instructed.

I agreed, though reluctantly.

I have never had to rely on the supernatural to win my wars. But what this soothsayer said made logical sense. He explained that the only body that can ride against the stormy winds in time to recall the crown prince is my *other* body. Since the crown prince would only listen to me I must agree to do as instructed. I did not have any other choice.

I sat facing in the direction of where the crown prince was headed and simply concentrated on the thought of myself travelling across space. The soothsayer in the meantime helped me to concentrate by chanting. He said that, should I see the crown prince in my mind's eye, I must ask him to return immediately.

A miracle then happened which I cannot come to terms with even today. I seemed to be able in that trance to float past the division of soldiers led by the general.

Then suddenly I began to see the crown prince riding ahead of me. At will I was ahead of him and I spoke to him of the very grave dangers ahead.

As commander-in-chief I ordered him to return immedi-ately. I warned him that if he failed to do so I would order the men from my personal guard – every one of whom was loyal to me personally – to arrest him.

Indeed, my men seemed to have heard me speak as such. In my vision I saw the crown prince pull to a halt along with my men and head back.

Later on the crown prince told me that he actually saw me riding in the air ahead of him as I spoke. And so did the men!

4 6

The soothsayer understood my deeper sentiments. For this same wrinkled-faced, long- and white-haired soothsayer told me – without my asking – that there would emerge, a few generations after my death, one truly great ruler, but that the people would first have to undergo year upon year of untold suffering.

This ruler was predestined to rule like a sun of intense brightness: one that blinds and scorches at the same time as it unifies and restores the kingdom. And if I am able to choose to be reborn much later, then there would also be another, even mightier king of kings. But he would appear not amidst our fertile yellow earth but in the barren soils of the northern, wind-swept plains, and born as one of the barbarians.

These signs are all – according to this revered sage – written on the night sky. But men, drunk on their possessions, or power, or pleasures, or obsessions, or loves, choose simply to ignore these signs from Heaven.

Nor do they learn to read the signs from Heaven so as to act in unison with the evolving nature of things.

I had long wanted to serve under an enlightened king so as to explore more deeply the interrelationships during a period of war between the king, strategist (strategy adviser), commander-in-chief (when appointed) and the generals.

4 7

I have written in *The Art of War* about how critical it is for the sovereign or king to ensure flexibility for his commander-in-chief in waging war within his theatre of operations, even

Thought

when the king has issued orders for engaging the enemy but the situation is one of certain defeat. The commander-in-chief ought not in such circumstances comply.

Conversely, when the king has yet to order an attack but the situation is one of certain victory, the commander-in-chief ought to be able to lead his army into combat.

I would argue for ultimate responsibility to be vested in the commander-in-chief, who should act in accordance with contingencies in the face of changing war scenarios.

War situations are often so fluid that a sharp-eyed and capable general fighting at the front should be able to find gaps in which to implement tactical and sometimes strategic thrusts.

So when I assigned my officers tasks I would always allow for some flexibility in implementation on the part of my commanders.

4 ▰ 8

In the same way Heaven may decree that the rainwater which falls to earth should venture forth to the seas, but the rain-water as it falls must be left to find this path on its own initiative.

The movement of water down to the sea has often impressed me. How quickly these waters, that fall on the western ranges, adapt to the configuration of land as they head irresistibly east to the sea! In the process of their flow the waters bring benefit to more than a thousand things. Thus a thousand things welcome water on its natural course towards the sea.

In contrast the army, moving in hordes, often leaves damaged a thousand things in its path. So the army, under orders to act from an unenlightened king and commanded by an uncouth general, often goes about executing the order to the detriment of a thousand things they may pass over.

For they would leave in their path a trail of burning, torture, plunder, extortion, execution. The primary consideration of the commander-in-chief should be that of acting in the best interests of the state.

Tonight the northern star is shining exceptionally brightly. She dangles like a mystical jewel hanging in the night sky.

The more I look at the northern star the more I feel drawn to her. Unlike the moon that wanes and waxes, there is a certain constancy in the northern star.

For unlike other stars that twinkle here and there and then disappear altogether, the light of the northern star is a steady stream.

As I have also recorded in an earlier part of these memoirs, the northern star has guided me across the land. It was a featureless empty grassland.

394

How does one know which direction to take in the night?

I remember that episode well.

The exhausting heat of an unusually hot, dry and boring summer – windless, rainless, cloudless – was made worse as we crossed a featureless terrain.

In the daytime we would see nothing but stretch after stretch of grassland. It is surprising how easily the mind can be dulled by unchanging terrain. Grass on the horizons. Grass that sweeps against your waist as you ride on. Nothing but grass. The same green.

We chose to sleep by day and travel by the cool of night, guided by the northern star that always hung there in the sky – in that corner of the night sky.

It was during such times that I was stirred to think of the ideal characteristics of a general as resembling those of the northern star.

5 📖 2

There, in the midst of a raging war, he stands majestic among the men. In my mind's eye I see his figure well, towering above the ebb and flow of bodies locked in combat.

The great general is always there, ready to provide the leadership to spur the men on despite the overwhelming burden of war. He gives directions but is never domineering. He vies for neither personal fame nor special attention from the king. He, the great general, is easily distinguishable from the lesser generals.

When advancing his troops into battle he does so only after careful consideration of strategy. Nor is he fearful of punishment when he orders troops to be withdrawn from a pitched battle. Again his only considerations are strategic – in the best interests of the state to which he has pledged his loyalty.

His only reason for engaging in fighting, killing, burning is better to secure protection for his people whom he dearly loves.

In the execution of his duty he has only the interests of his king deep at heart. Such a great general is indeed a rare jewel of the state.

But are most kings able to appreciate the true qualities of a great general?

I doubt it.

5 ⚡ 3

Enlightened kings are scarce. That is why I chose to retreat to the safety of this mountain hut once my mission was done.

Treacherous kings are many. No doubt these kings would, when their most feared enemies were destroyed, duly honour those who had contributed. But immediately afterwards these kings would devise schemes to eliminate from office the very same persons so honoured, and they would often meet an untimely death.

A triumphant great general, having secured ultimate and glorious victory for the state, is for that very reason a thorn in the flesh of the sycophantic leeches who feed on the fears and fancies of the king. Whether ministers or some lesser officials or eunuchs, they fawn on the king day and night. These are the very people who apply their minds to hatch a thousand and one murderous plots to rid the state of her most able and loyal men.

But why?

So that such capable and talented men would not become a threat to their own precarious position *vis-à-vis* the king. The king himself would also fear a mighty, fearless and triumphant great general, who commanded the utmost respect of the many tough, weather-beaten but possibly war-weary soldiers.

5 ⟨book⟩ 4

These war-scarred soldiers who finally succeed in returning to their homes after all the years of fighting – sometimes bare-fisted deep in the throng of the battlefield – are so unlike the unruly youths they once were.

Even mothers are shocked by the extent of the transformation that years of soldiering in the heat of many battles could bring to their once docile child. Eyes that once would shy away when met now gleam with fire. Not the rousing fires one finds in a camp, but cold penetrating flames. In the dark such eyes would strike deep irrational fears into the heart. The fires in these eyes seem able to pierce through the body of any mortal creature.

Instead of being soft and fleshy, these palms are now hardened like rocks. Indeed, so removed have the soldiers been from refined and civilised living that, when offered the victory toasts in porcelain cups, these inevitably snapped in their hands.

Tanned knots of muscle ripple through the frame of such a soldier. There is absolutely no fat on the stomach, but muscles chiselled to resemble the rocky terrain over which these soldiers have traversed in their forays north.

A glance at these soldiers as they cross into the city and you could tell that they would obey no one – not even the king – but their great general. For only their great general, who had been their equal in enduring severe hardship, would be able to stand out among them as their natural leader.

5 ⟨book⟩ 5

The great general who is able to lead an army from triumph to triumph is no ordinary soldier. He must have mastered the art of leading men. As I have written in *The Art of War*, such a great general treats his soldiers like his very own beloved children.

No wonder that kings often feel relieved when such a great general retires from the palace and his army of fighters – whose allegiance was forged through the heat of battles – is disbanded.

On the eve of the anticipated victorious return of a great general many a lesser king would consult a hundred and one soothsayers on the future implications. The night sky would be scanned by these soothsayers to see if any major upheavals were indicated.

Only on receiving reassurance of peace and calm does the lesser king feel at ease. But had there been any contra-indication, the king would have schemed to delay the arrival of the great general.

The imperial messenger would be called to deliver an imperial edict to the great general to embark on yet another mission – simply to delay his arrival in the capital city since this would spell danger!

That a king might fear the soldiers of the great general should come as no surprise. For in return for the love showered on them, these children would not hesitate when called upon to die for their father, the great general.

5 ▦ 6

His children are in sharp contrast to those soldiers commanded by lesser generals: spoilt, ill-disciplined, unruly, soft-kneed, weak-muscled and simply useless. A mere glance reveals the difference.

Years of moulding by such a mighty general must have mattered. A hundred of the disciplined, tough and heroic are better than ten thousand of the unruly, weak and cowardly.

Years of gruelling, bitter fighting out in the cold of the north have made these children into a tough breed of soldiers. So cold and hardened are they that they seem indifferent to the wild screams and women's cheers from the crowds as they stride into the city.

Indeed, many a retired soldier who has been so hardened, through years of brutality in fighting the barbarians, finds it difficult to adapt to civilian life. For from enduring one extreme, these former soldiers of the great general now have to endure the other – the sheer monotony of living out a simple existence. Not because of insufficient luxuries of life, but due to boredom – a lack of stimulus or excitement. Ironically these soldiers now miss the danger.

For years they have been living on the edge. Compared to their struggles in the very thick of battle civilian life must be agonisingly boring.

After the initial euphoria of reunion with loved ones the soldier must now confront the brooding boredom of everyday living.

Given a little time, even the most enthusiastic members of the family grow tired of hearing about their exploits – no matter how glorious and truly exciting this must have been for the soldier.

5 ⬛ 7

His exploits now fall on deaf ears.

Sleepless in the night, these former soldiers yearn many times for the chance to go back yet again to the battlefield, this time to fight till they fall.

For they miss the feelings of comradeship so genuinely felt in the heat of battle. But you may rightfully ask:

How does Sun Tzu know the feelings of these soldiers so intimately?

I too had my share of leading true blooded soldiers through many battles. Even now as I make my journey through the land my former soldiers show me my banners. Many of my 'children' kept these tattered banners that bear my name in the secret recesses of their homes. As they speak, I see some of them are toothless.

The burial ground they dream of is no longer their ancestral site but the battlefield. Their ideal is to fight, and die in action serving the great general.

That is how I know their feelings and now record them in my memoirs.

6 ≡🔖≡ 1

Early dawn. I sit up on the bed, soaked with sweat. And this is not a hot summer's night but late winter!

The last I remember of the dream is the vision of a great general who stood tall and erect, like a pillar at the city gates.

Enemy soldiers reeled off into the distance and melted into the mist. This great general, who had died so many years ago, had reappeared in my dream.

He was already sixty but still leading his army into the battlefield when I, as a young man, first met him.

The story of his martial skills was already well known by that time. I had been told many times of his brave endeavours in war. So much so that even into my old age I now re-enact through dreams the exploits of this great general.

He was particularly well known for the tremendous powers with which he was able to wield his unusually heavy halberd. By virtue of his skills alone, he could hold back the onslaught of more than ten thousand enemy soldiers.

In earlier dream sequences I had seen his metallic frame in action, repulsing wave upon wave of enemy attacks. Enemy soldiers whose courage had to be drummed up to fight him could themselves hardly believe what they saw. Their fellow soldiers were easily thrown back when they engaged the great general in battle. Indeed, it was once said that his roaring laughter alone was sufficient to frighten away lesser generals.

His own soldiers stood in awe behind him as the great general battled alone. And so the fighting continued till night fell. Armed with lighted torches the enemy troops continued with the onslaught.

6 ≡🔖≡ 2

There was not a hint of the great general ever becoming tired. He seemed to plunge on with ever more vigour after each succeeding wave of enemy attack. To the onlooker it appeared that each new wave fed him with more ferocity, energy and determination. Strangely, his body seemed to be sapping the vitality of the very soldiers with whom he was fighting.

In desperation the enemy commander-in-chief, a far

Great general

lesser general himself, called in the archers and spearsmen. Despite the paucity of light afforded by the isolated torches the great general was able to repel one flood after another of arrows and spears.

But surely a human body must tire! The great general held off the attacks through the night till the early dawn, when the mist began to gather in the background. Dead bodies of enemy soldiers lay strewn on every side. In front of the city gates the dead too began to pile up.

Gradually the momentum of attack by the enemy soldiers began to slow down. Just then soldiers who rode on the crest of one wave of attack flung poisoned dust – or was it just plain sand? – right into the face of the great general. At that moment for once he stumbled and withdrew his right leg as he tried to rub his right eye.

Many an enemy archer and spearsman grabbed that chance to charge forward. A tidal wave of arrows and spears headed towards him, the great general.

None of the spears struck him but the arrows did. One arrow stabbed deep into his left eye through a narrow gap in his helmet. Thirteen arrows pierced through his left upper thigh.

In my dream I heard the thunderous cosmic roar of the great general: '*Shaaaa! Ahhhhhh! Shaaaaa! Ahhhhhh! Shaaaaaa!*...'.

6 ⚔ 3

He charged forward at the enemy troops, ever determined to slaughter those in the crowd of enemy soldiers who had resorted to such low, cowardly, dirty trickery. Some of the enemy soldiers were so shocked by the sudden outburst of energy from the great general that they stood there, frozen by fear.

Many heads flew into the air and fresh red blood gushed out of headless trunks as the great general cut mercilessly through the ranks of enemy soldiers. In my dream the air seemed tinged with a warm redness: the red of human blood.

Those who stood behind saw what was happening before them. Many lost their nerve to continue the fight. Some simply abandoned their weapons to flee as quickly as their legs could carry them. The great general had become transformed, through sheer disgust and anger, to perform what seemed to lesser men impossible feats.

Seen in my dream as a re-enactment in slow motion it was as though he was simply slicing up human bodies.

Fear was written in the eyes of those that stood there, immovable and frozen. Through such deeds he was known far and wide as a legendary general.

6 ⚔ 4

The echoes of his cosmic roar still ring loud in my ears as I sit here with my memoirs. I wanted to translate aspects of the dream as realistically as possible into writing.

Why legendary?

Despite the severe injury to his left eye and his left thigh he did not flinch from his duty as a great general.

The thirteen arrows that stuck in his left limb he simply had twisted out without so much as a '*yach!*'

For he immediately set to forming a strategy for the counter-attack. Mighty as he was as a great general, he had mastered the fine art of war.

He considered every element before embarking on a strategy. His success may seem too difficult to be believed but he had ensured it through careful planning.

He was, however, unique in one respect: he was endowed with the physique as well as the mind of a master strategist. He knew that with his skills he alone could hold back the tide of enemy attacks, as the city gates were so narrow.

Now with that spectacular performance he had struck deep fear into every single soldier – the enemy's as well as his own.

That very morning he called for a meeting of officers and men. He ordered that spies and scouts and special forces be gathered.

As details about the deployment of enemy forces were given he would note their precise locations. The map of the terrain surrounding the city was already laid out across the table.

As the physician extracted the deeply embedded arrow

from his left eye the general gave detailed instructions on how the forces were to be reorganised.

Officers and men stood there, shocked that the wounds did so little to dampen his enthusiasm to lead the charge personally.

He only asked for the embedded arrow to be dislodged by the physician. After that he poured wine on to what remained of his left eye.

But one change he did make as a consequence of his injuries. He asked the blacksmith to forge a new helmet, of a special design. It had a small square piece in front that could cover his left eye and a disk perforated with holes for the right eye.

It was said that thereafter he fought even better than before. His blows and shots of arrows more deadly.

Why?

6 ⚊🗡⚊ 5

Ironically the loss of his left eye had forced him to rely more on his instinct and the sixth sense: the mind's eye.

It was rumoured widely that in the instant his left eye was shot he transcended and attained the highest stage in the mastery of martial arts: the level at which fighting becomes purely instinctive.

So even if he were ever blinded in the right eye it would not have mattered. His fighting would be equally, if not more deadly.

The story of his capabilities as a great general fascinated me more than his skills as a fighter. For despite his obvious individual fighting talents he did not rush out to devour the enemy forces as they retreated. Instead he held a strategy conference to work out a plan for launching a massive counter-attack to root out the enemy forces.

For he must have realised that out in the wide open plains his individual skills mattered less to the outcome. There he could more easily be encircled, whereas at the city gates his rear was protected by his own soldiers.

Having mapped out a strategic plan he proceeded without undue delay to execute it. He also ordered that more new and bigger banners, with his personal name written boldly and clearly, be flown high in the winds as the army marched out of the city.

For he knew that word had by then spread far and wide among enemy soldiers of what a miracle fighter he was: many attested to how, when wounded, he would rise ever higher and fight far more vigorously.

6 ⚓ 6

Some enemy soldiers had even secretly deserted their stations. His army marched smartly out in the wind. For he had chosen a day when the wind would be blowing in the right direction.

Seeing his banners flying high, the enemy soldiers would abandon their camps to flee for their lives as quickly as they could.

And as I have written in *The Art of War*, those experienced in war move without a mistake, and for them their resources seem inexhaustible.

The more I analysed the stories of this great general the more I found his successes to be truly grounded on very sound principles in waging war. He struck at the heart of the enemy when his troops were ready and when other factors of ground and weather were in his favour too!

7 ▬ 1

Today the spring sky is clear – not a speck of cloud. An image I feel arising within me is one of *clarity*: seeing clearly into the scheme of things.

It is like seeing one's face reflected in a bucket of well-water. Even better, having one's entire body reflected in a pool of still stream-water.

The feelings experienced are like the flash that comes at the moment of strategic insight. That instant when I suddenly see clearly how all things, heard and seen in the process of formulating strategy for an evolving war may be interrelated in a distinct pattern. At this moment all bits of information and *mis*information fit together to present the whole picture. Logic binds separate threads of thinking into a single powerful rope.

As a strategist I must see the way ahead in the waging of a war. My role as a thinker of strategy is different from that of the ordinary soldier. It is to impose an order, a perspective, a framework, a model or a schema on seemingly disconnected disparate things concerning wars or wars as they evolve.

The role of a strategist goes beyond putting things together, though that may be the beginning.

7 ▬ 2

Thus as a strategist I must produce a map of the terrain: assembling the features – rivers, mountains, paths, towns and so on – whether on a piece of cloth, silk, shell, bone or whatever is available.

A map helps one to see more clearly the path to take in leading an army across a terrain. The best map is however one committed to memory, a map that resides in the recesses of one's mind. For once a terrain has been mapped on to something that very thing could fall into the wrong hands. But an enemy would never get to see a map kept inside one's mind. On some maps I would often disguise the features – a ravine represented by a path or by a symbol known only to me – so that unless initiated one would be misled.

Since terrain is a critical element in determining victory in war I often took steps to deny the enemy any knowledge of it. Or, if that was not possible, at least to make the acquisition of such accurate information difficult. At times I would deliberately let a misleading 'map' be stolen by the enemy, or have my trusted men pretend to have been long resident in the locality. When called upon to advise on the terrain these 'guides' would provide misleading information.

My strategy would be to trap the enemy into a designated killing ground – shown on the map as ground ideal to encamp the army.

So whenever I worked on a strategy I would always check and recheck my sources. Tests of reliability of informants – biographical details checked independently – were a matter of routine.

406

Only after I had ascertained the degree of reliability did I put any weight on the information so received. For the enemy must be assumed to be equally capable of *mis*information. Therefore maps obtained had to be validated by my own scouts before I relied on them.

7 ▰ 3

Besides the ground, another contextual element to be worked into the strategy is the weather. Like a farmer I am always sensitive to weather conditions.

Thus I have often noted in the opening sentences of these memoirs observations about the weather. Indeed flipping back these bamboo rolls I note how remarkably often I have been doing so.

Why?

Perhaps because of my habit as a strategist of always being alert to changing weather conditions. Also partly because I find such a detailed record enables me to recreate within myself precisely the mood I was in when I made an entry in the memoirs. On recapturing such a mood more of the past would flood back again. More insights would be generated. Little insignificant bits of information would become the seeds for growth of new ideas.

Now on weather.

Do I have any secrets in the art of predicting weather changes?

I collect as a matter of course all works on forecasting weather, compiled from every possible source. I study the night sky in order to anticipate what the weather may be like tomorrow. Not only that, but I always ask inhabitants about the weather when I am new to a place.

For I am conscious that some weather conditions may be ideal for implementing a certain strategy.

7 ⚏ 4

I am reminded of the time I besieged a city with tight defences. I used patience as a strategy to win. I simply kept the morale of my men high and made sure they were skilled with their weapons.

I waited for a night of pitch darkness: howling winds that blew towards the city; fearsome lightning that dazzled in the distance; thunder booming in the ears; and rain.

The wind-swept rain pelted into the eyes of the enemy soldiers as they stood guard on top of tall walls, lonely, cold and hungry.

Given days of inaction the enemy was lulled into believing that we were still awaiting reinforcements.

For many clear nights I had stirred the fighting spirits of the men by inspiring talk of how in the past an army prevailed by attacking on a night of stormy upheaval. I told them they would eventually strike like lightning. The attack would be accompanied by drum-like thunder, flashes of lightning, howling wind and arrow-like rain.

Enemy soldiers were simply idling on top of those walls. With poor vision – pitch dark in the distance – and the rain pelting in their eyes, the enemy soldiers stood paralysed by cold and wet.

That night, with the weather as I had described in the tale, finally arrived. So the strategic moment for action came as anticipated.

My men were fed with the best soup. The talk had stirred them into a frenzied state of impatience for real action.

For officers specially skilled in the art of story-telling had retold the same story but with a vividness that was possible because of the stormy weather conditions.

Loss

Having heard that story told again and again of how sweeping success was inevitable when an army launches an attack reinforced by the weather, they now wanted to enact it.

For they saw with their own eyes how the cosmic drama was unfolding before them: howling wind, pelting rain, booming thunder, blazing lightning.

The moment of action for them too had arrived. The yearning for some battle action was deeply felt among the men.

7 ▬▬ 5

So like the release of a caged ram the army bolted when I ordered the attack. My soldiers swarmed over the walls as ants over a molehill.

The enemy soldiers were overwhelmed by the ferocity of these wild human tigers, clawing their way through the defences.

The enemy general thought he was still in a dream when into his gold bedroom burst the heaving soldiers with warm blood still dripping from swords and spears.

I felt some remorse about how the enemy general was butchered as he stood there dazed. When his head was presented to me, it was dripping in blood mixed with rain.

For the soldier who drove the blade fatally through his neck was seeking personal revenge. I was told that this soldier then sank his teeth into the general's fat abdomen – whilst it was still moving and alive – and tore out the intestine and ate it.

He had to be stopped from behaving like a wild animal. His family had been buried alive by this enemy general.

Suddenly the face of the dead general appeared across these bamboo strips with eyes still open as I had seen him.

Always when I recall this episode I feel nauseous. I have to break off from the train of thought. Otherwise that sadness in the eyes would get the better of me. Perhaps I ought to pause by the window for some fresh air.

The wide expanse of heavenly blue reminds me how everlasting this colour is. Even in the darkest of nights the sky is still a deep dark blue rather than a sheet of black.

Without the moon the constellations of stars ensure the sky remains lit. No matter how dim in the starlight, a tinge of blue is always present in the night sky.

Yet those kings whom I had known preferred yellow. Yellow – the colour of the sun as the ruler of the sky.

Why yellow?

I believe that only through consistent application of the right strategy could kingship within a family be sustainable across the generations.

Colour may, however, work at the more primordial and instinctive level in the consciousness of people. For they may associate yellow with the sun, from whom the first emperor of the kingdom originated. And all farmers know that life would simply be impossible without the warmth of the sun.

In these memoirs I ought to set out clearly what I think should be the way of a strategist, or the *Tao* of the strategist. My strategic thoughts have matured over time.

What I am doing here is to reflect further on what I have already recorded in *The Art of War*. In my opinion the path for a strategist to complete success in war depends on knowing four things well: the enemy, yourself, the weather and the ground.

However, if knowledge is limited to yourself and the enemy, then I would still say victory is within grasp. To know the way of Heaven and earth is what truly distinguishes a master strategist.

11

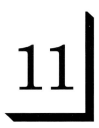

1 ▆▆ 1

A typical day in summer.

Today an interesting thought strikes me and makes me return to these memoirs: the classifiability of things – how our minds put things into groups.

I often feel that this must be the one quality which really differentiates the mind of a strategist from those of others.

Another way of describing this quality that distinguishes – rather than merely differentiates – the mind of a master strategist from another: he is skilled in providing an effective conceptual taxonomy for the varied things under Heaven involved in formulating strategy.

Conceptual classification is a tool that enables one to *see* more sharply and thus be better able to deal with things. I used it for the purpose of defining appropriate strategies in waging war, as recorded in *The Art of War*.

I classified grounds into various types.

1 ▆▆ 2

To be precise I wrote about nine types of ground. I drew on my extensive experiences in the battlefield to set out the do's and don'ts in relation to each type of ground.

I would say that this process of classification is necessary in the development of any knowledge or skills, including strategy.

Thus medical skills evolved with time to become more of an art as practitioners developed a typology of herbal plants that had been found to be effective in treating different kinds of illness.

So it is for different types of skills – be they farming or hunting or fishing. Over the course of time the occupation of a farmer or hunter or fisherman became established.

Skills related to an occupation emerged when persons were recognised as possessing distinctive abilities: skills to differentiate and classify related things and implement the right kinds of action.

Thus a seasoned hunter is able to give instructions on appropriate traps, weapons or devices for capturing different types of animal.

Similarly, a skilled fisherman is able to say what type of fish may be caught in different parts of a stream or river and by what means. A skilled farmer knows the best types of plant that may be grown – and how – on the different kinds of ground and in given weather conditions.

The skilled strategist is no different.

Indeed, I anticipate the emergence of the strategist as a retained adviser – distinct from a general – will become fashionable in the future.

If so, *The Art of War*, being the first written work of its kind, would be essential reading for such a strategist.

1 📖 3

I did not, however, draw a distinction between the role of a strategist and that of a general in *The Art of War*.

Ultimately any warrior – be he general or officer or even commander-in-chief – who has to compete for survival in the battlefield ought to master the strategy of waging war.

The skilful general must be able, as I have said in *The Art of War*, to vary his tactical deployment of forces according to ground conditions. In other words, how the general's forces should be configured depends on these conditions.

The general, in reflecting on this part of *The Art of War*, will quickly realise that the strategies which I have suggested for the various ground situations depend too on my own independent perception of human behaviour – soldiers in particular.

Thus I had prescribed in *The Art of War* that the general,

when fighting on the battlefield, ought to make it abundantly clear to his soldiers what are the odds against surviving. For, based on my own personal experience of battling in such a dire situation, soldiers may in turn be stirred to fight with unbelievable courage. Many of my own soldiers fought with a vigour and endurance that went far beyond my expectations, and beyond the ordinary limits of human endurance.

I noticed too how commands were readily and implicitly obeyed by soldiers in such circumstances. I was initially rather surprised by such a strong unity in spirit among the soldiers. They put up a long and fierce resistance – so long, in fact, that we were finally relieved from the pressure by the timely arrival of fresh reinforcements.

The behaviour of these same soldiers contrasted sharply with their earlier tendency towards divisiveness or a far less marked sense of unity when they were fighting within our own country – on ground which I have classified as 'dispersive'.

1 4

On some types of ground I found it critical that the general should keep the army together – especially that the rear was not left staggering behind. Thus when an army has just penetrated into the enemy's territory – the borderlands – the general must press the army on but at the same time keep it knitted together.

Strategic factors to be considered when fighting on the front are different when an army has penetrated deep inside an enemy's territory. For then the soldiers, by virtue of their unfamiliarity with a new country, tend to stick more closely together. Then problems of a different kind emerge: to gain adequate food, provisions and general supplies so as to sustain a fighting army.

Similarly, when enemy forces are deep within our own territory I would act to deny them resources even to the extent of burning down granaries, storehouses and villages.

I once trapped an entire army in bitter cold through a simple stratagem of luring them deep inside the country to a point where their supply lines became far too stretched to be protected.

Ground

I also denied them of every available resource, even wood. Thus many of the soldiers were frozen to death in the unusually cold winter that greeted their arrival in a burnt-down, deserted town.

1 🕮 5

The true skills of a general in devising stratagems are especially tested on ground that is tightly restricted. Hilly ground, marked by tortuous, twisting paths is the kind of place where the general's shrewd deployment of the different types of soldiers – especially archers – becomes critical in determining success.

Indeed, the very complexity of such ground suggests the applicability of stratagems. In this context I have remarked in *The Art of War* – as an exception to the rule – that a smaller army may profitably engage a larger one.

A different strategic consideration would apply to ground that I would see more as difficult to travel over – marked by the presence of ravines, swamps, high mountains, deep valleys.

Here I would say that the general's prime consideration should be to move the troops quickly out of this terrain. Use roads and well-trodden paths so as to avoid getting lost. Never linger around such places, especially if unfamiliar. There is always the danger that the morale of troops may be weakened if travel has been unnecessarily and unduly delayed.

1 🕮 6

The art of diplomacy is essential for success in waging war, especially when alliances have to be forged, for example, when a general is leading his army into a state which is surrounded by three others.

Given such a ground configuration it would be unwise for the general to engage in a war with any state without first securing alliances with the other two.

If possible the alliances should result in support in terms of resources too. Such alliances have to be forged; otherwise the general may end up having to fight on all three fronts at the same time.

Despite such alliances, however, the general must realise the possible dangers that may still be lurking in the background.

An alliance may no sooner be made before it is broken again. So the general must be wary of exhausting a state's resources.

In war the situation is always fluid. For a stronger state that stays neutral or, worse, pretends to be an ally, may seize the opportunity to deploy its army and gain both the other states in one sweeping action. These two states would then be easy prey, as they have been weakened through the wars fought between themselves.

1 ⚌ 7

In a situation involving three kingdoms or more, consummate strategy skills are called for. Such a situation is inherently unstable.

Human desires being what they are, strife may be expected until one kingdom finally emerges as the ultimate ruler.

Inter-kingdom relationships – whether 'an ally', 'good', 'friendly', 'bad' or 'sour' – are determined not by personal ties alone but more by strategic considerations.

The long-term self-interest of the kingdom concerned would be a primary strategic factor to consider.

Indeed, in such a situation of three kingdoms or more, the struggle for dominance would persist even if no war had been declared.

For war must be understood not only in the strictly military sphere of human endeavour but also as encompassing more widely the political, economic and social dimensions.

The psychological preparation of a people for war is a fundamental aspect of a long-term defensive strategy. So is ongoing training and improvements in weaponry.

2 📖 1

A day of incessant wind.

I stood by the window and heard the rustling of the leaves, and saw how the wind bent some of the trees into arches.

I extended my arms through the windows. By closing and opening these outstretched hands I could sense the flow of air currents curving through my fingers.

After a while, even though this is already spring, and the wind is not icily cold, I began to feel a biting chill inside my bones.

Another sign of aging. I remember how I withstood the cold even in the depths of winter up in the far north.

Old age has its compensations: deeper understanding of the things of the world; a seeing more into the roots of things, but as a result a tendency to be melancholic.

Just compare these memoirs with my terse statements contained in *The Art of War*. I hope there is some deepening of my thoughts through quiet reflection.

How a person's writing changes with the context too! *The Art of War* was written as I continued to wage war – partly to instruct my officers in strategic thinking – but these memoirs are the writing of a recluse up here in a mountain hut.

I tend in my old age to search for root and fundamental causes of things. And I have a greater tendency to philosophise.

2 📖 2

Oh, I wish I could manipulate the direction in which these gushing winds are blowing! That is something even a master strategist is not able to do.

Better still, if I could direct the rushing waters of the rivers. Imagine the power in my hands if I could make these waters flow and flood the enemy camps.

Wind and water are but natural sources of power and energy. Perhaps one day these powers may be harnessed by mankind in waging war.

As the wind whirls across the room my mind becomes

Winds

focused on one theme: the art of manipulating the flow of energy and power.

In the army too resides energy and power. As a commander-in-chief leading the charge of an army I could strongly sense their power and energy as the soldiers on warhorses thundered down the plains.

Directing the flow of energy and power of my own army required skill. But the true test of a consummate strategist lies in mastering – through expert manipulation – the flow of an enemy's energy and power.

I must capture these thoughts now flooding my mind. I must return with urgency to my memoirs before these thoughts escape me.

2 ⬛ 3

I now recall how in *The Art of War* I have often emphasised the role of the strategist in manipulating power.

The master strategist must be able to direct not only the power of his own army but also the enemy's. I have said this categorically in *The Art of War*. The strategist must be able to use such sources of natural power – the weather or the ground – in waging war.

The ground, by its configuration, has latent, invisible power: witness the momentum of a rock that is hurled down on an enemy below. Or the shooting of arrows from a cliff at the enemy trapped below.

Conversely, how much more difficult it is for an army to charge uphill! In doing so the army is pitting itself against the 'power' of the ground. It is like rowing a boat upstream against the tide. Or horsemen riding against the wind.

The extreme cold of winter and heat of summer: these powers of the weather may also be tapped by the strategist in waging war.

These – ground and weather – I have already addressed in the earlier parts of these memoirs. What is especially interesting is countering the power and energy of an enemy.

To destroy an enemy using his latent energy must be the epitome of skill of a master strategist. Consider the implications: the stronger an enemy the more harm, damage or destruction a strategist is able to inflict.

Directing an opponent's flow of energy against himself is illustrated clearly in *Taoist* martial arts. In the martial arts of Wu-Wei – which are grounded on the principles of the *Tao* – an expert exponent can harness the forces of an opponent so as to overthrow him.

Thus the heavier the opponent, the greater the impact of his fall, since the idea is to direct the opponent's force against himself. This I believe is the secret of the martial arts originating from *Taoist* philosophy. To be able to redirect the flow of energy successfully the *Taoist* martial arts exponent must act as if 'at one' with the opponent.

In war – although the scale of conflict is far larger than combat between two individuals – the situation is sufficiently similar for the application of such principles.

Thus, as commander-in-chief, I always emphasised keen observation of the enemy. I want to be 'at one' with my enemy: to so understand him as to be able to anticipate him.

My scouts and spies follow every move, initiative, decision, plan, idea or action of the enemy. By collecting such detailed information a master strategist can enhance his own manipulative powers over the enemy.

One basic principle is to cause imbalance or instability or dispersal in the configuration of the power that resides in the enemy. Thus one technique lies in causing him to shift his focus from the important and crucial to the merely trivial. Another associated technique is to disorientate the enemy so that his balanced perspective of the war is lost.

In *The Art of War* I have written of specific techniques to create disorder inside the enemy camp.

How?

By seizing something that the enemy treasures, so as to force him into compliance with your wishes.

420

As power once concentrated is more difficult to deal with, I gave instructions in *The Art of War* on preventing the enemy forces from amassing, that is, on devising ways to keep them dispersed. If the enemy forces are already amassed in a single locality then the alternative is to coin stratagems that throw the enemy into disarray.

Never allow the enemy an opportunity to consolidate themselves. For when they do so they become more formidable. If I allowed an enemy to consolidate their forces, they would be able to direct their concentrated powers against me. In such a situation there is great danger; indeed even annihilation is possible.

2 🔖 6

The power of an army is dependent on a tight unity in the command structure: rank and file obeying the orders of the higher officers.

So another way – again prescribed in *The Art of War* – of diluting the concentrated power of the enemy army is to cause disunity in the ranks. The idea is to cause the superior officers to suffer from a lack of unqualified support from their subordinates.

Another possible approach requires a thorough analysis of the composition of the enemy forces. I would take advantage of the fact that no army is uniformly weak or average or good or excellent in their fighting capabilities.

Clearly it is easier to score a victory over those identified as 'weak' rather than 'excellent'. By dissecting the enemy forces into their 'excellent', 'good', 'average' and 'weak' divisions I would be able to devise ways of preventing the 'excellent' from salvaging the 'weak' when I seek to subjugate the latter.

Nor would I allow the enemy's vanguard forces to be reunited with the rear after I had sliced the enemy through the middle.

And if the enemy forces are formed into large and small forces I would turn my attention to disrupting their communications. The idea is to prevent the small from cooperating with the large.

Another principle instrumental in causing disorder, imbalance, confusion, discontinuity or disruption in enemy forces is the element of surprise.

I stated in *The Art of War* how an enemy may be surprised. One way is to do things at a speed unanticipated by the enemy.

The enemy general might exclaim:

"It is impossible that their horses are able to fly through the sky to reach there so quickly . . . ".

A much greater speed is made possible through the use of special horses and more skilful riders.

The key, however, in effecting surprises is to be seen to succeed in doing things that are completely beyond expectation. Therefore another secret in enhancing the surprise element of speed is to be deliberately slow on occasion. If the enemy observes this 'slow' pace, he will never anticipate an early arrival in distant places. Alternatively, the surprise may be enhanced by the army advancing through unexpected paths or routes. Another technique is to strike the enemy in those places where I am the least expected.

How do I know I am not expected?

There are two distinct indications: degree of preparations by the enemy and extent of precautions. If both are lacking, then surprise, shock and disarray will be more strongly felt.

2 ⚏ 8

Now as I sit here writing on these strips of bamboo the wind has begun to blow more strongly. My reminiscences on things past and strategic tend to become stronger when the wind blows strongly.

Perhaps these winds are laden with thoughts of the distant past. Not just mine alone, but those of others too. All that is needed is the time and inclination to draw on them as I have done in the process of writing these memoirs.

3 ≣⧚≣ 1

Thirst. Another dry day.

Perhaps the start of a dry season?

Hardly any rain for many days past.

A dryness that seeps into the trees that line the path leading to my hut. The forest behind seems destined to enjoy a reduced green luxuriance.

There is danger with the pervasive dryness that dullness, leanness and hunger may creep into the forest, affecting the many lives that flourish within.

Is such dryness equally foreboding for other people?

I think not.

I breathed in air crisp, thin and dry as I walked back: so deathly still is the air.

The rich colours of the leaves are on the verge of fading: the edges of some of the leaves are becoming thin. The branches look drier, rougher and more brittle: the more fanned outwards the more obvious. Pile upon pile of fallen dried leaves have accumulated on the outside of the hut: the work of winds that only blew in the night.

I make these observations and I am still living out the remaining days of spring!

3 ≣⧚≣ 2

This dryness takes me back to my earlier days at war and the experiences which I later used to extract the principles expressed in *The Art of War*.

The mental impressions from these experiences – some marked by long spells of dryness – still remain with me in my old age as I sit here etching out my story in these memoirs.

I remember in particular one incident which happened very early in my military career: how my men and I were misled into a dead end by a map very carefully crafted by the enemy.

I led about ten thousand men in hot pursuit of a fleeing

Sun

prince after we had seized his city in a surprise attack. We followed a map found in the prince's study in order to make our way through an underground maze of tunnels dug beneath his residence.

The map showed one underground path that led to open ground. From that open ground – as indicated on the map – wide roads led to a neighbouring town.

Since the city was taken in one daring sweeping action I did not suspect that the map might be part of a deliberate ploy to mislead us.

Was there really such a ploy?

I learned a lesson from that experience about relying on maps. That underground path led us instead to a killing ground.

3 ⚔ 3

For when all my soldiers had emerged from the tunnel the entrance was automatically shut tight by a hidden mechanism.

Ten thousand soldiers and I, as commander-in-chief, were stranded on a flat, barren, sandy ground enclosed by steep cliffs.

The sun's heat scorched the earth dry and with every step dust was stirred up from beneath the feet.

The enemy soldiers who stood on top of the cliffs were surprised to see so many of us below. The alert was immediately sounded.

The echoes of the drums roared.

Immediately before us was a narrow path that seemed to be the only way out. From where I stood I could see on both sides of the high ground enemy archers and spearsmen were scrambling into position.

Fires were started and boulders pushed to the edge. My soldiers and I knew that to charge through that path would be to court certain death.

Where we stood too was dangerous. It would be what I later called in *The Art of War* a classic example of a killing ground.

My soldiers knew at once the grave danger they were in. I was surprised at how quickly and resolutely they faced it.

Immediately the men with shields who had successfully scaled the walls of the city – in spite of all the arrows, rocks and hot oil being hurled at them – formed a protective cordon of shields round the troops with me at the centre.

From the gaps in the shields I could see that the enemy troops themselves were still recovering from the shock of seeing so many of us below.

The first wave of arrows that fell on us was sporadic, shot weakly and uncoordinated. Many of them were easily fended off by my men. But moments after the alert had been sounded we saw bows and arrows ringing round at the top of the cliffs. The waves of arrows that followed did find their targets, some even through the narrow gaps between the shields used by my men.

We responded by banding ourselves together ever more tightly, even though I had never drilled them to respond so rapidly. They quickly moved the injured to the rear for safety. Those behind tended their wounds.

The arrows fell like rain for some time. They were then followed by spears and what we feared most – heavy boulders. I myself had to ward off many arrows that seemed to be directed at me specifically.

3 ⚜ 4

Within our own ranks were archers. But the onslaught of the enemy arrows was such that it was impossible to do anything other than stay cringing beneath and inside the shields.

Then there seemed to be a slowdown in the arrows that came at us. My archers took that chance to brave the continuing avalanche and charged forward.

They shot arrows upwards at the enemy soldiers who stood exposed at the edge of the cliffs. They were taken aback by such a surprise move.

Many enemy soldiers were wounded by these arrows. They fell off the cliff and crashed to their death.

We were granted a brief reprieve from the onslaught of arrows, spears and rocks as the enemy stepped back a little.

That split second was, however, sufficient for the rest

of my men quickly to recover spears lying on the ground.

In a perfectly timed and well coordinated action they threw the spears back at the enemy soldiers. The timing was perfect: the moment when they bent themselves forward for a look at the situation below.

Many were speared dead and fell off the cliff, far more than I would ever have thought possible, given our disadvantaged position: we were standing at the bottom of these steep cliffs and sending the spears upwards.

Then we smelt smoke and I knew the danger lay in front of us, so immediately shouted to the men to withdraw.

Hot burning oil was poured on to us from the top of the cliff. Many in the front were badly scalded. They screamed loudly and jumped and reeled about wildly.

More oil was poured.

3 5

This time fewer were hit as many had by then withdrawn to the rear. The enemy, roaring with evil laughter and jeering noisily, only agitated my men more.

Then out of the clear sky we saw pots, meltingly hot, coming down on us. Those hit by the pots had their skin charred black as soot. The larger pots were seen rolling down the cliff. The pots cut a path through our ranks as men avoided the molten heat.

I saw my men near me gritting their teeth and clenching their fists ever more tightly. I knew the men were so angry and bitter that they would do whatever they could to tear the hearts out of the enemy.

I asked myself:

"Could that be a sign that the enemy has run out of arrows, spears and boulders?"

Then one of my men started to jeer back at the enemy:

"Cowards! If you have any guts come down here and fight us!"

The rest of my men joined in. Soon the jeer became

rhythmic. But what was even more inspiring was a chorus that arose out of the incident as the men sang:

"Together we shall fight. Till the last we shall never surrender. Our souls united, no one dares challenge us to a real fight. We crave a warrior's death ... "

3 ⚔ 6

The enemy general, who had all along been hiding himself at the top of the cliff, suddenly appeared on the scene. He shouted at the top of his voice, betraying a sense of impatience:

"Let us grant them a warrior's death."

Perhaps he had expected us to dash through the narrow path. From where I stood I saw coloured banners being waved in the air as a signal to some distant troops.

Immediately my scout put his head to the ground whilst my men fearlessly advanced to block off the path that led into our enclosure.

The archers picked up the stray arrows that littered the ground. My suspicion was confirmed: the enemy had run out of arrows, spears and boulders.

Perhaps the enemy troops were finding their way down on the other side of the cliff. Then my officer seemed to read my mind. He ordered the men to let the warriors charging on horses through into the enclosure. For these warriors this would mean their end. The enclosure was their death-trap.

The archers had already lined themselves up for a quiet wait. Immediately after the warrior-horsemen were let in my men would close the opening again.

The warrior-horsemen thus trapped were shot with several arrows at once. They hardly had a chance to raise their spears, halberds or swords.

My men were determined not to yield even a little ground. They resolutely held the ground against the onslaught of the enemy forces. For they knew the dire consequences if they failed. It would spell the end of what remained of a badly battered division.

They took turns to fight off the advance. Indeed the fighting continued through the night. The next day the toil of fighting off the enemy began to tell on my men. Some lamented the passing of the night. The sun would mean more burning dryness in their throats – for some men that was worse than fighting.

3 ▥ 7

When dawn broke we were pleasantly suprised by two happenings that signalled the end of our ordeal.

First, the enemy had drummed a withdrawal. We later learned that the map was a trick devised by those in the enemy forces who wanted to depose the prince. But the ploy was discovered – moments before our attack – by the elements in the enemy armed forces who remained loyal to the prince.

To this day the reason for the withdrawal of enemy forces remains for me a mystery. Perhaps these enemy forces which attacked us formed the bulk of the enemy forces which were anti-prince.

The commander of these anti-prince forces may have decided that little purpose was served by fighting us: after all we came to fight the prince too! Such were the intrigues of court politics that to this day this question – *why the withdrawal?* – still remains unclear. Things like this remain buried deeply in the memory of time.

Second, the door to the underground passage had sprung open after my other division found their way to us!

And I lived to write the lessons of this episode in *The Art of War:* that soldiers, when in desperate situations or having to face certain death, naturally become more vigilant and fight to their utmost capability.

The psychological trauma has remained with me into old age: dryness in nature reawakened within me recollections of this event!

429

Mystical

4 ⚏ 1

A day in late spring.

Though still soaked from the rain I am moved to record a strange occurrence, an event that took me back to *The Art of War* and the memoirs.

I have just stepped into my mountain hut. During my journey back, thunder, lightning and the wind-swept rain greeted me as I reached the bank of the river. I was caught by inclement weather that engulfed the entire stretch of the river, the river long and wide meandering across the grass-land.

In the distance the silhouette of an isolated boatman perched on his tiny boat against a backdrop of stormy weather struck a poetic chord in me. Despite the rain, dark clouds, flashes of lightning and rising waves of river-water the boatman was unperturbed.

When I approached the boat he seemed hardly even to notice me. He appeared absorbed in a world of his own and oblivious to the happenings around him.

I asked myself:

"Why would he be standing there alone if his intention was not to ferry people across to the other side of the river?"

The boatman struck me as unique. He stood at the end of the boat, unmoved – perhaps even immovable – by all the cosmic uproar and disturbance.

He appeared to have read my thoughts and nodded his head as I moved nearer. Just when I was about to ask him the fare he raised two fingers – two copper coins. This was another surprise – no increase in fare despite the obviously more difficult journey ahead. At the point where I embarked the river must be at its widest.

With the mist on the waters the wooden platform on the far bank was hardly visible.

These factors – the weather and the strange boatman – added a touch of the unusual to what should have been a routine crossing of a river.

Interestingly, I found his stoic look – almost hidden by the straw hat, half-closed eyes and thick but tightly sealed lips – reassuring.

As a former commander-in-chief I would have thought the weather to be somewhat too rough and dangerous for a crossing.

I was like any other old, tired and worn-out traveller eager to be back in my hut. The way the boatman stood so firmly on the boat despite its being tossed about on the river gave me added confidence.

He steered the boat almost effortlessly.

As I sat there my mind was brought back to *The Art of War*: two enemies on a boat tossed about by the strong winds and waves would cooperate just like a pair of hands – the right assisting the left.

Would that happen on this boat too?

There was something mysterious about the boatman and his art of boating. It went beyond my perception of the boatman and boat as one.

I sensed that they were at one with the river too. It was as though the river itself was pulling the boatman and his boat across to the other bank.

His movements seemed so perfectly synchronised with the waves, the wind and the rain.

So calmly did he ply his oars. Indeed so rhythmic was the rise and fall of the boat as it cruised across the river that I fell into a sweet slumber.

As the boat approached the platform I rose from the wooden plank that served as a seat. To my utmost surprise I saw a huge dark brown water snake swimming right below the boat.

It was as though the snake was carrying the boat along as it swam. The boatman was quite unflustered by the sight of the giant snake.

His reaction further calmed me – any other man would have been paralysed by fear. I had experienced enough terrifying situations to stay calm, even in a calamity.

The boatman's eyes opened slightly and I was shocked to see that he had no pupils – simply a dark pigment. Despite that I caught a glint in his eyes as the boat neared the platform. It was as if he knew I was Sun Tzu.

I gave him two copper coins as I disembarked. As I stood there on the platform I saw the snake more clearly.

It was nearly thrice the size of the boat. As the boat turned to head for the journey back, so did the snake, in perfectly coordinated movements.

Even more extraordinary, the boatman threw both copper coins into the river, obviously aiming at the snake, which swallowed them in one gulp.

Could this be the snake of Mount Chang that I wrote about in The Art of War?

4 ▰ 4

There were many more questions than I could ask, for example:

Was it the boatman or the snake or both that actually brought me, seated on the boat, across the river?

Never in my travels or military exploits had I encountered such instantaneous coordination between a man and a snake.

I wrote in *The Art of War* of troops being able to coordinate instantly like the snake that dwelled in Mount Chang: if hit at the head it attacked with the tail; when its tail was struck the head responded; if hit in the middle both the head and tail would immediately counter-attack.

Everybody knows how such deep intuitive understanding may be possible between a rider and his horse. The rider and horse act as though they were one.

Famous warriors of the past often attained such a level of unison with their horses. So much so that when the warrior was endangered the horse could sense it, even though the warrior might be miles away.

How?

By the oneness of mind that had been achieved by both warrior and horse. For the troops too such reflex responses would be possible if their hearts and minds functioned as one.

A seasoned military observer may, from the way an army has been responding to attacks, discern the degree of unity in spirit.

Also, even though the battleground may appear chaotic – swarms of soldiers clamouring and milling about in circular patterns, columns of dark smoke arising and dead bodies, equipment and weapons strewn all over the ground – the trained eye would be able to discern a strategic intent and design behind the coordinated movements of troops.

But unity of spirit between a snake in the river and a boatman?

This must be something worth investigating.

4 ⚜ 5

I left the memoirs on the table as I continued with my enquiries into the boatman and the snake.

I ventured down to the river and to exactly the same platform. This time the sky was clear and the river calm.

Despite a cluster of boats, the boatman I had met before was not there. Those who stood waiting at the platform were not able to help.

I crossed the river to the other side and faced the same disappointment. I chatted with some villagers who took the boats across.

Nobody knew about the boatman as I described him. Now I began to wonder if I really had met such a boatman and the snake.

Or was it pure, vivid, imagination?
I dozed off during the ride, did I not?
Could it then have been a dream?

I have never been superstitious by nature and have always believed in grounding my principles on empirical observations and learning through experience.

This encounter, however, was somewhat unusual. It seemed impossible for me to find any plausible explanation for what had happened.

4 ⚏ 6

Along the path up the mountain I happened by chance to meet the famous *Taoist* hermit, about whom I and everybody living around this mountain knew.

He was called White Cloud. Somebody once told me that White Cloud was actually a few hundred years old.

According to some very old villagers the name was given to him a long, long time ago. It originated after many villagers claimed to have seen him floating on top of white clouds.

In my eyes, however, he appeared with his flowing white hair to be like any normal old man I knew. But there was one noticeable difference – there was a youthful exuberance about him.

It was he who unravelled the mystery, as I stood there in utter disbelief – I tried hard not to show it.

4 ⚏ 7

For according to him, the boatman was none other than the alter ego of the snake of Mount Chang, the snake that I wrote about in *The Art of War*! Due to very long years of self-cultivation the snake was able to transform itself to appear as a human being.

No wonder there were no pupils in the eyes of the boatman. He had the eyes of a snake.

More interestingly, the snake still resides in Mount Chang but would occasionally travel through the rain-clouds to the river.

Now I realised why I had noticed the strong sense of oneness between the boatman, the snake and the river.

White Cloud was certain that the snake of Mount Chang must have anticipated my difficulty in crossing the river in such stormy weather.

For that reason the snake made a special appearance. I

could only speculate on the reason: perhaps the snake had learned of my reference to it or him in *The Art of War*. This might explain that glint in the snake-like eyes of the boatman.

But why did the boatman throw two of my copper coins into the river?

The snake, according to White Cloud, may possibly have swallowed those copper coins to enhance that metallic glow of brown on his skin.

Now that everything strange about the incident had been explained by White Cloud I felt a sense of relief.

I therefore hurried back to record the details related to this strange event in the memoirs.

5 ▚ 1

A misty morning in autumn.

I would have ventured out had the mist been less dense. I could hardly see even my hands when stretched out in front of me. Or perhaps this could be due to the decline in the power of sight as I grow older.

I sat here facing the window – how it framed a picture of the mist outside! – and unrolled the memoirs to do some writing.

But as I gazed into the misty nothingness I lapsed into that indeterminate state of mind when one is neither asleep nor awake.

In such a semi-meditative state of consciousness one's grasp of the immediate present slowly weakens as the mind drifts on to other things.

The realm between pure imaginative reflection and dream grew more and more indistinct.

Over the many years of surviving out there in the battle-field I found myself able to coin my most innovative strata-gems or strategic ideas in moments such as these.

Parcels of time when I could not say for certain whether my mind was residing more in the *reality* of thinking or the *unreality* of dreaming.

With my mind in such a state of *reality–unreality* I found myself to be most productive in terms of generating the most innovative ideas.

What truly surprised me as a young man was that the less the conscious will to do the thinking, the better the results of unconstrained thinking.

For innovative stratagems that could help me resolve a difficulty would come to me as flashes of insight rather than as an outcome of logical deduction.

Thus if I recounted those occasions many could be seen to involve moments of plain idleness. People would be sur-prised to learn that there are such moments, even during times of war.

5 ▚ 2

A typical situation would be that of me, as commander-in-chief, seated in my war carriage, waiting for the army to reorganise itself.

In those moments of idle waiting before I set off to another battle-ground, fresh insights would stream into my consciousness out of nowhere. These processes are distinct from the more conscious strategic thinking that I often practised.

During my travels from one place to another in the carriage, I had the habit of using such time – sometimes many days on end – to reorder my thoughts.

I used to like to reflect quietly on what I had read that evening. For in the evenings, if I had any available time – apart from my duties as commander-in-chief – I would read whatever records might be available on the many wars fought in the ancient past. My men had been instructed to locate in any new city or town or village whatever records there might be on past wars. Often I would study etched tortoise-shells from antiquity in my efforts to learn the ancient skills in waging war.

It was from these ruminations over antique records that I drew useful lessons. I tested these principles using my own direct experiences from war.

I distilled the crucial lessons – the essence of the principles – for future strategists in my work, *The Art of War*.

5 ≡ 📖 ≡ 3

Of the many kings from the past who had waged war I found that the hegemonic kings of antiquity, or rather early antiquity, to be by far the most instructive.

The generals who commanded the invincible armies of the hegemonic king must themselves have been just as skilful in the art of waging war. Some, from the records of their exploits, appear to have been more than equal to the task, compared with the illustrious hegemonic king.

Thus from the historical records I acquired the secret principle of how to deal with a strong enemy: never allow an enemy to concentrate his forces.

Obviously the way to prevent this would depend on the circumstances. If the strategy of keeping the enemy army dispersed proved effective, then the enemy would be denied any possible gains from concentrating their entire strength against my inferior force.

Their combined strength would not be of immediate significance unless – and only unless – the enemy were afforded that opportunity to amass their forces.

Throughout wars I had applied a strict rule of discipline: I never allowed myself on any account to enter into a fight with a force reckoned to be stronger.

I would always wait for that opportunity when the enemy's strength had declined sufficiently before striking.

That I did not take any unwarranted risks may explain my triumph over my enemies, which I attributed to my reading about the hegemonic king.

5 ⬛ 4

The hegemonic king of old must have understood what moved the ordinary soldier. He understood what made men fearful and frightened, and what made them panic. This deep understanding of psychology was instrumental in his successes.

He mastered the skill to awe his enemy into submission without fighting. That many cities have been recorded as having fallen into his hands through strategy is a measure of his talents as a strategist.

Sitting here, I can easily imagine city walls collapsing under the weight of incessant attacks.

But can I imagine the walled cities of a numerically stronger enemy falling on account of strategy?

The secret ploys and machinations of strategy that worked towards beating a city into submission were far less well documented in ancient history. That would have required more substantive thinking, imagination and greater understanding.

The hegemonic king truly mastered the concept of power; nobody knew better how to nurture, gain, retain, exploit and foster power.

In order to deprive his foe of power he would, as a consummate strategist, prevent others from allying with his enemy.

King

This he did through projecting an awesome image of his power as hegemonic king. Thus his power base grew while that of his enemies declined.

I could also visualise how defeated the other kings must have felt to be cowed into handing over cities.

Imagine a former king down on bended knees pledging allegiance to him– outside the gates of his very own capital city.

For the hegemonic king had mastered the skills of weakening and finally depriving other, lesser kings, of their powers.

5 5

So long as the hegemonic king breathed he would be regarded as the king among kings. But his successes also depended on the capable generals that he had nurtured.

From reflective reading and analyses of past records of how the generals of the hegemonic king had fought I identified some common characteristics. These reflections I duly recorded in *The Art of War* as a distillation of my thoughts: knowing the plans of neighbouring states so as to form timely alliances, gaining familiarity with the terrain and using native inhabitants to gain strategic advantages from the ground.

These precepts I too kept when waging war.

5 6

I believe there is another form of reflective strategic thinking which operates at a deeper, subconscious level.

How else could anyone explain the emergence of a stratagem so unexpectedly?

What perplexed me were glimpses of a stratagem which my mind could literally 'see', the rushing air washing my face as I rode along on my horse across some waste battle-ground.

Even more shocking: in the most unexpected moments of immediate danger my mind could again suddenly 'see' through the secret schemes of an enemy. Yet days before I had still been puzzled. That is, even after I had strolled in the garden, trying to figure out the scheme that might explain a myriad of apparently unrelated events.

Suddenly in a flash of intuition – when I was fending off stray arrows – my mind seemed able to 'fit' unrelated things into a coherent whole. How mysteriously the mind works!

After a series of battles – some more successful than others, some indecisive and a few which I almost lost – my mind would, as my horse galloped rapidly through a long, narrow and dark pass, draw on these concrete experiences to derive some prescriptive principles for success.

Some of these found their expression in *The Art of War*. That the mind works in this manner still fascinates me.

5 7

And I had thought all along that my powers of mind would decline with old age. On the contrary, I found that my strategic mind seemed to work just as well, if not better, as I aged.

For as I grew older I began to look more deeply into certain things that I had glossed over during youth. I began to ask more fundamental questions, not just the 'hows, whats, wheres, whens' of things, but increasingly the multi-faceted 'whys'.

For this tendency I may have found a plausible explanation: as I grew older I began to realise the inevitability of the return of my body to the soil – unless of course I should attain immortality through *Taoist* meditative practices.

The soil is the medium in which all life seems to be rooted – the ultimate source of all things that move under Heaven.

Or is it?

6 ▦ 1

Impending rain?

Dark clouds filled the sky as I prepared to retreat to the mountain hut and perhaps spend the entire summer there.

My eldest son had just read some parts of my memoirs. What he said this morning concerning these memoirs echoes in my mind:

"Father, your thinking as a strategist has mellowed somewhat. These memoirs reveal more of the inner you than did The Art of War! *The family should preserve these for posterity. Our descendants are likely to follow after you and be strategists too."*

How time flies!

In my mind's eye I could still see my son as a little child. Today he is reminding me of something all of us have to accept – strategist or not – the inevitable flow of time. This reminder of my own mortality is most timely.

I ought to preserve these memoirs, now so extended and voluminous, with many more rolls of bamboo strips than I had anticipated when I first began the work.

Would my grandchildren and their line of descendants want to master the art of waging war?

How many would by that time seek a career in royal courts as strategy advisers?

Perhaps time passes even faster when you are living in a period of war. But war or peace, life goes on as it always has.

6 ▦ 2

I have benefited from recorded histories and writings on the many wars fought since ancient times.

When I read these records aloud in my mind I seemed to hear the echoes of their voices from the past.

Yet despite my wide reading of all that was available I found something to be missing. I hope the memoirs can fill such a gap.

I could not find anything that reflected the inner thoughts, feelings, intuitions, meditations and reflections of strategists who lived through times of war.

These memoirs, in which I try to mirror the inner mind of a strategist – using my own inner thoughts as a source – may be valuable for that reason alone.

My son, though years younger, is right. I should ensure that these reflective thoughts on strategy – my memoirs – are preserved for posterity.

The very fact that the style in which they are written differs from *The Art of War* may make the work even more useful to strategists of the future, perhaps those that come many generations after I am dead and gone.

Here in the memoirs I have deliberately allowed my thoughts to wander. If my work *The Art of War* is viewed as a farm, then these memoirs are the undulating greenery of nature.

So whilst *The Art of War* is prescriptive and constrained to thirteen chapters, these memoirs are free and overflowing with the ideas, thoughts, fears, worries and concerns of a strategist. Each complements the other. Each was written at very contrasting times of my life as a strategist.

The Art of War is a work forged out of the ruins of war. The embers of the fires of war can still be felt when one reads it. These memoirs on the other hand were written during my retreat up in the mountain hut. The reader can almost feel the remoteness of living so high up on the mountain.

Another difference is in my age at the time they were written. I was a much younger man when I wrote *The Art of War*. In contrast, I am now old and wrinkled, writing these memoirs.

Also there is a difference in my position. I was in command as a commander-in-chief directing my army in their operations when *The Art of War* was written. Now as a reclusive old man I am completing my memoirs.

Both works share one thing in common: they deal with things strategic.

6 3

Some aspects of strategy, however, remain constant over

time. Indeed some of the prescriptions may even be relevant in other spheres of human activity.

I believe that *The Art of War*, if it survives the vagaries of time, will remain relevant. For it contains the fundamental principles on strategy. So no matter how far it has to cruise down the river of time it will still appeal to strategists.

What then are some of the constants?

They are the qualities that I have emphasised in *The Art of War* as critical for a person to succeed as a general. The morale, fighting spirit, skills and determination of an army – all these depend to a large extent on the personal skills of the general.

Even if the tide of war has turned against the general, he must hide his true feelings. His face should look unperturbed.

In meting out rewards and punishments the actions of the generals must be seen to be entirely unbiased and objective.

Of utmost importance, the general must gain complete mastery over himself: he must never let his anger or temper show.

Another quality of the general that remains desirable – regardless of time and place – is inscrutability. The enemy must not be able to discover his inclinations one way or the other from studying his facial expressions. So during long conferences, despite provocative and agitative statements by the enemy, the general should stay as inscrutable as ever.

The enemy must always be left in doubt as to the true intentions of the general. Keeping his actual plans hidden is critical for success in waging war. Any untimely leakage of plans may be disastrous not only for the army under his command but for an entire state.

Thus in *The Art of War* I stressed that the general should always maintain the secrecy of his true plan – even from his own officers and troops and ordinary people.

His ultimate responsibility is to gain the final victory that may seem to the state and its people to be elusive.

But does the end alone – to finally prevail over the enemy – justify the means which I prescribed in The Art of War *should guide the general in his conduct of war: the utter secrecy that includes even deceiving his own people as to his true strategy?*

Sitting here I often wonder if war could ever become more civilised; if the parties to wars could come to agree on rules of war.

Or are these prescriptions in The Art of War *only appropriate for the time and conditions, so wicked and wretched, that I have lived through?*

6   4

Whatever rules of war may be agreed upon between states, the role of the generals is likely to remain unchanged: that of leading men into actual combat.

Like the artist who must appreciate the qualities of paper and brush before painting, the general must appreciate the context of war and the motivation of his soldiers. So a general must recognise that his soldiers, when thrown into desperate situations, become ever more resolved to fight for victory. Thus I prescribed that the general should even create these situations by his own actions: burning one's own boats and smashing one's cooking pots. In doing this the wise general is only ensuring that the law of human behaviour works to his best advantage.

In order that the confidence of men to wage wars successfully remained undisturbed by talk of things super-natural, I prescribed that the general should disallow any superstitious practices.

Yet another prescription in *The Art of War* came out of my experience as a commander-in-chief. I had often found my men to be doubly cohesive, the deeper they penetrated into enemy territories.

The importance of keeping things strategic secret is so great that I would never announce in advance the places to which the army would be headed. Also nobody – not even my own men – would be told in advance the time I planned to move. So the enemy found it extremely difficult to lay traps for me.

Would such strategic approaches remain valid in the many, many years ahead of us?
Would the art of war be so different a thousand or more years later?

I sit here and imagine the battle scenes of old. My lessons in *The Art of War* had been derived in part from ancient teachings. Perhaps I ought to consider too the context in which those wars had been waged.

6 ▥ 5

Time.

I often ponder over the essence of time.

What it is? and what it is not?

In waging war timing is critical to winning. There is a right and a wrong time for any planned military action.

Now as I grow older, I begin to think of the coming of an end of time – my time. Many of my fellows have gone before me and I need not fear the going.

But what puzzles me still today is why so many of my men – some whom I knew well and were close to me – have gone over to the other side but none has ever returned to tell me what it is like there?

The battlefield may be strewn with dead bodies but none ever returns – except occasionally in my dreams.

Is death then a journey that my men who were killed in battle embark on immediately upon their death? A journey that somehow is irreversible?

Perhaps it is just like going down a waterfall in a river. It is simply impossible for one that has gone over to paddle back.

I know that at birth a lot of blood is spilled.

I was once asked by a soldier if death in the battlefield – especially with that much blood being shed – meant instantaneous birth somewhere else.

I shall never know, as I am more likely to return to the soil than die in the heat of battle!

Time

7 ⟨⟩ 1

Lightning.
    Many flashes.
        Appearing
    disappearing
reappearing.
      Disappearing
        reappearing
          disappearing.
     Many times.
          Lightning.
        Blinding.
     Terrifying.
    Swift.
Lightning.

This is a piece of calligraphy in which I tried to capture the essence of speed of lightning on paper.

I took out my memoirs from the open shelf and flipped to that strip of bamboo where I last stopped.

I remain, despite being old, as fascinated by the way lightning traverses the sky as when I was very young.

Today promises to be yet another stormy autumn day. With the rain-laden clouds looming in the distance the sky appears ready to strike with a heavy downpour.

I sit by the window waiting for the storm that hangs above to unleash its energy.

What is so similar about the storm and the army?

Both are, from my abstraction, simply bundles of energy. Energy which, when unfurled, would wreak havoc on earth through sheer destructive power. Surprisingly, despite all the turmoil that has been brewing on the horizon – lightning, thunder and wind – *not a single raindrop has fallen.*

What a disappointment!

I looked for another opportunity to study the nature of water. For I have always held the qualities of water in very high esteem. These qualities, as written about in ancient books, have been validated by me through direct and fascinated observation.

Turbulence

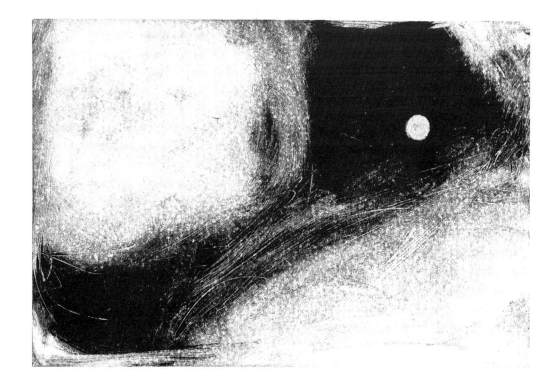

Indeed, through the deep reflection of images in water I have derived insights that are simply inexpressible in words. Words limit as much as they illuminate. For that reason in *The Art of War* I kept my message brief.

My preferred mode of instructing my officers in the art of war was to direct their minds to the phenomena of war. So as wars evolved I took pains to explain to some of my chosen disciples – often my own officers – how some of the basic principles are inherent in certain phenomena. How speed, for instance, was the essential principle for success in one exploit (to be discussed later).

I was concerned that too many words might distort the fundamental ideas that I had discovered and validated empirically on the battlefield. So I chose to state only those that I believed would be of continuing relevance in wars to come. Also men have a way of attaching themselves to words rather than seeing for themselves the reality, of which words are merely tools of description. No words can describe the essence of speed better than if I direct the eyes of my men to the lightning in the sky.

Yet how many of them will seek out lightning for deeper study and reflection?

Such a study is essential if one is to fully comprehend the concept of speed as I intended it should be understood.

Also, words often become dated. Look at how quickly the books of old become obsolete. Alas, the book, *The Art of War*, is composed of nothing but words.

Could I ever write a wordless *Art of War*? a book that constitutes, if you like, the essence or *chi* of war?

How timeless will The Art of War *remain?*

I know not.

As the water, the storm, and all that is part of nature seem unchanging, so must those principles of war that were derived or grounded on direct observations of nature.

451

Human nature, being an integral part of nature, may too remain unchanging across the vast expanses of time.

But is nature so unchanging and eternal?

What is founded on the ever-changing will always change, whilst that which is grounded on the unchanging (or unchangeable?) will remain unchanged.

Tonight, after such a long observation of flashes of lightning across the sky, it would be timely for me to reflect more deeply on their quality.

Perhaps embedded in these observations are lessons in the art of war.

Some flashes of lightning are like the heavenly calligraphic brushstrokes executed instantaneously across the sky: swift, powerful, bold, dynamic – even majestic.

7 ⚊ 4

The best generals are those scholar-swordsmen who wield the brush as they would the sword. Both the sword and the brush are moved by the same source of energy inherent in nature: the *chi* that is the essence of the life-force.

In nature I find *chi* in things. That which sustains life must contain within itself *chi* or energy. Every army, too, has its energy.

So the wise and careful general stores up the energy of the army till that incisive moment.

Even in unleashing the *chi* of the army the superior general seeks to ensure that the army is thereby strengthened rather than weakened.

How?

Now as I write I sense the strong *chi* of the rice that I have been cooking in the back corner of my little hut. Yes, even the grains contain within them the life-force or *chi*.

For how else would you explain their growth when these grains were planted in the soil?

When cooked the grains unleashed their vital *chi* into the air, and hence the fragrance.

How else would you explain why no roots will sprout from grains that have been cooked?

I see in the gathering of the storm an accumulation of *chi* in nature. As I studied the evening sky a pitch darkness crept inside the room. I retreated from the window and ignited the wick. Slowly the light returned as shadows were cast about the room.

Outside the clouds dispersed as quickly as they had formed. The flashes of lightning decreased perceptibly in intensity and frequency and at last all became quiet.

I am left only with a memory of what I had witnessed earlier.

I recalled my writings in *The Art of War* wherein I had emphasised speed as being the essence of war.

"*Strike...*" I would say to my soldiers "*like the lightning!*"

Hidden in the dark clouds the lightning would strike down from the sky so quickly. And as it unfurled its power I could see it spreading out wide and dashing downwards to the ground.

7 ▓ 5

In my mind's eye I could recall my army emerging from the clumps of bushes and trees – like the clouds in the night sky – and charging down at such thunderous speed that the enemy below was simply shocked into inaction.

Though the incident had happened so many years ago, the impression stayed with me. The enemy was completely unprepared. Many a soldier was frozen by fear: cold sweat trickled down their faces.

The enemy general was himself lulled by the deceptive quietness of the mountainous passes into complacency. He was in the carriage, dressed in silken undergarments.

He died with his head stuck to the wooden pole of the carriage, nailed by an arrow that shot through his neck.

The killing was not unlike the flashes of lightning that lashed out and mercilessly felled the tallest of the defenceless trees that grew in the thick forest.

453

Many an enemy soldier surrendered, swords still undrawn. And the arrows of many an enemy archer remained tightly strapped.

These images were replayed vividly in my mind as I read the passage in *The Art of War*:

"... *be swift as the hare so that the enemy will not be able to resist you.*"

But on that occasion we were swifter than the hare – more like lightning in our speed and destructive force.

7 ⬛ 6

That was the opening we had yearned for. Many of my soldiers knew the principle that speed would maintain the element of surprise.

Indeed, we had been trailing the enemy before that decisive moment when I ordered the strike. The enemy general himself had caused the downfall of his army by being so relaxed.

My army was put on the alert the moment it was reported to me that the general – probably due to the heat of the day – had changed from his distinctive armoured outfit into something made of silk.

His soldiers took that as a signal for them also to relax. Consequently, the swords were sheathed, halberds, long spears, axes and other weapons kept in boxes and bows and arrows packed behind the archers' backs.

Later the captured soldiers, some half-drunk, confessed that they thought an army of ghost-soldiers had attacked them. For in the darkness of the mountain pass at night they could only hear thundering noises and roars but could not see any soldiers. Many simply panicked as the roar of the attack echoed down into the mountain passes below.

But rather than order the slaughter of the masses of soldiers who surrendered I spared many of their lives. Only the most evil of the officers were killed. Many whose lives I spared later volunteered to join me in my military expeditions. Therefore I was able to reinforce the *chi* of my army as a consequence of the attack.

12

1 ⟨book icon⟩ 1

A CLEAR, WINDLESS, wintry day.

As the years catch up with me I have become ever more wary of the cold wind from the north. Against these winds I have had to act more defensively over the years, especially these last few. With declining health the cold has become less and less tolerable. For no matter what clothes I wear these northerly winds always find their way into the marrow of my bones.

Thus a windless morning is one of the few remaining pleasures that I yearn for when living through an otherwise bleak winter.

I took a stroll during the early dawn of the day – one of the many that I had taken. A morning walk is revitalising to the body as it is refreshing to the mind.

A refreshed mind brings new memories. In old age memory is important, especially for a once highly active commander-in-chief like me.

I am trapped in a bodily frame that creaks like an old, little-used door. Yet the martial spirit in me remains very much alive.

I sometimes feel – despite my old frame – the pangs of hunger. Not for food but an insatiable hunger for action.

My mind, in contrast with my body, remains clear despite the years. Besides letting memories flood my mind I also work on these memoirs.

I simply have an inner compulsion.

On some occasions in quiet recollection – seated as I was, my legs folded under me – I would see my past reflected in a still pool that existed inside my mind. The stillness of that pool seemed to correspond to the quietness of my heart. In those moments of absolute stillness I saw past events unfolding.

But when emotions arose in me about what had been portrayed in that pool of the mind, then the imagery quickly became blurred.

It was as though somebody had thrown stones into that pool. That somebody was none other than my other self: my strong, alter ego.

456

Interestingly, the facets of my past that the pool reflected were often sparked off by what I saw in the day, not directly but indirectly.

This morning I saw charred remains of branches snapped from old desolate trees: dashes of black against the pervasive whiteness of snow. A familiar scene, and one that I had seen so many times before. But never with such evocation of strong emotions.

For the hands of nature seemed to be at work etching out an impressive calligraphic piece – dashes of black on white – for my eyes alone: Sun Tzu the Fire Strategist.

Indeed, I had been known during my military days for my expert use of fire as part of the strategy for waging war.

In *The Art of War* I had laid down how fire ought to be employed. Thus a basic requirement is to have some things – wood, cloth, grass – that fire may consume in the process of burning.

Fire cannot, however, burn walls of stone or sand. Nor can fire contend with water, even though it may melt metals.

To raise a mountain of fire requires thorough preparation and special equipment, including incendiary missiles.

I had also recorded in *The Art of War* the times when it would be most appropriate to use fire: during a dry spell as a result of scorching heat, and when the wind is strong.

The time of day for the use of fire is also critical to

success: the idea is to strike where and when it is least expected. For example, in the dead of night, with high winds after days of scorching heat will be an appropriate time, as people are likely to be deeply asleep.

As fire may be put out by water the choice of the place to launch the first strike must be where access to water is tortuous and difficult.

Fires once raised can be ferociously destructive, roasting whatever lies in their path: people, stores, equipment, arsenals, grain, almost anything.

1 ≣ 4

As commander-in-chief I often asked my officers and men to study fires, to learn through their own observation what it meant to fight as ferociously as these roaring flames.

I would instruct the officers thus:

"Emulate these fiery qualities through thinking deeply about what is now unrolling before your eyes."

This I learned from a cook turned soldier whose style of fighting much resembled burning flames. When he was a cook he would spend many hours observing how fiercely the fires would burn in the stove. As a result he had acquired some of its fighting qualities. I had witnessed him *burning* through the ranks of the enemy.

How he died was rather strange. It was reported to me that he had drowned when tossed into the waters of the river by an unexpected surge of a wave.

He ought to have known better: fire fears water. But the river crossing was unavoidable. Perhaps his death was simply fated.

1 ≣ 5

From close observation of the use of fire in many battles I derived further lessons on its use in waging war.

The overriding principle is clear: act according to the changing circumstances. These situations are often fluid. For

Fire strategy

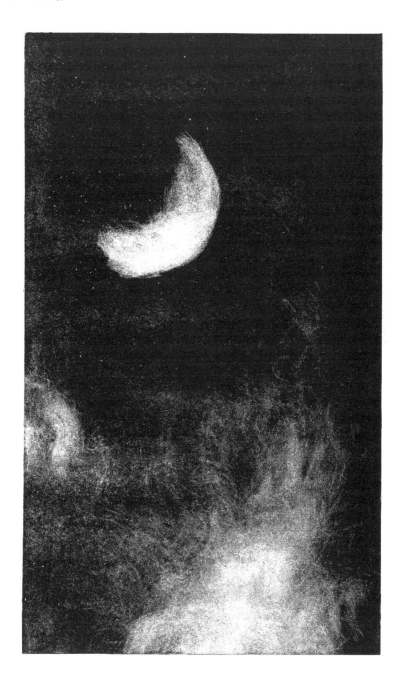

each of them I tried in *The Art of War* to state what seemed to be the most appropriate actions for the commander-in-chief to take.

One is simply that when the fire has broken out inside the enemy's camp the commander-in-chief must immediately coordinate military actions on the outside.

Do not, however, launch an attack immediately if, despite the fire, the enemy has remained calm inside his camp. When the fire has reached its height, take such follow-up action as circumstances may best indicate.

But to do nothing except wait may also be a wise strategy: much depends on how the situation evolves.

The wind direction must be anticipated: never attack from down-wind if the fire has been raised up-wind. Otherwise a calamity may result.

1 🕮 6

Even though I have written in *The Art of War* about fire strategy, the role of fire has long been rooted in human lives. Fire has for so long been a tool for man. Since very ancient times its destructive powers have been acknowledged.

Some even attribute supernatural powers to fire. I know of people who worship fire. A seer whose skills I have come to respect – I usually avoided discussion of the supernatural in my earlier writings – uses fire as an oracle. For his eyes only, fire opens up vistas of the future. The enquirer merely has to choose a piece of firewood and toss it into the burning flames.

He also uses the sounds of fire. Through the crackling sounds of burning wood he can hear the voices of the future. Even the dead, it seems, speak through the crackling sounds of the fire.

But how is it possible for the past and future to be read and heard through fire?

I still do not know.

For it to be possible, time – past, present and future – must by necessity be unchangeable, or rather, change must already be predetermined.

If so, the seer was one endowed by nature with skills to let his eyes roam and his ears listen, and thereby 'read' a heavenly bundle of bamboos that contains the story of our past, present and future.

The logical conclusion would be that it must be possible – somewhere and somehow – for eyes and ears to traverse time, as one would unroll and read the memoirs.

The nature of time may just be too complex to be un-ravelled or understood by means of words. Instead of a single continuum there may well be very many levels of time, as there may possibly be many bundles of my memoirs. If so, then one may logically move across different time levels in the same way that, by analogy, different floors in a palace may be accessed and thereby explored.

So changing one's future may simply mean moving to another plane in time. The seer may simply be using the *chi* of fire to journey through time.

Or is it a transposition into a different medium of existence, as ice changes into water?

The seer, in my view, must have seen images of the future in the fire – not just flames – or heard voices of the past – not just crackling sounds.

Or are these merely images picked up by a mind more sensi-tively attuned than mine?

I have often been intrigued by such phenomena but I am at an utter loss to account for their supernatural qualities. Thus I decline to rely on the superstitious.

Why should I turn to superstitions when I can learn enough from the past to control forces of the present and in the process determine outcomes for the future?

The essence of time may better be grasped through

direct experience of its flow, as I am now experiencing through aging.

1 ▰ 8

The other fire I would employ in waging war is invisible to the human eye. Unlike the fire without, this other fire resides within the body.

These other fires are often just as effective – if not more so – in enabling me to reach the very goals for which a war may have been waged: the fires of lust, greed, temper, anger, hatred.

Both fires share common characteristics. When one is truly angered there is a fire that rages within and the internal body heat is such that sweat is generated. When one is near a burning fire there too is heat and sweat.

Both consume. The fire without consumes the substances which it is burning. The fire within consumes the body fluids and dries the internal organs.

Both kill. The fire without kills through roasting human bodies. The fire within kills by its disruptive effects on a person's flow of *chi*.

Both have an effect on focus. A raging fire quickly focuses the attention of the people so affected. An internal fire – be it anger or hatred or lust – takes the attention away from the person so afflicted.

I was able to defeat an enemy by a timely 'gift' of a peerless beauty to a lustful general: she so consumed him that he had little energy or time left for matters of strategy!

The fire of lust raged in him till his *chi* was depleted and his military affairs ignored. I finally took the city with very little bloodshed.

That one beautiful woman did the work of an army!

Autumnal winds.

Oh how gently these winds rustle the leaves off the trees! The dance of leaves – those of a brown-golden hue – to the accompaniment of autumnal winds is so delightful to watch.

Could the dances of these leaves have inspired the early kings to introduce dancing as a form of courtly art?

The sharp edges of the leaves floating in the wind remind me of sword dances. Their twisting and turning made me recall the days when shining blades glittered amidst rising camp fires.

I seem to hear too the distant beating of drums: '... *dum, dum, dum* ...' as the leaves spin, turn, fall to the ground before my eyes. These sounds in my ears recall my own past experiences.

During the war, when on the move in the forest, my ears would be attuned to noises carried by the wind. For when strong winds blew my senses were alerted to smells and sounds. The sounds of the forest are easily distinguished from those made by soldiers on the move.

When silence was critical in executing a mission I would order my men each to bite on a stick. The hoofs of their horses would be bound with cloth. In this way no human voices nor other noises would be heard, even if the wind blew from us towards the enemy.

When I set up camp I would instruct my soldiers on guard how to detect signs of soldiers in hiding, using the wind as an aid.

For many a guard would think that on a windy night it would be impossible to detect untoward movements in the bushes.

I emphasised a sharpening of their senses – eyes, noses and ears – as keys to early detection. When the wind blows in one direction be alert to the movement of bushes in the other. Know the smell of the forest and when that changes, be more circumspect.

2 ⚌ 2

As I stood there images of the past again flooded my mind. Again I was stirred to write.

I turned to that strip of bamboo in *The Art of War* where I had recorded my own observations on the behaviour of wind. I read these aloud:

"Wind that blows in the day will die down at night."

I remembered being emphatic about the wind to my officers.

"These are the invisible soldiers that nature provides for us to do battle..."

I would often tell the soldiers. Arrows carried by the winds have more impact '... *thud, thud, thud...*' when the victims have been struck.

I once used the wind to carry the aroma of cooked food into the besieged city. That would effectively lower the fighting morale among the enemy troops. Fighting on an empty stomach is like going to war unarmed: *what is the use of a sharpened halberd if the arms are too weak to wield it?* A weakness due to an agonising hunger.

The leaves in their dance also unveiled the otherwise invisible shapes of the wind. Yes, there is one quality I have always admired about the wind: its formlessness. In other words, it makes its presence felt yet remains insubstantial.

No sword can penetrate a force that has no substance. Water has no form but can be contained. But nothing can hold the wind. It simply disappears. Clouds, though insubstantial, differ from the wind in the visibility of their forms.

2 ⚌ 3

I often wondered at the might of the wind that blew across the plains.

Could my army acquire some qualities of the wind?

Imagine how difficult it would be to fight an army such

as the wind: it would inflict damage but, because invisible, would flow past, could not be encircled, would always be fluid and impossible to stop.

Another aspect of the wind on which I had often pondered:

Is the wind that blows over these mountains always the same wind?

The army that fought under my banner had an identity of its own. Similarly, I will be greeting the same wind year after year as it returns to the same place. Just like the same moon.

If this has gone on since time immemorial, imagine all the things the wind would have witnessed!

2   4

Now I recollect the image of a person everybody called the Divine Hearer. She was grey-haired, heavily wrinkled, paralysed from the waist down and blind yet able to 'see' through her ears.

She lived in a small hut like mine, perched on the edge of a cliff with a middle-aged lady attendant. Something about her told me she had just emerged from a long period of meditation. Some said the attendant was her sole pupil. Others had earlier whispered very softly into my ears that she was almost on the verge of attaining immortality.

I understood later why, when she was spoken of by those who knew her, they always kept their voices low and soft.

It must have been from my voice that she knew I was no ordinary soldier. I thought that was very possible, given my authoritative tone. But her remarks were more incisive. For she said I was more than an ordinary general – a commander-in-chief of the king's army.

This she said – as if she read my thoughts – was from the sound of my footsteps and not from my voice. That would have been remarkable even if she could see, for I was dressed in simple clothes.

I had asked her:

"How could you know the precise location of a particular ancient battle that had actually been fought?"

She replied, simply by attuning her ears to the wind. For all the human yells, cries, screams and shouts of battle – the *"Shaaa, yaaak, ehhh, ahhhh ... '* – were contained in the wind that blew over this ground.

"What about the clanging and drumming?"

I asked myself. From her facial expression I knew she read my thoughts but chose to ignore them.

Then she claimed that by concentrating her mind she could even hear distinct voices, but the desperate human cries of pain from war were the most audible.

"How could the past ever be heard in the wind?"

That was the first time the question arose in me.

"Could it be that, like a mandarin duck can dive into the depths of a lake and reappear in another place, time could be traversed, enabling one to recover a piece of the past?"

I began to wonder. I almost forgot my purpose for visiting her: to enquire about past works of strategy. Many had – despite knowing my disinclination for things superstitious – suggested that I visit her.

I had wanted to locate a classic work on strategies for waging war in open terrain. It was widely believed to have been hidden by its last known owner somewhere near his base camp: he was none other than the commander-in-chief.

That infamous battle – one of the fiercest ever recorded – had raged on for many days and nights.

As if reading my thoughts she spoke:

"You will get what you are looking for in the Fragrant Village. Just ask your men to dig on a spot ten steps to the east of the only

well there. You are predestined to read that text on the art of war."

I was shocked beyond words.

2 ▭📖▭ 6

By her facial expression I knew she wanted me to bid her farewell so that she could resume her quiet sitting.

Since then I have tried in vain to provide a logical explanation for all these happenings. For the text was found precisely where she had indicated.

I had seen too many generals fail on account of acting purely on superstitions and therefore had prescribed against these practices in *The Art of War*.

But what I witnessed that day was clearly the work of an exalted human being who must have been an astute follower of the *Tao*.

Now, after having for many years read the works of *Taoist* masters, I began to understand my encounter with her better.

One thing still remained vivid in my memory. From the distance as I descended the cliff, I could see through the thickening mist a glow. First it hovered over her hut but later it seemed to float swiftly over us. What I saw I dismissed as probably due to effects of cooking fires and the mist.

But later I learned from the people living nearby that she had neither stove nor cooking utensils. They, she and the attendant, survived purely on wild fruits plucked from the forest. Perhaps there was another explanation.

Could she, after all these years of self-cultivation through meditation, be able to transmute herself?

I could only speculate here.

It dawned on me that it might not be impossible for her to transmute her material body into pure energy or light: something that is able to glow and ride the wind.

The entire episode remains a mystery to me even now. But as I grow older I become more inclined to ponder on the after-death.

For there is one certainty if nothing is done: my body will be buried and ultimately returned to the soil.

Could that be the reason why the earth has been called the Mother?

And if what is widely believed is true, I would then be reincarnated sometime and somewhere in the future.

Or should I instead devote the time that remains to deep medita-tion and walk the path of the Tao?
Is the answer to be found in the wind?

A thousand questions may be asked and yet not a single reply found!

A day when autumn turns into winter.

Change.

Something that has always intrigued me.

More so as I am currently experiencing slow inevitable change myself. I am now far less supple than I was before.

As I stroll in the grounds after the rain I can sense the difference. My eyes can see less well than before, especially when I have to write on the bamboo strips. Now as I continue with my memoirs I need to light up two separate wicks instead of one.

Out in the open space, however, my eyes appear to function just as well if not better in looking into the distance.

And whether I do some exercise in the day matters more than before. I sleep better if I have taken a long walk in the day.

This morning again I saw how the little raindrops had crystallised into bits of ice. For me this transmutation signals the coming to an end of autumn.

With that the birth of a new winter.

These observations triggered in me deep thoughts on things past which involved processes of change. In particular how things take shape: emerging, forming, consolidating, hardening or solidifying. And how wars emerge from mere jealousy between kings, jealousy that grows into hatred of each other.

Then, to wreak vengeance on each other, people from disparate backgrounds gather and form large standing armies. When people are taken away from their farms it must be expected that the ricefields will be left unattended. Thus it should not be surprising that whenever large armies are being gathered there will be a country-wide shortage of grain. Prices will escalate, given such shortages. Famine and hunger will be the dire consequences.

In war farmers are turned into soldiers. And soldiers consolidate their shooting skills to be assigned roles as archers. Along with that wild horses are turned into warhorses.

I was also aware of the process of change in the hardening of attitudes among the ordinary people towards the necessity of going to war, even though the original cause may initially have been trivial.

468

I was reminded as I stood out there observing the change in the season that the present climatic conditions would also change – ice would melt back into water.

That is only possible with the coming of spring, another new beginning.

3   2

I have noticed too that when hostility has been allowed to ferment for a long time war simply becomes inevitable.

The hardening of attitudes among the populace is one thing that the master strategist must be conscious of at all times. For example, a series of events as they evolve may eventually consolidate the attitudes, beliefs and thinking of the masses.

This transmutation – the hardening of water into ice – has wider symbolic relevance for me. One of the skills that I had honed to perfection as commander-in-chief lay in being able to transform a motley group of people – from all different walks of life – into one cohesive fighting force.

The process is akin to the transmutation of water into ice. I used to watch with deep pride as the army – once only a loose gathering of people – formed themselves on the battle-field in their shining uniforms. They looked so compact and disciplined.

Sitting here writing inside my hut I smell the sweet fragrant steam emerging from boiled rice in the clay pot. There in front of my eyes I witness the transmutation of water into vapour – also formless but easily carried away by the wind.

Insubstantial.

Is that fragrance not the smell of chi *or the life-force?*

There is no possibility that cooked grains can change back into rice grains again. In other words, the *chi* or life-force, once released, will be lost for ever into the atmosphere. No rice plants can grow from cooked grains for lack of *chi*.

Chi

I have devoted a great deal of time to mastering the use of water as a technique in *The Art of War*. I would often lay down a rather detailed scheme so as to engineer a successful inundation of the enemy's base camp.

So whenever an enemy's camp had been reported to be sited on low ground near a river or stream my mind would quickly frame a strategy for either inundating or isolating the enemy forces through the use of flood-waters.

The ploy worked especially well during the spell of change in the weather from winter to spring as the sun began to thaw the rivers.

I was often thrilled as a commander-in-chief to see how my army, perched on a hill-top, would fan themselves out to attack the enemy below.

As they gained momentum in the downward thrust I could feel the energy or the *chi* of the army unfolding.

From the faces of the soldiers I knew they were confident in prevailing over the enemy. Indeed many of the enemy soldiers, on hearing such a thunderous roar and seeing many thousands of hoofs, simply became panic-stricken.

Many enemy soldiers just reeled away from their defences in hordes. That must have been my proudest moment as commander-in-chief.

My saddest moments were those when I had to disband the armies that I had trained and moulded, or when they were transmuted. For when victories had been secured old soldiers, used weapons and their adored commander-in-chief would no longer be required. This was especially sad in the case of armies widely known to be personally loyal to their commander-in-chief rather than the king himself.

I, too, after securing victories had to withdraw from the king's palace. Perhaps that is in the nature of the *Tao*.

Like the ice greeting the coming of spring by changing back into water and flowing back to the rivers, the army melts away as the disbanded soldiers return to the villages to work their farms again.

471

I once ordered the army to chip off rocky pieces of ice to use as boulders. These were hurled down on enemy attackers who had to brave a stormy winter before attempting to scale the walls of the city which I was defending.

At other times I instructed boiling water to be poured down on enemy soldiers scaling the walls. Boiling water had so scarred them that the moment they saw any sign of steam on the walls they would quickly scatter away to safety.

So there are many uses of water implicit in the art of war.

I recall that as I stood and watched the fires being set up to boil the water how much the process was akin to stirring up the feelings of soldiers before battle.

As water turns into steam when fired by the flames, so I witnessed how troops may be inflamed by words to fight the enemy. As the bubbling water reflected the agitation caused by fire, so was anger seen on the reddened, frowning faces of the soldiers. I remember their faces well.

For these were the very men I had first gathered from the farms when asked by the king to build a formidable army.

Then their blank faces were like blank pages without words. Through months of military training and indoctrination they became known and accepted as soldiers.

For they now thought, acted and behaved like true soldiers. Like bamboo strips covered with words all along their length, the soldierly profession was written all over them – in their faces, bodies, actions, speech and behaviour.

Unmistakable.

The ultimate test remained however to be taken – that of survival through pitched battles. That was when I practised the art of fiery speeches so as to incite the men into full action. I had no doubt whatsoever that my many victories on the battlefield would simply have been impossible without these properly trained and disciplined soldiers.

Sometimes I had to absorb soldiers from defeated generals into my army. I began to appreciate the blank faces of my early recruits.

For these soldiers were poorly trained under their former generals and I had first to cause them to *un*learn what they had learnt, which was often a great deal. Poorly disciplined soldiers led by weak generals are of little use to a commander-in-chief.

No writing is possible on a page already filled with words. So I began a process of retraining for these soldiers who had deflected before they could be integrated into my main army.

In the meantime these soldiers were given secondary duties – cooking, husbandry, stores – rather than primary fighting roles in the army. But I made sure they were eventually given the opportunity to be assimilated into the main fighting force – the pride of the army.

I strongly believe in the strength of an army bonded together by commonly shared beliefs, values and principles. By many other things, too – songs, food, recreational activities and so on – I would seek to differentiate my soldiers from the others. I would actively cultivate in my soldiers the importance of keeping up the martial spirit.

Even today after so many years I could tell whether a soldier had been with my army by merely observing his behaviour: the song he would sing, the wine and food he preferred, but more importantly, his determined fighting spirit.

Cruelty

A cold winter.

Again I am experiencing the biting cold winds of the north. Oh how strangely penetrating are these winds!

Despite closed windows the wind and thus the coldness seem to seep through somehow. Their presence is keenly felt in the currents inside the hut.

Whenever my teeth begin their involuntary chatter due to the cold I recall something told to me long ago, about the sheer brutality of one fat, egoistic, ill-tempered general, by my former teacher.

This fat general once ordered the ears, noses and lips of surviving rebel officers and soldiers – some of the bravest in the land – to be severed and the men then forced to do a season of slave labour.

These were men who were known to be against him being appointed by the king as the general of the army. He was recommended for promotion by the sole surviving son of the king, the effeminate prince.

The rumour that circulated so widely in the palace was that the recommendation was made on account of the 'services' rendered by the fat general. He was widely believed to be a secret lover of the prince. In the palace it was whispered that the prince was referred to by the eunuchs as the future queen.

Once appointed, the burly, uncouth general acted quickly to use his authority to wreak vengeance on these officers and soldiers.

The reason for scarring their faces was to deeply humiliate these once war-honoured men. The general also wanted to frighten others into blind submission.

When winter came the streets in the city were littered with their dead, chained bodies. For when the strong cold winds blew directly onto their faces they were chilled to death!

Noseless and lipless, these once loyal officers and soldiers were defenceless against the cold north winds.

When the news that such cruelty had been meted out to

their own kind reached the capital the 'queen' acted to prevent the information from reaching the ears of the aging king.

The king was partly to blame too. For in his advancing years he had grown to be more interested in courtly music than military affairs.

When the story circulated among the army and the people at large, it caused such a stir that it sparked off a revolt that spread throughout the country. The souls of these dead men must have been placated when the general himself died in a most barbaric way. The method was devised by family members of the dead soldiers and officers. They sought revenge – as savage and cruel as any imaginable. The general was tied to four corners of a table. Then the family members who so hated the general sank their teeth into his flesh and ate him alive.

It was said afterwards that every member had eaten their share: nothing but the skeleton remained – even the skull was sucked dry.

Even the king was forced to abdicate from his throne for his utter neglect of military affairs. His son, the 'queen', was also severely punished for his role in bestowing the generalship on an evil man.

The mob that burned down the palace could only be appeased if the country were rid of the 'queen'. He was not only castrated but had a red hot iron rod driven through his anus.

He, sexually mutilated, was banished to live out his remaining years in the distant northern wilderness as an outcast.

The general, in his impulsiveness, had given no thought at all to the possible longer-term consequences of his inhumane order to cut off the noses, lips and ears of loyal, battle-honoured officers and soldiers.

These comparatively small things – noses and lips – eventually caused him to suffer a more savage death: he was literally eaten alive. The king too paid for his leisurely pleasures.

So I often emphasised in my talks that kings, so long as they remain kings, must be deeply concerned with military affairs. No general should act lightly in handling matters of punishment and reward.

4 ▬▬ 3

The howling of these north winds has intensified somewhat. I am made to wonder if the 'queen' could endure such an utter wilderness, having led a cushioned life in the palace.

Even now inside my hut I find that no amount of clothes seems able to prevent these insidious winds from penetrating deeply into the very marrow of my bones.

How my bones ache in the cold!

In moments like this I fear that the coldness may even still my heart. Only a burning fire could dispel such cold. I always collect sufficient wood in the summer in anticipation of a possibly long, cold winter.

I remember writing in *The Art of War* that it is the enlightened king who ponders over plans while the good generals implement them.

I remember how I first came to realise the significance of thinking ahead. Only through that can one be prepared for contingencies.

Somewhere within my collection of ancient writings on strategy is a highly valued stone. On it is carved a story using inscriptions so ancient that at one time I could not read it. I later took the trouble to learn this particular mode of ancient writing just to be able to read the inscriptions which I was told had long been abandoned and that only a few old scholars known to my father could decipher – and that with some difficulty.

They did not know whose writings these were. One scholar even told me these writings could be thousands of years old.

Is that possible?

4 ▬▬ 4

For the writer recorded a time when the people still wore animal skins, walked barefoot, lived in caves, though they ate cooked food. That must have been a time when some communal life had begun to be a feature of ordinary living among the people.

I remain fascinated even though I must have been told of this tale by my elders many times since my early youth. Some stories seem to gain vitality when retold again and again. This is such a tale – at least, I believe, for strategists.

For embedded in the tale is the timeless rationale for planning: being prepared by thinking ahead.

The tale recounted how an ancient tribe of people owed their continued existence to one thoughtful person among them. This person they later made their tribal chief, the equivalent of a king. In that year the tribe encountered a severely long winter.

Nobody among them was able to foresee such a disaster. Not even the esteemed tribal high priest and priestess. But neither did the tribal chief.

He had a habit of thinking ahead. He always collected far more wood than his own family ever needed. For he feared a prolonged winter. Thus over the years he had built up a large collection of wood inside his cave.

His keen observation told him how wood collected during a hot, dry summer would burn so much better. The crackling noises that such wood made: '*Klick, klizz, klick, klizz, klizz ...*' were so reassuring, especially to his children when seated there, surrounded by the howling winds from the north. He heard his older daughter say to his little son when such woods were burnt,

"*These sounds frighten away the cold winds and that is why you and I are no longer shivering as before.*"

That made him, as a father, determined to collect as much firewood as his caves could possibly store. For nothing pleased him more than to see his children reassured of warmth during a long, cold and dark winter.

4 ▆▆ 5

The summer preceding that winter was scorchingly hot and dry and still. It seemed to last so long that many tribe members were lured into forgetting about the seasons.

Did summer overlap into autumn in that unusual year?

For from the story as recorded that appeared to be the

case. It seemed that the weather turned its back on the tribe. The signs of impending change seemed to be lacking that year. People were shocked by the sudden transition from days of sweaty heat to days of shivering cold.

As the writer recorded:

"Many had never witnessed nature turn from green to white in so rapid a transition ..."

The still, noiseless air suddenly turned full of cold energy, resonating with eerie howling sounds.

That year it seemed that the winds were especially ruthlessly bitter, cold and strong. Children sleeping in the night could *hear* that the wind came from the north.

So many leaves fell that the forest paths were covered with them. Indeed in many places the leaves piled up knee-deep.

Peering out from the caves, with the moon hovering in the background, the people saw clumps of trees that now looked skeletal. All were being stripped bare of leaves.

Such barren trees looked frightening – like officers and men with their noses, lips and ears sliced off.

4 ☙ 6

Even if the tribesmen had wanted to do something during the transition to fight the cold – such as gathering more wood – it would have been impossible.

Too many had fallen ill. Their bodies were unaccustomed to such a sharp turn in the weather. The transition was too quick for the tribesmen. Many had to rely simply on their own stock of wood to feed the fires so as to counter the biting cold.

Animal skins – if there were any spare – were taken out and shared among the tribal people.

When the snow fell, confirming the arrival of winter, there was an impending sense of doom among the tribal people:

Whatever had happened to the autumn we thought we knew so well?

But fortunately for the tribes people one person among them had more than enough firewood to keep them alive through the long, vicious winter.

4 ⬛ 7

That story was always at the back of my mind whenever I advised kings to build huge granaries to store grain for the people, storehouses to keep supplies, and armouries for weapons.

5 📖 1

The coming of spring.

As usual I took my early morning stroll.

A mild mist.

Exercise out in the open is beneficial to an old man like me. The sun seems to hang in the sky longer than before.

The distant mountain ranges, still snow-capped, appear – from the outer edge of the path which I had traversed – to be greening.

The whiteness seems to be on the decline. This sweeping view of the mountain scene reminds me of a fundamental principle that I had always subscribed to as a strategist when deploying the army.

That reminder propelled me like a shot back to the memoirs. I had not looked at my writings for some time now.

In my youth I was repeatedly given one piece of advice. I later learned that my father and grandfather and his father before him must also have been told this:

"Keep that mountain green and you will always have firewood sufficient to meet your needs."

I wonder how far back in time I must go to trace the root source of this thought.

Possibly a thousand years?

Or even as far back as when men first learned to use firewood? That piece of information is of timeless value to a strategist.

5 📖 2

On some occasions as a commander-in-chief I had been criticised by the king, impatient for quick and spectacular outcomes, for a lack of fiery martial spirit.

If there is anything I am not, it is an emotionally-laden, loud-voiced and roaring general.

I had resolutely refused, despite his numerous imperial orders, to plunge the army, encamped on a mountain, into battle.

Why should I venture out to meet the enemy troops eager for action, when I could hold them off from behind high walls that linked two hilly peaks cutting across this narrow but critical pass?

Indeed, I had ordered my men to put tiny pieces of cloth in their ears to prevent them from hearing the verbal abuse hurled by the enemy, hungry for action, who stood far below and outside those walls. The walls were far too high up for the ladders to reach. I did order an onslaught on the enemy below, but that was much later when their rations had run low along with their morale to fight.

After about two full moons, from the top of the walls I remember seeing an army in surprising disarray. The enemy had by then assumed we would never open the gates to engage them. Clearly the enemy troops had become so restless that their officers had difficulty controlling them.

By then, too, the wine had run dry and the rice sacks were empty. The enemy troops were seen in a disorderly fashion killing wild animals and climbing trees for berries simply to stave off hunger.

That was the moment for decisive action.

In one quick sweep we tore down the enemy's base camp and captured their general alive, still in his underclothes.

The king was once again pleased.

5 ▰ 3

As I have written in *The Art of War*, the commander-in-chief out in the field ought never to be subject to imperial edicts formulated behind the confines of the capital city.

For the king lacks first-hand knowledge of the situation on the ground. Based on my extensive experiences as a commander-in-chief I later prescribed that the only interests a war strategist should have in regard to war are those of the state and the state alone.

What may be in the interests of the state may not necessarily be reflected in the whims and fancies of kings, especially those recently enthroned and hungry for early victories.

So the truly loyal strategist may often be caught in a

difficult situation: his own strategic analysis, based on available information, may dictate a course of action diametrically opposed to the desires of the king.

Thus, once I received the imperial edict from a king whose pride at a banquet had been badly hurt by the others mocking him for having a toothless army.

Having turned down two earlier imperial edicts I received the third with just one word inscribed: 'Fight'.

I simply had to ignore the imperial edict as it was not an opportune time to act. I would still condemn acting against your own best judgement merely to please the king.

5 ☰ 4

I had audaciously and for good reason told the officers and men that a displeased king now may be pleased again in the future. But I find in a thousand years of history rarely any instance of a state reviving itself once it has been crushed at the hands of an enemy.

Once lost a state is gone.

For ever.

As a result of a crushing defeat due to an error in strategy an entire civilisation may be buried in the sands of time and forgotten. Its existence may even be obliterated from the pages of history.

Perhaps a less evil fate than death may befall the losers in wars. Nobles and peasants alike, their state fallen and their families torn apart, may be made to lead meaningless lives as slaves. Like commodities their bodies and souls are bought and sold in the market place. For generations the descendants of nobles and peasants will have to live out their lives in enforced slavery. So a strategist must keep in mind the dire consequences of moving troops simply to momentarily please the king.

Also, never act on the spur of the moment or out of raw vengeance. I have never fought a battle out of passion. Only after detailed, logical and strategic analyses would I contemplate my moves.

I always had to be certain of victory before leading forces out of well-entrenched positions high behind mountain walls.

Supreme master

The only reason for using troops is to seize certain victory. For that is the way to keep the mountain green for ever.

I have learnt from meditating on the virtues of the mountain spirit the possible roles for immobility in wars.

Why is the mountain so ever lasting?

Perhaps the answer lies in its calmness and immobility.

In the classic canons on *Taoist* meditational practices I am struck by how, towards the final stages of self-cultivation of the *Tao*, sitting still is emphasised: be like an uncarved block of wood.

Or a mountain.

5   5

I begin to comprehend why an aged supreme master of a martial arts clan who specialised in advanced forms of crane-fighting techniques chose to retire deep inside the recesses of a mountain cave.

I had wanted, as a young commander-in-chief, to gather the best fighters in the country to engage the enemy. Using powers vested by the imperial edict I sought an audience with him.

His fighting skills were already known far and wide. But when I met him I found him to be already as old as I am now. Yet there was a radiant glow on his face.

Seeing him so old I decided against persuading him to join me in battle. When I was younger I did not understand why a supreme master of crane fighting (a title bestowed on him by the founder leader of the clan as his successor) would choose to be reclusive.

His cave in any event was sited just next to the temple where many of his ardent novices and followers lived. His goal, despite his exalted status, was to continue to live in simple quiet isolation so as to attain perfection through self-cultivation.

In the process he also fulfilled his role of supreme master in taking the art of crane fighting to higher degrees of physical power and attainment.

He would sit on a cold stone inside the dark cave, alone for many moons without a break. Fruits were the only foods he took during such retreats.

The clan members were under strict instruction never to disturb the supreme master. Even I, as commander-in-chief, had to wait for some moons before he could emerge from his meditation to meet me.

Mundane matters concerning the martial clan were all delegated to a nominal leader. But when the supreme master emerged from his long self-cultivation I was told that his martial prowess was often enhanced greatly.

Though I did not personally witness these powers I was told he could raise winds by merely waving his sleeves.

5 ⚔ 6

I remember meeting this supreme master again before I retired, as I was crossing those mountain passes. This time it was simply by sheer chance.

Even now in my mind's eye I can see him there in front of me. His looks did not seem to have changed since the very first time that I had met him. No signs of aging, even though more than twenty years must have passed. If at all, he looked younger than I was, and endowed with more vitality and energy.

Then I realised how wars could weary, stress and age a person. Sitting here writing these memoirs I would not be surprised to meet him once again, and to find him looking younger than myself.

He may even have unravelled the deep secrets of age-lessness. Or at least his body lasts like the mountain and no longer ages at the same rate as any other ordinary mortal being.

I may have begun my personal cultivation of the *Tao* just a little too late in life. But I have no regrets. I have accomplished what I wanted in life by distilling my experiences in *The Art of War*.

6 ▰ 1

Behold!

Distant flashes of lightning in a late evening sky. My anticipations are confirmed as I sit here capturing these emerging thoughts.

In the distance low thundering noises are beginning. Just then I could almost feel the anger in the air as I stood there alone outside.

Through the eaves of the roof I had peered into an ever changing dark cloudy sky. Somehow, perhaps for me alone, the sky with its strange contorted images spoke of the potent powers of Heaven.

Like the contorted face of a general who has difficulty in suppressing his emotions when infuriated by remarks that he has heard: enemy soldiers outside shouting abuse to his face.

I remember how surprisingly demonic this general's usually pleasant-looking face – which I knew so well – could become when he was angered.

For the enemy troops had hurled insults at him: '*Cowardly! Useless!*' and shouted names: '*Dog! Idiot!*' just outside his walled defences. I had refused, as the appointed commander-in-chief, his repeated requests for permission to open up and engage the enemy.

To me, detached from the scene, it was clear that this was nothing but a stratagem to lure him, in a well-defended position, to come out into the open.

6 ▰ 2

As a precaution I then ordered that he and his army of loyal soldiers be immediately replaced. I had to assign another contingent of troops. For somehow I had sensed intuitively from the way his requests for permission were worded that at any time his emotions might simply get the better of him.

A continuing defensive posture by his army at that spot was essential for my *overall strategy* at that stage of the war to work. I could not therefore risk having another front to deal with should the enemy forces succeed in filtering through the narrow mountain pass.

I was concerned that the general might lose his head and

act rashly. He had once before flared up when the enemy piled on him incessant insults.

Except for his inability to stay collected when in a defensive position he was in every other respect a fine general. He was a fiery warrior on the battlefield, with superb fighting technique, though that alone did not make him a good general. In addition he was a master in stirring up the will of his soldiers to fight till the bitter end. His only weakness was his temper, which he had difficulty in reining in.

His replacement, I later learned, was a timely move. For the general had been preparing to dash out into the open to slit the throats of enemy soldiers with his own hands – those very soldiers who had stood outside, screaming insults.

6 ⬛ 3

The howling of the wind is beginning to be heard now. A storm seems imminent.

Staying up here alone in the hut I have become ever more attuned to subtle atmospheric changes, more so than when I was an active commander-in-chief.

Often I find myself able to discern from sensing everything that surrounds me – the air, warmth or cold, winds, clouds and so on – the likely changes in the weather.

I am beginning to appreciate the teachings of the *Taoists*: of realising oneness with nature.

Interestingly for me, having written *The Art of War* and now these voluminous memoirs, I now come to realise how limited words can be for imparting the finer aspects of a skill, for example, how to sense impending changes in the environment.

Earlier in *The Art of War* I emphasised the role of weather in influencing outcomes in war. Yet I am not able beyond that to give details on how a strategist may be able to predict possible changes in the weather by being more attuned to nature.

The art of sensing change is something that a strategist must master if he is to perfect his skills, and it must be cultivated as part of his very person.

These skills must be mastered to an intuitive level of perfection. For only through mastery of picking up signs of change can the strategist become effectively proactive rather than merely reactive.

In the past I have relied as a commander-in-chief on weather charts compiled by the ancient scholars who had studied and recorded such patterns of change in a given locality.

Over time I have learned to predict likely changes in the weather from my own intuition. Now I can sense an unmistakable depth of unquenchable anger that fills the air. This is unlike the usual downpour that provides intense relief after a long spell of dry weather.

6 ▬▬ 4

I am certain Heaven will wreak havoc over the next few days when the latent powers are unleashed: more lightning and thunder; slashing rain coming in torrents; strong, high, irresistible winds (even whirlwinds) and so on.

It is like a hot-tempered general on the verge of throwing the whole weight of his army so as to avenge his deeply wounded pride, where the primary motivation for launching the punitive attack is to vent his anger. From the perspective of a child standing by, watching the soldiers march past, there seems to be little difference between the two – an army moving out as part of a well-thought-out strategy and another, moving on the spur of a moment's fury.

For a strategist any movement of an army is a momentous one. For moving an army may create a vacuum that may lead to the demise of an entire state.

Just as through the wrath of Heaven an entire string of villages may simply disappear beneath the raging waters, so could a state be buried in the river of human memory through the rash actions of a wilful general.

Even if the waters recede afterwards the destruction may be such that little of what remains could remind us of the past.

6 ▬▬ 5

In *The Art of War* I cautioned strongly against any impulsive actions by a general who chooses to fight simply because he feels resentful.

Such a hot-tempered general is an easy prey to stratagems coined by the enemy to trap him. When the main army of a state is trapped, defeated and demoralised, then an entire people is in danger.

This applies as much to the appointed commander-in-chief who should never engage in any battle lightly, even though the imperial edict is for him to engage in war.

I ought to have written that more explicitly in *The Art of War*.

Or should I?

Matters related to war, such as the raising of an army or the despatch of an imperial army must never be decided hastily.

The least appropriate moment is when the commander-in-chief is himself overwhelmed by anger. For anger clouds the rational mind and makes logical and strategic analysis impossible. One's thinking is simply clouded by raw feelings and crude emotions.

Even Heaven, when unleashing emotional outbursts, will lose all sense of balance and proportion – the thunderous outpouring is such that the land below becomes a brownish sea of water. Drought will inevitably follow. After such a downpour, that may last for many days, very little water is left. Even Heaven may find difficulty later in relieving the people of their sufferings from the long drought that may follow. Since ancient times people have feared that after the floods come the droughts. It seemed to the peasants that this is like night following day.

6 ▰ 6

When troops guarding the garrison have all been mobilised to avenge the hurt of a general's pride, the base camp will be vulnerable to easy capture by the enemy.

Once lost such a base camp, if well nested on high ground, may be irretrievable. Such joyful emotion that the general may have experienced – like a child watching the march of the imperial army out of the city – may indeed be short-lived.

So I had to soothe the general who stormed into my residence in the capital city demanding to know the reason why he had been ordered, by a letter written in my own hand, to yield the command of the garrison to another far less senior but more scholarly officer – a person unmoved by emotion.

I had to lend this youthful and scholarly man my own imperial sword, a symbol of ultimate authority. For I had to prepare him for a possible refusal by the general to comply with my orders.

6 ▆▆ 7

I still remember speaking these words to the general, as he fumed uncontrollably with deep anger:

"You may have abandoned the garrison to the hands of a younger man, but at least your army remains intact and under your command.

"Imagine what it is going to be like if you are lured out by the enemy into open battle.

"I have received information from spies that behind and far below those hills the enemy has deployed more troops lying in wait.

"Those shouting abuse outside your walls are but decoys. Once your temper has cooled I have new orders for you . . ."

Now the rains are beginning to slash on the thatched roofs: *'tut, tut, tut . . .'* as I record these thoughts. I hope through relating such an experience that what I had prescribed in *The Art of War* as important is reinforced.

7 📖 1

A very hot and dry day in summer.

This morning I went to fetch water from the stream below. Instead of the gushes of fresh water I saw mere trickles.

I am told that since the last flood many moons ago – when I last made an entry in the memoirs – the villages below have been undergoing a drought.

The morning sky is empty of dark, rain-laden clouds. Some white clouds are spattered about on a stretch of eternal blue.

Perhaps even Heaven, since the last stormy outburst, is now dry. At least for me the stream is still trickling with some water.

Inside my hut I keep my wooden containers covered and filled with stream-water. Precautionary attitudes like these have been ingrained in me since my early days as a commander-in-chief.

I had a reputation as a man of prudence. The security of any state rests on its commander-in-chief and I therefore had to ensure adequate supplies and provisions at all times when waging war.

Without a continuing sufficiency of food, water and supplies an army is easily put at risk. Of all people, including the commander-in-chief, it is the king who must master the art of prudence.

By thinking and acting prudently the king ensures the long-term survival of his state. A glorious kingdom, despite many generations of governance by the same ruling house, may still be lost through the reckless acts of an imprudent descendant who ignores the lessons of the past.

So when I was called upon to advise as a strategist or before accepting any appointment as a commander-in-chief I had to study carefully the ways and practices of the king of the state concerned.

How prudent is the king?

7 📖 2

I emphasised prudence of the king in *The Art of War*, and wrote that an enlightened king is always prudent.

But what constitutes acts of prudence?

These are reflections which I ought to record in the memoirs. There are now so many rolls of bamboo relating to the memoirs that the shelf looks somewhat crowded.

I remember hearing when young some long-forgotten stories of royal acts of prudence woven from the past. Some of these acts seem pedantic but are nevertheless illustrative of the frame of mind of a prudent man.

Take the simple actions of a king when presented with a young, handsome steed captured from the northern plains: a horse of a rare breed with stamina to run through the day and night and able to cover long distances, as far as a thousand *li*, without ever resting.

A prudent king will admire such a horse but not immediately ride on it. Instead one of his men will be ordered to test-ride the horse.

Only when it is shown that the horse is safe will the king himself ride it. Such prudent practices will be implemented in other spheres of mundane activity.

7 ⬛ 3

The king represents the people of the state and as such is the living personification of its unifying principle.

It is not inconceivable that an enemy of the state will find various ways and means to depose the king and thus cut the fibre that binds the society together.

So prudent measures will be instituted by the prudent king. When cooked food is served, palace servants will be asked to taste the food before the king does. Such a measure rules out the possibility of the king being poisoned. The practice, if known, will also discourage such attempts.

Also it is possible for assassination of the king to occur while he is deeply asleep. Such attempts may be made by paid assassins sent to cross the border. Or members of the personal guard of the king may be given heavy bribes or be coerced by other treacherous schemes to undertake the assassination.

Again, the prudent king will have thought through these matters and have implemented counter-measures. One such measure is to have a number of possible places within the palace grounds rather than one fixed location to spend the night. The precise bed on which the king will spend the night is decided personally by him, so that it is impossible for anyone to know in advance.

7 ▰ 4

Kings of the past have also been prudent in verifying even those deeds said to be performed by loyal subjects.

Thus when an enemy general, widely feared by all, is claimed to have been killed in battle the prudent king will demand that his head be presented in a box for inspection.

The prudent king is also aware of human weaknesses in given circumstances. Virile men often find beautiful women irresistible. Thus out of prudence kings of the past often insisted on castrating male servants, those serving within the inner chambers of the palace.

Thereafter these servants were known as imperial eunuchs. By such measures the prudent king would have little to doubt on the question of the legitimacy of any pregnancy conceived, whether by the queen or imperial concubines living inside the inner chamber.

The prudent king, although he values trust very highly, realises that nothing is better than effective control measures.

7 ▰ 5

Since military ventures are often risky undertakings the king, as an act of prudence, takes advice before embarking on any initiative.

Indeed the practice of retaining strategy advisers may constitute an act of prudence: to explore other less risky alternatives.

Even if a plan has already been decided upon, the role of strategy advisers remains invaluable: to map out detailed actions to be implemented.

Besides having a retinue or team of personal strategy advisers, the king also holds conferences with ministers and generals when a major strategic initiative is to be implemented.

In *The Art of War* I should have emphasised more the role of the king in formulating appropriate strategy. Techniques in strategic thinking, if mastered, should help a king reduce the risks in whatever the state undertakes while yielding better results or outcomes.

Another facet of strategic thinking which should help the king evolve contingency plans is the 'what ifs'! Thus secret tunnels and passages are dug in palaces even in the most formidable states.

But why?

That is the essence of contingency planning: to be prepared even for the worst possible outcome – the palace under siege by enemy forces. These underground or between-walls passages are known only to the king and a few other people.

For the contingency plan to work care is needed to ensure that even during construction those involved see only an insignificant part of the overall maze of passages. Even then these people are often banished to live their remaining lives in remote places.

To ensure the utmost secrecy for some of the more vital passages – escape routes for the king – those involved are sometimes, in the more ruthless regimes of old, murdered by hired assassins.

As a precautionary measure only the king has a map of such intricate passages. Such prudence ensures the survival of the state as symbolised by the person of the king, even if the palace should fall into the hands of the enemy.

7 ▰▰ 6

I remember an old drawing etched on a tortoise-shell. The sketch is of a special conference room reserved for use by an ancient king. The room is designed specifically for him to confer with visiting foreign dignitaries on matters of vital importance to the state.

I remain intrigued by the design of that room. The picture showed a king seated on a raised platform and behind him stood two maids, fanning him. On a lower level sat two foreign dignitaries who had not, according to the sketch, been disarmed. I remember seeing their swords still dangling at their sides.

That must be a most unusual practice – allowing foreigners to carry their swords when conferring with the King. On closer scrutiny I saw that *outside* the room and hidden from the eyes of these foreign dignitaries were the special imperial guards.

On every side of the room behind the screens or walls stood these guards, with drawn swords, ready to dash out.

Even beneath the floor of the room and above in the ceiling there were guards whose bodies were shown ready to strike out.

Their etched faces showed them to be straining their eyes and ears in following the dialogue. This must surely be the idea of a prudent king!

Such a king must have intended to lull the foreign dignitaries into believing that he is a simple, straightforward person – someone to be trusted.

Indeed, according to the records, many foreign dignitaries believed the king to be incapable of coining stratagems.

Yet elsewhere it was recorded – not surprisingly to me – that this same ancient king was a master in the art of using assassins to deal with those who opposed him. And he never used one but two assassins: one to perform the act and another to confirm that the assassination had indeed been successful as well as, on occasion, to silence the doer.

This prudent king never crossed a river unless the imperial boat on which he sat pulled along another smaller boat. He was wary of the contingency: *what if* the imperial boat should capsize?

An act of prudence no doubt. Only through these memoirs could I illustrate the concept so vividly.

13

A SCENE THAT stays long in my mind.

With the memoirs before me and in my mind's eye I see a red radiant sun setting in the far west. The sun emits rays that cast a golden hue over the distant horizon. The rays of light are more soothing than burning to the skin.

Then in a moment an image of many gold pieces wells up before my eyes. I remember *The Art of War* and the unfinished memoirs in my hand. Indeed, I wrote in *The Art of War* about the pieces of gold – hundreds and hundreds of them – paid to gain secret information on the enemy; how in my days as a commander-in-chief I would lavish money on accurate and detailed data on the enemy's strategy, the deployment of their troops, morale and location of their supplies and so on.

I have even briefed the king on some occasions to bestow rank, honours, riches or whatever on any person who was able to help me obtain top secret information about the enemy.

For a person who contemplates anything less or begrudges such payments and honours is condemned by me in *The Art of War* as lacking in humanity.

Such a person is no general; nor could he ever be a support for the king. Nor could such a person ever gain mastery of victory in war.

How could he when he values money above reliable information on the enemy?

Pieces of gold, even hundreds of pieces, could hardly compensate for the enormous cost incurred in waging war.

There is just no basis for any comparison. Imagine the cost of raising an army of one hundred thousand from a variety of professions across the country: farmers, artisans, dealers, fishermen, carpenters and so on.

To raise that many will mean so many households being denied of the recruited soldier's civilian earnings. And then there will be the recurring costs of feeding, clothing, arming, training and drilling before engaging these soldiers in battle.

What about the cost of those killed as a result?

Should not the state compensate those households so affected for the permanent loss of future earnings?

What about the cost of the suffering, commotion, acute stress and distress that a war inevitably brings?

It is little wonder that a state after long years of war is easily bankrupted even though the treasury may once again be overflowing with gold, jewels and precious stones.

A thousand pieces of gold a day, as I estimated and recorded in *The Art of War*, may not suffice with today's rising prices and grossly enlarged scale of war. This rate may have to be revised in the light of the current scale of war. How costs of war have escalated over such a short period of time – now as compared to the time when I first conceived of *The Art of War*!

I cannot imagine how much may be needed if a war is waged many years hence. One thing I am certain of: it will be more and more and not less.

If a state's treasury is bankrupted, how can there be glory even if victory is finally won over the enemy?

Prolonged wars do not benefit anybody. Years of contrived efforts in waging war, even with victory, never bring lasting joy to the masses. For any joy from victory will quickly evaporate once the costs of war are counted. The situation is even worse if a war is being waged in distant places.

Imagine how exhausting the effort must be regularly to transport by human labour war supplies to sustain a one hundred thousand-strong army in war. It is costly too for a state to wage an indecisive war.

Imagine, besides the measurable costs, the costs of the toil, struggle, anxiety, tension, agony and frustration, associated with an indecisive war!

So no strategist of any repute will advise a king to become embroiled in an indecisive war. I would prefer, when waging war, that it should be brought to an end decisively. There should be no lingering self-doubt when a war is being fought.

1 ⚔ 4

To reduce the risks of uncertainty in waging war to a minimum I would advise the king to reward richly those in the know. If reliable information on enemy secrets is available at a price then no king should hesitate.

For with inside information on the enemy's intended strategy the strategist will be able to work out a stratagem that either counteracts or benefits directly from the enemy's planned course of action.

Nothing is more effective than to attack an enemy's strategy. A network of spies that brings in timely information is vital to the war effort. Without such information it is like asking an archer to shoot blindfold at a moving target in pitch darkness. With detailed and accurate information an archer is then shooting in the light at a fixed target from a known distance.

Clearly the odds of succeeding are greater in the latter situation than the former. So efforts by intelligent spies that garner timely inside information are like the lighting and fixing of a target that enables an archer to be deadly when firing his shot.

Thus if a secret alliance is being planned by the enemy

then envoys may be quickly despatched to disrupt it.

Another more graphic illustration relates to the exact timing and scale of an attack by the enemy on a border city which may be uncovered by a spy planted inside the enemy's camp.

Details such as size, composition, leadership, weaponry and formation relating to the attack are useful for developing a strategy that may lead to ultimate victory.

1 ≡▮≡ 5

I can easily configure one such strategy. Thus if the enemy's main army is to gallop out of their base camp for the attack then it is possible, given adequate time, to turn the city into one massive trap. The trap appears to 'welcome' the main force of the enemy. As part of the strategy the general guarding the city is to feign surprise when attacked by the enemy.

Soldiers must appear to scuffle in a disorderly fashion into position when alerted to the attack. At a critical moment the city gates are made to collapse in response to mounting attacks by the enemy.

The idea is to lure the enemy deeper inside. The young, old and female in the population within the city will have been evacuated secretly the day before.

The city is to be stacked with rolls of dry hay in preparation for the attack. More are placed on the roof-tops where they may then be lit and rolled down on to the enemy forces trapped below.

Once the enemy's main force with their commander-in-chief is trapped inside the city steps may be taken to hem them into a designated killing ground through the use of fire.

In addition, troops stationed on standby some distance behind the city will then advance towards it.

Inside, at all corners of the city's streets, through which enemy soldiers will inevitably have to pass to avoid the fire, I would order trenches two body lengths deep to be dug. These trenches will be camouflaged in order to deceive enemy soldiers. On the floor of these trenches will be planted upturned spears and knives and sharpened bamboo rods.

The overall scheme for trapping the enemy in 'the city of roaring fire' will be mapped on a piece of cloth laid out on the floor.

I would study it closely to ensure that no enemy soldier will be able to stray out of the city except through one narrow route made by a hole deliberately cut in the walls. That path should however lead towards ground where my soldiers will be waiting. Those that surrender will have their lives spared.

Inside the city the enemy troops are to be cut down systematically through raining on them wave upon wave of arrows tipped with oil and fire. These are to be shot by archers situated in strategic roof-top positions. Beneath these buildings where the archers stand will be dug tunnels that lead to outside the city perimeter.

If the fire proves too overwhelming then these skilled archers will be able to escape from the burning fire. In my mind's eye I see and hear the roaring flames consuming an entire city on that day the enemy is trapped inside.

Gradually these flames will in turn become glowing embers of burnt wood. The glow of this burnt wood casts a golden hue in the night sky.

Somehow the scene, though imaginary, reminds me of the late setting of the sun out there in the far west.

As the flames that engulfed the city die down a sizeable contingent of my troops will be re-establishing themselves after taking over the entire base camp of the main enemy force together with the stores, supplies, arms and so on.

503

Through such a strategy as described I am certain to prevail over the enemy: an empty hollow city in exchange for the destruction of the main army of the enemy together with their major base camp.

Such a deal is *only* possible through the timely and accurate information that I may obtain from paid spies.

Is such an exchange not worth the hundreds of pieces of gold?

I do not deny there is still suffering being inflicted on

Attack

the population of the city in having to vacate their homes. But that is a lesser evil than being slaughtered, plundered, raped, tortured, burnt, knifed and enslaved should the enemy forces succeed in launching a surprise full-scale attack.

Putting aside my brush I cast my eyes outside. I see a golden hue: *is it the sun setting in the West?*

Or is it another city being burnt?

2 ⚏ 1

A mid-winter's day – so cold. The snow outside is already knee-deep in some of the places along the path.

Sometimes I fear, living alone in this mountain hut, that I may doze off and be frozen – *and remain frozen forever!*

In these circumstances I often ponder what lies beyond life.

If I am frozen is there an ethereal body that continues?
Or is that the end?

I do not know the answer, even though I am already in my twilight years. I simply have to keep the fire in the hearth going.

So I turn to work on my memoirs.

2 ⚏ 2

I know in *The Art of War* I cautioned against relying on the supernatural when waging war. Some generals believe it is possible to gain foreknowledge through the spirits or gods.

Thus some will consult seasoned practitioners of these spiritual arts. There are many possible methods.

One that relates to fire is most intriguing. Some will listen to the crackling sounds when a piece of wood is placed in the fire; others through studying the patterns of a tortoise-shell that has been burnt.

Indeed, many generals will be on the lookout for omens that foretell of future success or failure of a military mission. Such a belief by the general in omens will create hopes and fears among the soldiers.

So if the army encounters ill omens, such as the un-explained snapping of the general's own command banner in a slight wind, then the soldiers will become discouraged. Some may even desert the army.

As a commander-in-chief I would often employ the tactic of a haunting voice to implant fears among enemy soldiers of their impending death in coming battles.

I would employ men skilled in voice inflection to create an eerie atmosphere – especially in the dead of a rainy night –

by making sounds that seemed to come from the other world.

In these sounds the men would convey the message of impending doom. My idea is to weaken the will of the enemy soldiers to fight.

At other times I ordered my men to lay signs of ill omens – mutilated heads of animals and even owls, ravens or crows – along the path which the enemy soldiers were known to be taking.

2 📖 3

The more scholarly generals will try to gain foreknowledge by relating the past to a current situation. These generals believe that history often repeats itself. So by use of analogy they believe it is possible to gain some foreknowledge of likely future developments.

These generals ignore the fact that forces at work, even in a situation that may appear analogous, could be entirely different. It would be risky in war to rely on pure analogy to foretell the future.

Some generals rely on detailed calculations and try through extrapolation to gain foreknowledge. The problem here lies in the reliance on assumptions in making the fore-casts. But what is assumed may not necessarily hold, especially in the very fluid situation of war.

Although it is useful to be able to estimate how fast an enemy is able to cross the river or march through the forest this is not the same as knowing for certain the direction in which a war is going to evolve.

These projections are made based on assumptions that the enemy will indeed be crossing the river or marching through the forest. Again such assumptions may not be valid.

2 📖 4

In *The Art of War* I stated clearly that the only reliable way to gain foreknowledge is to ask men who know of the enemy situation. Other methods are more conjectural than definitive.

I still subscribe to this: gaining foreknowledge from using spies who have direct access to enemy plans.

As one lives to be as old as I am, often alone, it is inevitable that things spiritual and eternal become more relevant than when one was younger.

So today I ought to discuss my deeper reflections on these things. I was, when younger, against spiritual consultation to gain foreknowledge, for I was shocked by the absolute and blind dependence of the generals on these methods.

These generals fail as a result to build a network of intelligent spies. Even when such secret information is made available I am surprised that these generals prefer to rely on forecasts made by the crackling noises of firewood.

Wars are to be fought and won through the efforts of soldiers led by generals within the human and *not* the spiritual realm.

That is why when I was commander-in-chief I forbade such superstitious practices. Generals who depend too much on these spiritual methods often end up even failing to apply strategy in waging war.

Such prohibitions do not however mean that I deny the presence of spirits. I recognise that there has to be a spiritual realm but in waging war it is critical to use the most reliable methods for gaining foreknowledge of a plan, strategy or stratagem residing in the mind of the enemy general.

2 ⬛ 5

As I sit here by the fire my mind often wanders into a dream-like state. In that surreal state I hear the metallic-sounding voices of long-dead childhood friends, compatriots, soldiers, generals.

Each come in their turn. Despite the strange medium through which these sounds from the other world are filtered I am still able to recognise distinct voices – voices which my mind is able to put faces to.

Or are these faint images an integral part of the process of communicating with the other world rather than my mere imaginings?

My personal *aide* to whom I am forever indebted (he was killed in combat shielding me from a stray arrow) spoke to me thus:

"Sun Tzu, your men and I on the other side are all waiting for you to lead us again into combat.

"Many are delaying their rebirths so that they may again be led by you in a future time and place: to be reborn together with you.

"The men are also waiting to welcome you to ethereality. There is a feast waiting once you have crossed to the other shore."

It is reassuring to know that I will not simply be plunging into the murky depths of the unknown.

No wonder some kings of the past had those closest to them buried alive together with them when they died.

This same *aide* alerted me once to the danger of the flames dying down, uttering these words:

"Be awake, Sun Tzu; otherwise you will be chilled to death."

That tells me that my end is still some time off. I have been told that when one comes towards the end of one's life familiar faces will welcome one to the other shore.

My own father had the same experience when he was nearing seventy. I did not think much of these happenings then, but I do now.

2 ▃▃▃ 6

Sitting here before these fires I think back 2,500 years ago to the time of Fu Hsi, the emperor who had taught men how to harness fire, initiated agricultural practices, tamed animals and so on.

I remain in old age fascinated by the sixty-four hexagrams in the *I Ching*. Each hexagram depicts a situation in life. Using yarrow sticks one is supposed to be able to depict the forces influencing change from one situation to another.

More importantly for me, there is a deep and meaningful philosophy that underpins the *I Ching*.

How did Emperor Fu Hsi conceive of these things 2,500 years ago?

Ethereality

I must admit that despite my preference for relying on men who know the enemy's situation I would still as a commander-in-chief study the *I Ching*.

When all rational thoughts on deciding an issue related to war have been exhausted I would not hesitate to consult the *I Ching*.

Similarly, should I receive conflicting information from long-trusted spies and there is pressure on me to act one way or another I would refer to the *I Ching*.

Invariably I find the passages related to the two hexa-grams (*now* and *future*) stimulate in me more profound thoughts. These passages encourage me to explore a wider range of issues related to military strategy.

2 ▤ 7

I remember how I came to admire *I Ching* or the *Book of Changes*. On one occasion as a newly appointed general I had to lead an army which was under siege. We were severely out-numbered by enemy forces. All my officers were in utter desperation and looked to me for a plan.

It was then that by sheer chance I came to read hexa-gram 33 from the *I Ching*. The book was open at that very page when I came to it.

In the *I Ching* hexagram 33 is entitled 'Retreat'. I was struck by the direct correspondence between the situation depicted by the hexagram and my current circumstance.

The admonitions contained in hexagram 33 were most timely in instructing me how to conduct a constructive retreat, which must be distinguished from flight.

Retreat is an act of strength whereas flight is one of weakness. I acted according to the advice in hexagram 33 and we succeeded in retrieving ourselves from a most vexing situation.

Even now I remain very impressed that a work written some 2,500 years ago can still be of such timely relevance to me.

How could the author of I Ching *configure in his mind sixty-four unique situations?*

For that reason alone I often ask myself if I could travel back in time to meet the author of *I Ching*.

What in essence is time anyway?

Perhaps in ethereality I shall rediscover the meaning of passing time.

3   1

As I unroll these memoirs the autumn sky outside darkens and the starlight struggles to emerge from a sea of deep impenetrable purple blue.

This is a moonless night and during times like these I know my network of spies that I had once helped to establish for the state will again be busy.

The spies will be exchanging bits of vital information under the cover of night darkness. Bamboo strips, inscriptions on shells, slips of paper will be passed down the spy chain.

In such a night, too, horses will be heard hurrying crossing the borders, relaying information vital for the survival of the state.

Wars may be planned, started, escalated, averted, prevented on the basis of these secret exchanges. Little except what is found in *The Art of War* has been written about this.

Those initiated into these secret services for the state must be very carefully chosen and nurtured. One requirement for choosing them to act as spies is their ability to keep quiet on secret matters.

Without a network of spies providing the state with critical and timely information, the strategist, be he the king, general or commander-in-chief, will encounter difficulty in implementing timely strategies.

3   2

The setting up of such a network of spies is no simple matter. So even though I have long retired from my position as commander-in-chief I still have occasional visitors from distant states – many, many *lis* away – who come all the way to my little mountain hut.

They beseech me, often on bended knee, to lecture them in person on how to establish a spy network. These visitors must come in secret. For although they hold very powerful ministerial and command positions in their respective imperial courts, they come dressed simply.

Their retinue of bodyguards and servants often relieve me of my daily chores as I spend time lecturing to these dignitaries.

Some are even crown princes who want to learn the finer aspects of the art of intelligence gathering and evaluation.

So dedicated are these 'students' that even the crown princes willingly put up with the spartan living conditions of this mountain hut.

Many have read my work on how to establish a spy network in *The Art of War* but are nevertheless still eager to hear from me first-hand as the author of these ideas.

The remoteness of my mountain hut is no obstacle to those truly ardent to master the art of war. No wonder the *Taoist* masters living in these mountains are still found to be the most able students in the study of the *Tao*.

These students of mine are grateful for the instruction. I too gain from the ensuing, often exciting discussion on building up a network of spies.

Somewhere in the hut I have kept in a bundle standing invitations from these crown princes, ministers and commanders from the various different states.

3 ▰ 3

Some of these invitations come with offers of exalted positions and honorific titles with high remuneration. I never intend to take up any of these. I am just too old to travel that kind of distance. More importantly, I should devote whatever energy and vitality I have left to recording my further reflections on the art of war.

At my advanced age, and living alone, I am keenly aware that the time remaining for me to do productive work may be limited.

Occasionally my eyes fail to see clearly, despite working with two lights. Also my hands are less steady than before as I write on these bamboo strips.

Yet my mind is still rich with ideas, memories, anecdotes, concepts, lessons – if only I were young enough to tap all these sources.

Life is such an irony. When I was young, full of energy and eager to contribute I found myself out there too busy seeking positions and offices to apply my thoughts to the art of war.

Now old, weak and often even lacking strength to write, though enriched by decades of experiences, I find myself bestowed with titles and offices waiting for me.

But what is more befitting for an old man than to retire quietly in these peaceful surroundings amidst the fresh mountain air?

As one waits in a mother's womb for birth so it must be for the old man to have to wait for his rebirth into another realm.

Perhaps this aging, when one loses the sharpness of one's vision, hearing, taste, and agility of the body may be but an extended process of preparation for the long journey home.

Old age brings a sharper clarity of thinking to one's work. There is added depth and a multi-faceted approach to looking at issues. That is far less likely when one is much younger.

3 📖 4

On the matter of spying, all who made their journey to this little hut know by heart the five types of spies that I had classified in *The Art of War*.

A spy network is truly an invaluable asset to the state. Indeed I counselled those crown princes that their day should begin and end with the readings of reports gleaned from fresh information submitted by spies. Needless to say there should be a system for keeping and retrieving such information.

Each class of spies has its own unique role and different contributions to make. The spies in place are those natives of the enemy's country who are able to provide an intimate knowledge of various aspects of the country. These range from matters of farming, weaponry, economics, politics – anything that may have broader implications.

Thus whether it is a famine or revolt or bumper harvest that is happening in a neighbouring state, each piece of information may have broader strategic implications.

Such information enables the king to be alerted to possible new initiatives that may be taken by another state. Thus a state that has enjoyed good years of harvest may have the economic strength thereby to wage new wars. Conversely a state that has been weakened by years of famine may simply be too debilitated even to be a meaningful partner in defence.

3 ▬▬ 5

I often use in these lectures a simple example to illustrate what constitutes a good spy network. If a lot of smoke is seen in the distance inside the enemy's camp one knows a major fire has been raised. But before such a fire is possible a great deal of firewood must first be gathered or trees felled. Now before firewood is gathered to make the fire somebody must have first ordered that this be carried out.

If there is an intricate network of spies at work this decision by the enemy to raise a fire and the rationale for doing so will be known in advance. For that to happen there must be spies inside the enemy's senior rank of officials. Spies able to penetrate deeply into the causes and reasons why certain decisions are being made are very valuable. Even more valuable are those spies able to influence the decision-making process so that the outcomes – decisions by the enemy – are in our favour.

Thus let us presume that the lighting of a major fire that creates smoke in a certain way is discovered by our spies to be a signal for the enemy to concentrate their forces. Assuming this is to our disadvantage then we need spies within the upper reaches of the enemy's official hierarchy to prevent it.

But even if that fails – thwarting enemy strategy is uncertain at best – there is already an early warning of con-centration of enemy forces.

For the complex system of spying to work effectively double agents are required: enemy spies who have been bought to serve our purposes. Double agents are most valu-able but their loyalties have to be assured time and again.

3 ▬▬ 6

When the discussion turns to expendable spies my eyes often well with tears. For these people end their lives in the most cruel ways imaginable.

Why?

To discourage others. Seldom are they given a quick death. Most suffer a lingering death. For I remember with utter sadness in my heart the fate of one such expendable agent. The enemy had parts of his body dismembered piece by piece and returned across the border to his family: first the ears, then his nose, followed by the lips, eyes, fingers, toes, hands, legs and finally the head.

No beast is as cruel as man.

I felt terribly sorry and I am still full of remorse for the family of the expended spy. Yet to my surprise there are people – from my own state and that of the enemy too – still willing to sacrifice their lives by volunteering to act as expendable agents.

Little does history recognise the role of these unrecorded heroes in the waging of wars.

3 ▆▆ 7

There is one lesson I learned from my years of tapping this network of spies. If a regime is cruel, harsh and hated by the masses then there is little difficulty in recruiting expendable spies from all walks of life.

I found that people are willing to sacrifice themselves for a good cause. Certainly for the system to work there must be expendable spies who are never told they are to be sacrificed.

The more fortunate are those spies allowed to live out the rest of their lives incognito as a reward for their long years of service. These spies can no longer live in their own country, having worked for our state. But they are likely to live their remaining lives in fear of being hunted down by special, nameless killers sent under secret imperial decree issued by their own king to ferret them out.

Even many years after the event I still hear of former spies being killed in cold blood. That is the price to pay for being a spy!

I woke with a terrible nightmare that the secret imperial killers from the inner chamber of the palace were on a secret imperial decree to silence me.

Perhaps I ought to have been more circumspect about whom I lecture to on aspects of the art of war. Matters such as the nurturing of a spy network are indeed sensitive.

The writing about secret spies in these memoirs must have reawakened in me great fear, even though I see myself as a teacher of the art of war.

The best gift to a teacher is a dedicated student. And if these students happen to come from other states, so be it.

Since my retirement from the court I have been left largely undisturbed by the late king. I was told that the crown prince who succeeded him is hardly interested in matters of war.

So although I have received in my retirement occasional invitations to court ceremonies, as the years have passed these have been on the decline.

The court is just too embroiled in its own internal politics. The officials have little time to be bothered about my absences, even at stately functions.

I am told by my family members as a result of my long absences that my name may have even been deleted from the court invitation list.

That frees me from having to make the long and troublesome journey down from the mountain hut to the capital city.

When a person reaches my age even exotic food, courtly dances and elegant robes have little appeal.

The only desire left burning in this old frame is to complete these memoirs. I am glad still to be making good progress towards finishing them.

On the use of spies in waging war I wrote in *The Art of War* that one of their major roles is to gather accurate and detailed information.

Thus if an attack is being planned it is useful to gather details such as the names, family background, habits, weaknesses and personal tendencies of the garrison commander and his staff officers.

If our spies are sufficiently penetrating, even details relating to ushers, gatekeepers and bodyguards may be obtained. Such information should be gathered as a matter of routine when an attack is being planned for a city, town or military installation.

Success in such secret missions or planned attacks is contingent upon these matters being kept in utmost secrecy.

It is therefore necessary, even though cruel, to put to death all those people that the spy had spoken to in case there had been any premature leakage of these secrets. Even the spy himself is seldom spared the blade of the secret imperial killers.

4 ⬛ 3

The establishing of a spy network is a difficult task that requires finely honed skills, but what is even more intricate and challenging lies in extracting the truth from spies.

Not all commanders are able to fully harness the web of information that may be woven from the network of spies in action.

The commander or general must, as I wrote in *The Art of War*, be able to relate with spies in a most intimate and confidential manner. Above all the general must inspire the absolute trust and respect of the spy concerned. Another quality that the commander must have is overflowing generosity when rewarding spies for their efforts.

Indeed in *The Art of War* I prescribed such sterling qualities in the commander – sage and wise, humane and just and delicate and subtle – if he is to be able to extract the truth from spies.

No doubt to be a commander-in-chief as I was requires being resolute in meting out punishments, especially when there has been proven betrayal of trust by spies.

A betrayal, if tolerated by the commander-in-chief, may lead to even more disloyal acts down the spy chain. One betrayal may be all that is required for the state to be vanquished.

The leakage of a detailed plan for defence and attack by

a double agent to the enemy may result in the early demise of the state.

Seen in perspective these extermination orders are necessary to prevent the possible future losses of thousands upon thousands of civilian lives. This is when I would seek the secret imperial order issued only by the king. These orders are written on a special piece of yellow paper carrying the imperial seal of authority.

In these orders would be specified the names and addresses of those to be exterminated. These would then be handed by me in secret to the head of the secret imperial killers from the innermost chamber of the palace guards.

4 🕮 4

Given the sensitive nature of these assignments, I would often handle these matters personally with the chosen secret imperial killer. Such bizarre killings, I am told, are happening with ever greater frequency since I left the court.

The local village magistrate will often find it almost impossible to investigate these killings as no trace of evidence is ever left behind.

Every person found at the given address is killed by a swift slit of the throat. All persons known to be related to the spy will also be massacred.

During the time when I was still commander-in-chief I had to handle the case of an overly diligent and inquisitive magistrate. His exhaustive enquiries – the finding of an odd insignia – almost led him to suspect the imperial palace guards to be behind a series of outrageous murders. I had to intervene personally or the magistrate's life would have been put at risk.

Even though I was the commander-in-chief, in certain matters of internal security regarding palace secrets the head of the secret imperial killers is authorised in certain situations to act without first getting the sanction of the king.

These are the ugly truths about palace politics. Heinous murders are often committed under cover of maintaining internal security of the state and the palace.

I therefore acted quickly in my capacity as commander-in-chief immediately to quash further attempts by the young magistrate to investigate further. I could not explain to him that he, his family and everybody connected with the enquiry would simply be exterminated if he pursued further with his investigations. I simply ordered him to leave such matters in my hands.

4 📖 5

Outside the palace so little is known of these secret imperial killers. Except in these memoirs I too often had to deny their existence to outsiders. Even my family knows nothing of their presence. Although there are only a handful of them, the secret imperial killers are most formidable and fearsome. I consider them to be lethal fighting machines. The closest analogy is a newly devised machine that I am told is able to fire multiple arrows. Both these machines and the secret imperial killers are efficient in killing and devoid of human feelings.

These secret imperial killers (SIK) have no identity of their own. They are given numbers, not names. Their training has shaped them into what they are. I learned they are recruited from the toughest of the surviving war orphans. Their whereabouts are so secretive that only the king and the head of the SIK have access to their special quarters, hidden beneath the palace.

These killers are also trained in a tightly kept secret method of being able to terminate their own lives in such a way that their bodies will never be recovered. They have been taught to act this way should any mission fail in unexpected circumstances. Even as a commander-in-chief I was told no more than what I absolutely needed to know about how the SIK work.

4 📖 6

From what I have been able to piece together it seems that the training is so arduous that very few of the original batch of recruits survive.

I had met some of them when I had to issue them with the secret imperial decree. They clearly do not owe me any allegiance – or for that matter to anybody.

They only operate in the dead of night. Their eyes, hands and bodies reminded me instantly of cold, sharp blades of shining metal.

I have no doubt that if my name had appeared on this secret imperial decree they would have carried out a perfect and clean act of killing on me too.

I was told that they lead unusual lives – sleeping in the day and trained to manoeuvre and kill in the darkness of the night.

They are at their peak in the art of killing on moonless nights. They are very different from the soldiers I commanded. Whilst my soldiers were trained to fight in wars, these killers are dedicated to killing and are most efficient in pitch darkness. They kill by primordial instinct. So reputed is their precision killing in total darkness that everybody refers to such skills as the killer's instinct.

523

Their belief is that once a killer's sword is drawn it must draw fresh blood before it is put back into the sheath. Otherwise they are doomed to fail on the next mission.

4 ⚌ 7

They learned early in their training that to be a supreme master killer one has to be devoid of human feelings. For feelings are premonitions of death for the secret imperial killer.

Their only measure of self-worth is in the tally of secret imperial decrees that they have successfully implemented.

Even as I write these entries into the memoirs my hand wavers. Not out of fear of any secret imperial killer – I am already so old – but that this work may be destroyed simply because of such revelations.

5 ▰ 1

Heavy downfall of rain on a windless and hot summer noon-day.

Sitting here by the window and listening to the monoto-nous sounds of the rains: '*tat tat tat tat tat*' on the roof I entered into a deep meditative state. I experienced a true stillness of mind. In that state of being nothing seems to disturb me.

I am beginning to sweat now.

Profusely.

This despite the rain falling outside. I turn naturally to my memoirs.

I find this process of rethinking more deeply and reflec-tively on *The Art of War* very enjoyable. My feelings now are exactly like those of the ceremonious court musician whom I once knew. Towards the end of his performance his eyes would be full of tears, no matter how joyful the music. For he felt sad that the musical performance he had created for the court had to come to an end.

In moments like this I realise the profound truth of the saying: 'That which begins must also end.'

My own theme in the memoirs is now on spies, espe-cially double agents.

5 ▰ 2

I wrote earlier in *The Art of War* about the crucial role of double agents. As the word 'double' implies, these are spies who are still operating as agents for the enemy.

Their loyalty however has been cultivated and bought by heavy bribes. These spies must always be given the proper instructions and be well looked after.

From them further details may be garnered of the enemy's spy network. It is through them, too, that a network of native and inside spies may be established within the enemy's country.

I advocated in *The Art of War* that double agents be given the most generous treatment.

I did not however mention a special breed of highly skilled military spies who reported directly to me as comman-der-in-chief.

These military spies are now being created in some of our neighbouring states. What differentiates these special military spies from the others is that they are an integral part of the army.

Unlike the others but similar to the secret imperial killers (SIK) these special military spies receive unique and extensive training from a very young age.

Also like the secret imperial killers, the special military spies are recruited from war orphans.

Only the most intelligent and fast-thinking are to be selected. They remain utterly loyal to their master. It is he who trains and nurtures them like a parent.

5 ▆ 3

I had as commander-in-chief some special military spies reporting to me. Till now my lips have been tightly sealed, for this is an utmost secret.

I think it was right to leave the special military spies out of the mainly prescriptive book *The Art of War*. For completeness of my memoirs I ought to reflect their special contributions. These special military spies have their place in my memory of things strategic.

Rarely do I talk to a special military spy in the presence of any person other than his master. For despite the small number of such spies their roles are often essential to ensure success in critical moments of war.

I clearly remember how twelve of those special military spies helped me in waging war. They did not have personal names, only impersonal numbers. For example it was Number 3 who was able to confirm a last-minute change of battle plan by the enemy. He was able to eavesdrop by stealth on secret discussions in the enemy's hidden chambers from where our other spies had been excluded.

5 ▆ 4

As was to be expected these special military spies had been trained to be extremely versatile. They were given expert training on the secret art of disguise. They were very quick to change their disguise, say from old lady into agile young man.

Special military spy

Their usual military attire, as I remember, was black, including gloves and shoes. Their heads and faces too were wrapped in black cloths. Only their eyes peered out through a thin opening. That was how they would report to me for assignments. Except perhaps for those pairs of eyes nothing else could give them away.

Unlike the special imperial killers, however, they had been trained to operate as effectively in the day as in the night. They had to be experts in voice imitation, ranging from a young female to an old man.

In trial runs these special military spies had no difficulty in imitating my voice. Their imitations sounded so real that time and again my men were tricked into opening the doors. That was how they were able to infiltrate the enemy's most heavily guarded places.

Deep in the forest they learned to communicate with each other through imitating calls of the wild.

5 ▰ 5

Another skill they excelled in was the art of escape, whether tied up or thrown in prison. For with their soft and pliable bodies trained from youth they could easily slip between the wooden bars of a typical prison.

When tied and bound by ropes their captors were shocked to find that these special military spies had been able to wriggle themselves free.

They were also masters in the art of concealment. As part of training in sharpening their skills my soldiers were ordered to hunt down these special military spies, concealed inside the base camp.

More often than not they escaped detection. They had been trained to remain immovable even when perched up on roof corners like a bird for long hours. They had the skills to survive in difficult situations: able to swim, glide through the forest, scale steep heights or leap down waterfalls. They could live in the forest on a diet of berries, roots, fruits, insects and small wild animals.

I owed my success in one major battle to a Number 8 who alerted me to a flanking attack by the enemy's main force. The general had decided that the army should secretly manoeuvre through a little known path in a thick forest. Little did the enemy realise that their movements had been watched by a pair of eyes in the forest.

A special military spy could remain for days beneath the river-water by depending on a reed to breathe. Number 12, I remember, was especially talented in this art. He infiltrated the enemy base camp which was tightly guarded by its moat. Though often lying beneath muddy waters he could still estimate the enemy's strength and condition, the detailed layout of the camp, including sites of stores and weaponry.

These special military spies had to be able not only to read but also to draw all sorts of maps: palaces, base camps, garrisons, cities, villages.

Once I was able to confirm a double agent's report of the situation in the enemy's base camp with Number 12's independent observations.

Another skill they had to be true masters of was the use of poisons. One of their weapons comprised a short blow-pipe. That pipe was to be used to blow toxic fumes into a bedroom or poisonous darts that immobilised the victim. The special military spy could then enter and search the room. Once immobilised the victim might be compelled to give information. No doubt they had been trained in the art of quick torture.

When at risk of capture these special military spies could exterminate themselves instantly by swallowing a special type of poison.

As a corollary skill they were adept in the use of medicinal herbs. Thus even if injured by poisoned arrows, these special military spies could concoct antidotes out of plants growing in the wild.

Their capabilities for surviving despite suffering severe injuries were legendary. For more than a year after the master and I had assumed Number 10 to be dead, he reappeared. He had last been reported seen falling off a very steep cliff into a stream below after having been shot by the enemy's ace archers: three poisonous arrows in the chest. His reappearance was most timely. He came on the day before we decided to select another trainee Number 10.

Besides the blow-pipe the spies had weapons and tools rarely seen by even experienced fighters. These included palm-sized circular sharp-edged metal darts, short knives hidden in their shoes, long ropes with metal claws on the end and gloves with sharp metal spikes.

I was awed even as commander-in-chief when shown by the master the full array of their special weapons and tools. The usefulness of some of these implements was clearly demonstrated to me on one occasion.

Numbers 2, 3 and 5 were able to scale the exceptionally high walls of an enemy-held city on a dark, rainy night to throw open the gates for the army to enter.

Such matters are kept so secret that only the very highest-ranking officers in my army would get to know of the operation of these special military spies.

My concern now is whether by putting these in the memoirs I may be jeopardising my own work – these many bamboo bundles may all be thrown into the flames on account of these records!

6 📖 1

A clear sky.

Great emptiness.

Quietness.

My mind a vast expanse of nothingness.

On my table are the few remaining blank bamboo strips. The last of the many bundles that together constitute my memoirs.

Once these memoirs have been written I must journey back home to town. I have to arrange for them to be brought down the mountain and have copies made.

I do not regard my responsibility as complete until that is done. With my health declining over the years I must set forth before I become too old to make it down the mountain path.

For me to feel certain that future readers of *The Art of War* are likely to have access to these memoirs surely more than one copy has to be made. War still rages in some of these places.

6 📖 2

My memory flashed back to the last few lines in *The Art of War*. Lines that I remember so well. I wrote them while still in the very thick of battle!

Indeed the gongs of the battlefield could be heard as I finished *The Art of War* in my commander-in-chief's tent. The enemy had finally mobilised their troops, as our spy had already forewarned.

It was not I but my personal *aide* who later arrived and kept the original copy of *The Art of War* as I rushed off to lead the army.

That must be why these lines remain so strongly etched on my mind.

6 📖 3

I wrote about I Chih, formerly of Hsia, who helped in the rise of Chin. Then there is Lu Yu, formerly of Yin, who contributed to the emergence of Chou.

These are great personalities in the *History of the Rise and Fall of States*. Both are extraordinarily skilled and talented.

In concluding *The Art of War* I emphasised that kings and generals should use their most intelligent men as spies to achieve success in things strategic. For secret operations are essential in war. The moves of an army are dependent on the intelligence gathered.

As a commander-in-chief I always valued spies of high intelligence. Though I did not have in my service any unusually intelligent spy with divine talents, I remain convinced from reading past records of their special skills.

6 4

The mind of a gifted master spy must be endowed with unusual, almost divine intelligence. Although such a person possesses no martial skills, his talents are more highly prized than those of many a warrior-general.

His eyes, ears and other senses are much more sharply attuned than those of others. He can detect even the most subtle changes in the affairs of an enemy's state. Perhaps his senses are even better attuned than that. The master spy can sense the coming tides of things early, even though the signs are hardly noticeable.

He is like the seasoned farmer who knows the taste of fruits from sampling the seeds. Using his sharp senses he can infer so much from so little. He is like the master strategist who infers the condition of the enemy's army from the wheel-tracks of their carriages or from the way banners are carried.

By observing the facial expressions among guests during stately banquets the master spy can determine whether a scheme for a secret alliance has been hatched. In the same way a master strategist knows from the drooping banners how disarrayed an enemy's army is when seen on the move.

6 5

Nothing that is in the least amiss can escape the master spy's eyes. An array of bodily postures alerts him immediately to the dispositions of the enemy troops.

Master spy

From the inflections in the voices of those who speak he knows the lies and half-truths. Though only a few words may have been exchanged he can ascertain another's true intentions.

A casual walk through town allows him to sense accurately the mood of the people. Hearing the name of a person or place, or seeing a face or a painting just once and he can instantaneously recall the details.

From on top of a high wall he can spot in the distance a lesser-skilled spy out of the crowd of people mingling in the streets below – even if the spy is heavily disguised. Perhaps that is due to the intuitive skills a spy develops over time to identify his own kind, like a eunuch is able quickly to identify without difficulty another of 'his' kind in a gathering of people.

533

 6   6

Anything once read by a master spy would stay long in his memory. Years later and despite the intervening turmoil of old states having fallen and new ones having risen he could remember all the memorials, imperial edicts and decrees and wall notices and letters. Even the different seals used as crests for paintings he could identify, having only seen them once.

More astoundingly, a master spy I once used seemed able to read the minds of people. This was claimed by those who had personal encounters with him. He could answer questions yet unasked but already formed in their minds. I have long wondered if such skills as mind reading could be possible.

Could the mind of a talented spy be cultivated through intense training?

6   7

Impossible.

The seed of talent must first be there for the mind of a master spy to be cultivated and honed to perfection. Even more so for the mind of a divine strategist.

There remain but two more strips of bamboo before I close the memoirs.

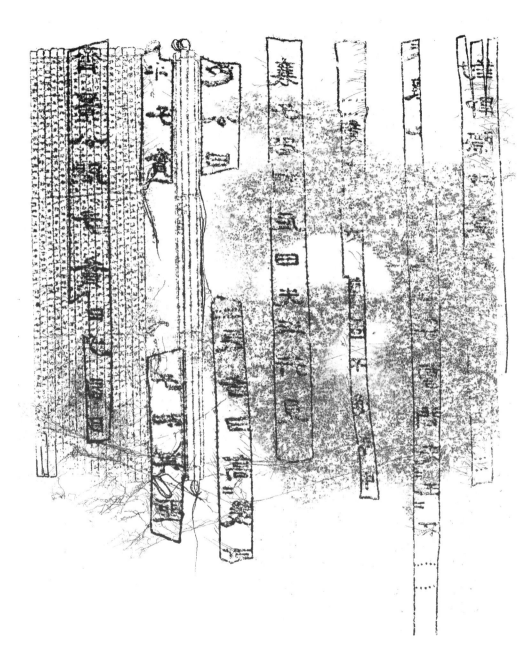

Behold!

Here in these many bundles I have compiled my memoirs. The sky remains just as clear as when I started work on them.

There is now a tinge of sadness as I write on these very last two strips, which have lost their freshness after mellowing over time.

In the process of deconstructing *The Art of War* I have gone on and reflected ever more fully, deeply and multifariously on the mind of the strategist.

These bamboo strips are very dear to me. For on each are etched my memories, reflections, subconscious thoughts, imaginings, insights, remembrances, dreams, recollections, meditations, reminiscences and so on.

I once stood by the stream and imagined the memoirs floating downstream. Today I plan to sit here and slowly run my eyes over these bundles of memoirs.

Each strip of bamboo.

Every little word.

Let each word re-echo inside me.

I begin to experience the memoirs as an embodiment of myself. This ought not to surprise me, for the memoirs are but my very own reminiscences on strategy.

As the sky darkens I feel drawn into the flow of time – along with my memoirs which will also float down that river, perhaps for ever.

535

Persons and organisations in the US, Europe, Japan and Asia who are keen to develop training courses or workshops based on Reminiscences of an Ancient Strategist: The Mind of Sun Tzu may send proposals to the author at the following postal address:

MacPherson PO Box 168
Singapore 348475

Currently the Japanese University Graduates Association of Singapore (JUGAS) is developing training courses based on Organising Strategy: Sun Tzu Business Warcraft for endorsement by the author.